Ecological Risk Assessment:
A Meeting of Policy and Science

Recent titles from the Society of Environmental Toxicology and Chemistry (SETAC)

Ecological Risk Assessment Decision-Support System: A Conceptual Design
Reinert, Bartell, Biddinger, editors
1998

Principles and Processes for Evaluating Endocrine Disruption in Wildlife
Kendall, Dickerson, Giesy, Suk, editors
1998

Quantitative-Structure Activity Relationships in Environmental Science-VII
Chen and Schüürmann, editors
1997

Chemically Induced Alterations in Functional Development and Reproduction of Fishes
Rolland, Gilbertson, Peterson, editors
1997

Chemical Ranking and Scoring: Guidelines for Relative Assessment of Chemicals
Swanson and Socha, editors
1997

Ecological Risk Assessment of Contaminated Sediments
Ingersoll, Dillon, Biddinger, editors
1997

Public Policy Applications of Life-Cycle Assessment
Allen, Consoli, Davis, Fava, Warren, editors
1997

Reassessment of Metals Criteria for Aquatic Life Protection: Priorities for Research and Implementation
Bergman and Dorward-King, editors
1997

Multi-Media Fate Model: A Vital Tool for Predicting the Fate of Chemicals
Cowan, Mackay, Feijtel, van de Meent, Di Guardo, Davies, Mackay, editors
1995

For information about additional titles or about SETAC's international journal,
Environmental Toxicology and Chemistry,
contact the SETAC Office, 1010 North 12th Avenue, Pensacola, FL, USA 32501-3370
T 850 469 1500   F 850 469 9778   E setac@setac.org   http://www.setac.org

Ecological Risk Assessment:
A Meeting of Policy and Science

Edited by

Ann de Peyster
San Diego State University

Kristin Day
Environment Canada

Proceedings of the SETAC Workshop on Ecological Risk Assessment:
A Meeting of Policy and Science
8–9 October 1993
San Diego, California

SETAC Special Publications Series

SETAC Liaison
Kristin Day
Environment Canada

Current Coordinating Editor of SETAC Books
Christopher G. Ingersoll
U.S. Geological Survey, Midwest Science Center

Publication sponsored by the Society of Environmental Toxicology and Chemistry
(SETAC)

Cover design by Mike Kenney
Indexing by IRIS

Library of Congress Cataloging-in-Publication Data

Ecological Risk Assessment : A Meeting of Policy and Science (1993 : San Diego, Calif.)
Ecological risk assessment : a meeting of policy and science : proceedings from a Workshop sponsored by the Southern California SETAC Chapter, 8–9 October 1993, San Diego, California / edited by Ann de Peyster, Kristin Day.
        p. cm. -- (SETAC special publications series)
"Publication sponsored by the Society of Environmental Toxicology and Chemistry (SETAC) and the SETAC Foundation for Environmental Education."
Includes bibliographical references and index.
ISBN 1-880611-14-7 (hardcover)
1. Ecological risk assessment--Congresses. 2. Ecological risk assessment--Government policy--Congresses. I. de Peyster, Ann, 1948– . II. Day, Kristin 1952– . III. SETAC (Society) IV. SETAC Foundation for Environmental Education. V. Title. VI. Series.
QH541.15.R57E255 1993
333.95'14--dc21
                                                             98-21948
                                                               CIP

Information in this book was obtained from individual experts and highly regarded sources. It is the publisher's intent to print accurate and reliable information, and numerous references are cited; however, the authors, editors, and publisher cannot be responsible for the validity of all information presented here or for the consequences of its use. Information contained herein does not necessarily reflect the policy or views of the Society of Environmental Toxicology and Chemistry (SETAC) or the SETAC Foundation for Environmental Education.

International Standard Book Number 1-880611-14-7
Printed in the United States of America
05 04 03 02 01 00 99 98   10 9 8 7 6 5 4 3 2 1

⊗The paper used in this publication meets the minimum requirements of the American National Standard for Information Sciences—Permanence of Paper for Printed Library Materials, ANSI Z39.48-1984.

Reference listing: de Peyster A, Day KE, editors. 1998. Ecological risk assessment: a meeting of policy and science. Proceedings from SETAC Workshop Ecological Risk Assessment: A Meeting of Policy and Science; 1993 Oct 8–9; San Diego CA. Pensacola FL: Society of Environmental Toxicology and Chemistry. 224 p.

The SETAC Special Publications Series

The SETAC Special Publications Series was established by the Society of Environmental Toxicology and Chemistry (SETAC) to provide in-depth reviews and critical appraisals on scientific subjects relevant to understanding the impact of chemicals and technology on the environment. The series consists of single- and multiple-authored or edited books on topics reviewed and recommended by the SETAC Board of Directors for their importance, timeliness, and contribution to multidisciplinary approaches to solving environmental problems. The diversity and breadth of subjects covered in the series reflect the wide range of disciplines encompassed by environmental toxicology, environmental chemistry, and hazard and risk assessment. Despite this diversity, the goals of these volumes are similar; they are to present the reader with authoritative coverage of the literature, as well as paradigms, methodologies and controversies, research needs, and new developments specific to the featured topics. All books in the series are peer reviewed for SETAC by acknowledged experts.

The SETAC Special Publications are useful to environmental scientists in research, research management, chemical manufacturing, regulation, and education, as well as to students considering careers in these areas. The series provides information for keeping abreast of recent developments in familiar subject areas and for rapid introduction to principles and approaches in new subject areas.

SETAC would like to recognize the past SETAC Special Publications Series editors:

T.W. La Point
The Institute for Environmental and Human Health
Texas Tech University
Lubbock, TX

B.T. Walton
U.S. Environmental Protection Agency
Research Triangle Park, NC

C.H. Ward
Department of Environmental Sciences and Engineering
Rice University
Houston, TX

Contents

Chapter 1
Ecological risk assessment: a meeting of policy and science 1
Ann de Peyster, Regina M. Donohoe, Steven M. Bartell, and Lawrence W. Barnthouse

Chapter 2
Ecological risk assessment guidance for Superfund sites 9
Clarence A. Callahan and B. Douglas Steele

Chapter 3
Guidance for performing ecological risk assessments at
hazardous waste sites and permitted facilities in California 23
James M. Polisini, James C. Carlisle, and Laura M. Valoppi

Chapter 4
Managing ecological risks: what information do
regulators need and want? 55
Bruce A. Macler

Chapter 5
Evaluating bioaccumulation in wildlife food chains 65
Harry M. Ohlendorf

Chapter 6

Chapter 7

Chapter 8

List of Figures

List of Tables

Preface

"Ecological Risk Assessment: A Meeting of Policy and Science" was co-sponsored by the Society for Environmental Toxicology and Chemistry (SETAC), San Diego State University Institute for Public Health, San Diego Toxicology Association (SANTA), and Environmental Science Division of Navy Command, Control and Ocean Surveillance (NCCOSC) in San Diego, California, October 1993. This meeting provided an informal forum for regulators, scientists, and others working in the area of ecological risk assessment (ERA) to share approaches and insights on regulatory and scientific aspects of this field. This gathering typified earlier efforts to design sensible regulatory approaches and specific methods for conducting ERAs that appropriately integrate meaningful science with widely accepted public policy. Case studies were selected to illustrate different scientific approaches that had been used successfully to assess risks in aquatic and terrestrial ecosystems. Other presentations on policy describe risk assessment guidelines or management practices from regulatory perspectives to encourage data gathering that is meaningful from a regulatory standpoint. Conference presentations that could be transformed ultimately into full peer-reviewed chapter manuscripts are included in this volume to illustrate both the then state-of-the-art and how thinking has evolved since the meeting.

The methods and policies used to evaluate and control health risks to ecosystems can be as dynamic as the systems they are designed to protect. Ecological risk assessment will inevitably continue to undergo significant changes as a result of new advances in science and technology and as social and political priorities shift over time. Those working to refine and improve ERAs should find some good advice in each chapter and should appreciate the early groundwork laid by some of the experts in the field.

Of course, the overall goals of any conference cannot be achieved in a single gathering, no matter how strong the desire to achieve them. We hope that readers of this book will be inspired to convene similar interdisciplinary gatherings to stimulate creative thinking on this subject. Collaborations among scientists working on similar sites and issues was promoted by interactions at the meeting. Informal discussions during and after the meeting also provided opportunities for policy-makers to work toward more harmonization of different regulatory approaches taken by government authorities. An unscientific poll of some of the approximately 150 attendees at the presentations and scientific poster sessions at this meeting, some from locations as far away as New Zealand, indicates that many ideas—in some cases significant "meetings of the mind"—resulted from the informal interactions among participants at the conference. These valuable outcomes involving compromises necessary for achieving shared goals are difficult to reflect in written manuscripts.

Ann de Peyster   Kristin E. Day
San Diego State University   Environment Canada

Acknowledgments

Substantial financial or in-kind support was also provided by the following entities:
  San Diego State University Institute for Public Health,
  Environmental Science Division of Navy Command, Control and Ocean
    Surveillance (NCCOSC) RDT&E Division, San Diego,
  San Diego Toxicology Association, and
  San Diego Chapter of Sigma Xi.

Editors

Ann de Peyster is a professor at San Diego State University (SDSU) in the Graduate School of Public Health. She earned her Ph.D. in Environmental Health Sciences with an emphasis in toxicology from the University of California-Berkeley School of Public Health. She joined SDSU in 1983 to develop the toxicology program and is now the program's director. At SDSU she has developed and taught numerous graduate courses in toxicology and related areas, including risk assessment and hazardous waste management. The majority of her publications involving mammalian and aquatic models focus on effects and mechanisms of toxicants affecting reproduction. Dr. de Peyster is active in the Society of Toxicology and is also a founding member of the Southern California Chapter of the Society of Environmental Toxicology and Chemistry.

Kristin Day is a research scientist with the National Water Research Institute, Environment Canada, Burlington, Ontario. She earned her Ph.D. in Environmental Biology and Toxicology at the University of Guelph. Throughout her career, Dr. Day has been recognized many times. She represented Canada on an OECD Working Group to harmonize protocols for whole sediment toxicity tests with the midge *Chironomus riparius*, and she lead the validated bioindicator research group for the Guelph Node of the Canadian Network for Toxicology Centres in a 3-year study to develop early warning biomarkers or bioindicators for a model compound. Dr. Day was elected to the Board of Directors of Society of Environmental Toxicology and Chemistry from 1992–1995, and she is a member of the Editorial Board for *Environmental Toxicology and Chemistry*. She also is a reviewer for *Environmental Pollution, Journal of Great Lakes Research, Hydrobiologia*, and *Chemosphere*.

Abbreviations

AAS	atomic absorption spectroscopy
AET	apparent effect threshold
ANOVA	analysis of variance
ARAR	applicable or relevant and appropriate requirement
AWQC	ambient water quality criteria
BAF	bioaccumulation factor
BCF	bioconcentration factor
BPTCP	Bay Protection and Toxic Cleanup Program
BTAG	biological technical assistance group
Cal EPA	California Environmental Protection Agency
CDFG	California Department of Fish and Game
CERCLA	Comprehensive Environmental Response, Compensation and Liability Act
COC	chemicals of concern
COEC	contaminant of ecological concern
CON	control site
CSMW	California State Mussel Watch
DBT	dibutyltin
DCM	dichloro-methane
DDT	dichloro-diphenyltrichloroethane
DFG	Department of Fish and Game
DRMO	Defense Reutilization and Marketing Office
DTSC	Department of Toxic Substances Control
EA	environmental assessment
EDL	elevated data level
EDR	exposure-dose-response
EIS	environmental impact statement
EOTW	end-of-test tissue weights
ERA	ecological risk assesment
ERL	effects range-low

ERM   effects range-median

FDEP   Florida Department of Environmental Protection

FFA   federal facility agreement

FPD   flame photometric detection

GC   gas chromatography

GERG   Geochemical and Environmental Research Group

HDAA   hydride derivatization atomic absorption

HERS   Human and Ecological Risk Section

HI   hazard index

HQ   hazard quotient

IAS   initial assessment study

IR   installation restoration

ISO   International Standards Organization

LBL   Lawrence Berkeley Laboratory

LOAEL   lowest-observed-adverse-effect level

LOD   limit of detection

LOQ   limit of quantification

MATC   maximum acceptable tissue concentrations

MBT   monobutyltin

MCAS   Marine Corps Air Station

MCB   Marine Corps Base

MCLG   maximum contaminant level goal

MLLW   mean lower low water

MTRL   maximum tissue residue level

MWR   Morale, Welfare, and Recreation Department

NBS   National Biological Service

NAV   Naval Station San Diego

NCBP   National Contaminant Biomonitoring Program

NCP   National Contingency Plan

NDDB   Natural Diversity Database

NOAA	National Ooceanic and Atmospheric Administration
NOAEL	no-observed-adverse-effect level
NOEC	no-observed-effects concentration
NOEL	no-observed-effects level
NRAD	Naval Research and Development Center
NS&T	National Status and Trends
NWR	National Wildlife Refuge
NWS	Naval Weapons Station
OAPCA	Organotin Antifouling Paint Control Act
PAH	polycyclic aromatic hydrocarbon
PAISI	preliminary assessment/site investigation
PCB	polychlorinated biphenyl
PEA	preliminary endangerment assessment
POLB	Port of Long beach
PRP	potentially responsible party
QA	quality assurance
QC	quality control
RCRA	Resource Conservation and Recovery Act
RfC	reference concentration
RfD	reference dose
RI	remedial investigation
ROD	record of decision
RPM	remedial project manager
RTE	rare, threatened, or endangered
SAIC	Science Applications International Corporation
SAP	sampling and analysis plan
SARA	Superfund Amendments and Reauthorization Act
SETAC	Society of Environmental Toxicology and Chemistry
SI	Shelter Island yacht basin
SID	Shelter Island deep

SIO	Scripps Institute of Oceanography
SMCL	secondary maximum contaminant level
TBT	tributyltin
TBTCL	tributyltin chloride
TSMP	Toxic Substances Monitoring Program
UF	uncertainty factor
USBR	U.S. Bureau of Reclamation
USFWS	U.S. Fish and Wildlife Service
WAWW	whole-animal wet-weights
WQO	water quality objectives

Participants and Authors*

Lawrence Barnthouse
Oak Ridge National Laboratory
Oak Ridge TN

Brock Bernstein
EcoAnalysis, Inc.
Ojai CA

Clarence Callahan
USEPA, Region IX
San Francisco CA

James Carlisle
Department of Toxic Substances Control
CalEPA
Sacramento CA

Ann de Peyster
San Diego State University
San Diego CA

John DeSesso
The MITRE Corporation
McLean VA

Regina Donohoe
CalEPA
Sacramento CA

Brad Davidson
Computer Sciences Corporation
NCCOSC RDT&E Division
San Diego CA

Roy Fransham
Computer Sciences Corporation
NCCOSC RDT&E Division
San Diego CA

Joseph Grovhoug
Computer Sciences Corporation
NCCOSC RDT&E Division
San Diego CA

Lora Kear
Computer Sciences Corporation
NCCOSC RDT&E Division
San Diego CA

Edward Long
National Oceanic and Atmospheric
Administration
Seattle WA

Bruce Macler
USEPA, Region IX
San Francisco CA

Harry Ohlendorf
CH2M Hill
Sacramento CA

James Polisini
Department of Toxic Substances Control
CalEPA
Sacramento CA

Michael Salazar
National Oceanic and Atmospheric
Administration
Seattle WA

Sandra Salazar
National Oceanic and Atmospheric
Administration
Seattle WA

Peter Seligman
NCCOSC RDT&E Division
San Diego CA

Douglas Steele
USEPA, Region IX
San Francisco CA

Aldis Valkirs
Computer Sciences Corporation
NCCOSC RDT&E Division
San Diego CA

Laura Valoppi
Department of Toxic Substances
Control
CalEPA
Sacramento CA

*These affiliations were current at the
time of the workshop.

Chapter 1

Ecological risk assessment:
a meeting of policy and science

Ann de Peyster, Regina M. Donohoe, Steven M. Bartell, and Lawrence W. Barnthouse

The views expressed are those of the authors and do not necessarily represent those of the Office of Environmental Health Hazard Assessment, the California Environmental Protection Agency, or the State of California.–Regina Donohoe

Scientific efforts have long focused on describing and quantifying the adverse effects from human-induced changes in ecological systems. However, only within the past few decades have these efforts become increasingly structured and formalized as a regulatory process. For example, only since 1970 have environmental impact statements, which describe the adverse effects on the environment anticipated from proposed human activities, been required in the United States by the National Environmental Policy Act. In recent years, the U.S. Environmental Protection Agency (USEPA) has extended and advanced its requirements for evaluating environmental impacts by developing more technically sophisticated assessment procedures based on a conceptual and methodological foundation of ecological risk (USEPA 1992, 1996). State governments (e.g., Florida, California, and Kentucky), international organizations (e.g., the Organization for Economic Cooperation and Development), and other countries (e.g., Canada, the Netherlands) are also in the process of developing formal guidance for assessing ecological risks. The continued development and refinement of federal, state, and international guidelines for performing and evaluating ecological risk assessments (ERAs) provide incentive for additional discussion and debate. The promulgation of guidelines produced by these various organizations will likely stimulate further evolution of the risk-assessment process (NRC 1983, 1994).

It was within such a developmental and evolutionary context that the conference, Ecological Risk Assessment: A Meeting of Policy and Science, convened in San Diego, California in 1993. The conference was organized by the Southern California Chapter of the Society of Environmental Toxicology and Chemistry (SETAC) with the purpose of offering participants an opportunity to contribute to the process of refining and advancing concepts, methods, and guidelines necessary for accurate characterization and meaning-

1

ful assessment of ecological risks. Furthermore, the conference provided an open forum that encouraged interactions among the regulatory user-community and the developers and practitioners of ERA. The organizers of this conference hoped that those participants charged primarily with the technical aspects of estimating ecological risks would benefit from a greater understanding of the stated needs of regulators attempting to incorporate risk-based management into policy and decision-making. Conference planners anticipated further that policy makers and the regulatory community might benefit through increased technical understanding provided by detailed presentations and in-depth discussions concerning the scientific complexities that define current capabilities for accurately and precisely estimating ecological risks.

In San Diego, a diverse group of policy makers, risk assessors, risk managers, and scientists from industry, government, and academia met and addressed the challenges of further developing and refining the risk assessment process. The group worked with equal intensity toward advancing the scientific practice of characterizing ecological risks. Risk assessors and risk managers emphasized again the necessity of a multidisciplinary approach in estimating and evaluating ecological risks. Conference participants also acknowledged the fact that technical skills borrowed from many disciplines within the environmental sciences (e.g., basic biology; population, community, ecosystem, and landscape ecology; environmental toxicology; environmental chemistry; geology; hydrology; and the atmospheric sciences) are required to assess ecological risks (Bartell et al. 1992; Suter 1993; Bartell 1996). Participants recognized that ERAs push current understanding and technical capabilities within these sciences to their limits. In addition to fundamental technical requirements, conference participants noted that frequent and effective communication between risk analysts and risk managers greatly increases the likelihood of successfully completing the process of assessing ecological risks (Mehrle 1993; Moore and Biddinger 1995).

The proceedings of this conference are offered as a reflection of the essential kind of communication required among specialists from many disciplines to refine and advance both the process and practice of ERA. Several important lines of thought or concepts were repeated several times during the conference discussions and are further addressed in the chapters that follow. These recurrent thoughts and ideas were summarized in the final commentary at the conference. The final comments emphasized several interesting perspectives and common themes concerning ERA that emerged from the presentations. The closing remarks also identified future needs for advancing the process of ERA, including the following:

1) The ERA process is developing, at least partially, "from the bottom up." That is, in the absence of officially recognized or legally sanctioned procedural guidelines for assessing ecological risks, those risk assessors, risk managers, and the regulated community required by existing laws to perform ERAs must necessarily collaborate, apply sound judgement, and implement scientifically defensible methods in

attempting to meet legislated obligations without such guidance. The regulated community can ill-afford to wait passively for guidelines to come "from above."

2) The many and diverse sources of ecological stress, the scale and complexity of ecological responses to stress, and the different regulatory objectives and jurisdictions pertinent to risk management act in combination to reduce the likelihood that a single or simple guideline for assessing ecological risks will emerge. It is equally unlikely that ERA will ever reduce to a simple set of formulas or computations that parallel guidance concerning human health risk assessment (e.g., NRC 1983 "Red Book"). However, as such prescriptions for assessing ecological risk develop and evolve under the auspices of government agencies, the regulated community should insist that resulting guidelines be fundamentally similar and consistent in concept, intent, accepted methods, and interpretation. Evolutionary convergence toward conceptual and operational similarity of risk-assessment guidelines developed by federal, state, and local governments should be apparent to the user-community.

3) Technical innovations in estimating ecological risks should be scientifically defensible and reflect an active partnership in development between scientists devoted primarily to basic environmental research and those who also assess risk. New data, information, and understanding produced (e.g., by ecologists and environmental toxicologists) and disseminated by the basic research and development community should be continually monitored and carefully evaluated by risk assessors for relevance in advancing current capabilities in characterizing ecological risks. At the same time, those environmental scientists engaged mainly in theoretical or basic research should be encouraged to consider the potential contribution of their work toward surmounting the many technical complexities inherent to ERA. An effective feedback loop between basic research and practical application must be established and maintained to accelerate the timely technical evolution of the ERA process.

4) Ecological risk assessment should be elaborated as a key process in deciding among alternative solutions to environmental problems based on an overall objective of reducing risk. Acceptable risks should be established as practical and effective alternatives to chemical concentrations (e.g., maximum contaminant levels), e.g., as the fundamental criteria for mitigation, remediation, and restoration at hazardous waste sites. The implementation of risk-based decision-making will become increasingly important as activities at contaminated sites shift from risk assessment to actual cleanup.

5) Future efforts in reestablishing the environmental integrity of, for example, hazardous waste sites, should strive for a balance between the costs of assessment and remediation and the ecological (and human-health) benefits that result from cleanup activities. Using the process of ERA in a decision framework aimed at obtaining the greatest reduction in risk per dollar spent in cleaning up can con-

tribute significantly to economical, effective, and justifiable reclamation of contaminated sites. Risk assessors, risk managers, and decision-makers representing government and the private sector will have to collaborate to realize this balance between risks and benefits. Importantly, the public should participate in evaluating risks and in determining who benefits and who is encumbered by risks associated with the risk-based remediation of hazardous waste sites.

This symposium's proceedings attempt to capture the novel ideas conceived during the conference and provide a more detailed, comprehensive presentation of the many issues presented and discussed at San Diego. Many of these thoughts and discussions have been modified, revised, or refined as the result of both transforming oral presentations to written chapters and from subsequent peer review. Chapters in this volume focus on the 2 basic themes of the conference: 1) establishing regulatory policy in relation to the process of ERA, and 2) developing an understanding among the regulatory community concerning the current technical capabilities for assessing ecological risk. The first theme examines the risk assessment needs and expectations of the regulators, while the second addresses previous implementation of methods and approaches in meeting these needs and expectations. The integration of these themes constitutes a conceptual and operational "meeting" of science and policy—the primary conference objective.

At the time of the San Diego Conference, the USEPA Framework for Ecological Risk Assessment (i.e., USEPA 1992) had been in circulation among the public, regulators, and risk assessors for barely a year. Not surprisingly, the framework has undergone significant refinement since then. Therefore, it is important for the reader to understand what these proceedings are not. The reader should recognize that the conference was not intended to provide a detailed methodology or prescription for performing an ERA. Furthermore, these symposium proceedings do not describe the content and format for an ERA to meet the requirements of current environmental legislation. The continuing evolution of the ERA process in the regulatory arena (e.g., USEPA 1992, 1996) precludes the development and publication of these much needed guidelines and documents. Since 1992, several books and references concerning ERA have been published, and the interested reader less familiar with the ERA process might consult these for background information (e.g., Bartell et al. 1992; Suter 1993; Kolluru et al. 1996; USEPA 1992, 1996).

These conference proceedings provide those readers more familiar with the ERA process some new ideas and fresh perspectives concerning the potential strengths and limitations of ERA derived from hands-on experience by several well-respected practitioners. It is hoped that their shared experience discussed at the conference and represented in this volume will stimulate the further development and refinement of the ERA process. Insights gleaned from careful and thoughtful reading of these chapters might perhaps help catalyze the needed collaboration among scientists and policy makers to establish ERA as an effective and meaningful process for evaluating human impacts on the environment.

Overview of chapters

Chapters 2, 3, and 4 address ERA perspectives from regulatory and policy points of view. A meaningful integration of science and policy requires a fundamental understanding of the needs and responsibilities of the policy makers. Resulting science policy can be expected to evolve with time and the advance of science. The USEPA framework and proposed guidelines, basic to the assessment of ecological risk (USEPA 1992, 1996), represent the products of years of discussion involving scientists and regulators. This approach comprises problem formulation, exposure analysis, effects assessment, and risk characterization. In Chapter 2, Callahan and Steele expand upon the USEPA approach and provide specific federal guidance for assessing ecological risks at hazardous waste sites. These authors outline ecological guidelines for the remedial investigation/feasibility study phase of the Superfund risk assessment process within USEPA Region 9. Callahan and Steele advocate the integration of data and information in an iterative risk-assessment process that differs somewhat from the existing USEPA Framework and consists of 5 phases: scoping, preliminary impact assessment, confirmatory impact assessment, risk characterization, and remedial guidance.

Similarly, Polisini and coauthors (Chapter 3) describe a multi-phased approach for assessing ecological risks and evaluating hazardous waste sites and permitted facilities in California. These 2 chapters stress that risk-assessment policies and guidelines should have similar basic objectives even though specific guidance might vary regionally and from state to state. These 2 chapters are consistent in their emphasis on a cost-effective, sequential approach to risk assessment that begins with simplistic preliminary assessments based on existing data and progresses through more detailed assessments using newly collected, site-specific field and laboratory studies.

Evaluations of ERAs conducted according to available guidelines (e.g., USEPA 1992, 1996) might help refine and validate these approaches. For example, the value of adequate planning as part of problem formulation, the USEPA prescribed initial phase of an ERA, cannot be overemphasized. Careful planning of an ERA helps to identify the necessary information and ensure that it is assembled in an efficient manner. In Chapter 4, Macler draws upon his experience as a risk manager for the Montrose Chemical Corporation Superfund site remediation efforts to further underscore the importance of initial discussions between risk assessors and risk managers in developing a technically sound risk assessment that will enter effectively into the risk-management process. Macler describes how close communication between the risk assessors and risk managers led to a clear understanding of the goals of the Montrose ERA. The potential limitations of the ERA, as well as the impact of both the ERA strengths and limitations on resulting management decisions, are also developed in Chapter 4.

Chapters 2 through 4 examine the potential utility of an ecological risk assessment for providing risk managers and decision makers with technical information for selecting among remediation or decision alternatives. Building upon these discussions of policy and decision-making, Chapters 5 through 8 present case-study risk assessments and analyses of site-specific environmental contamination. Important criteria delineated by the conference organizers for selecting each of these studies were that 1) each study should represent an essentially completed risk assessment, and 2) each study should illustrate important lessons learned and experience gained in the context of risk analysis. The authors presenting these selected studies describe the particular knowledge concerning environmental assessments gained by applying the methods and approaches of ecological risk analysis developed in the earlier chapters. The case studies include assessments of terrestrial and aquatic ecological systems. The studies also introduce recent innovations by ecologists and environmental toxicologists in developing and refining assessment tools beyond standard laboratory assays; such new methods include complex environmental modeling and in situ studies to estimate risk.

In Chapter 5, Ohlendorf focuses on the exposure-analysis component within the overall framework for ERA. He describes alternative methods for characterizing the bioaccumulation of contaminants by both terrestrial and aquatic organisms at 3 different study sites. In evaluating potential adverse ecological impacts at the Naval Weapons Station near Seal Beach, California, Ohlendorf advocates environmental monitoring of contaminant concentrations in saltmarsh sediments and other biota as an effective way to assess bioaccumulation by endangered birds occupying the area. In contrast, the author presents earthworm and plant bioaccumulation assays as contributing valuable information regarding contaminant exposure for a risk assessment performed at the Camp Pendleton Marine Corps Base. The third study introduces a complex environmental modeling approach. The model simulates future concentrations of contaminants in a risk assessment for Kesterson Reservoir food webs and forecasts exposure to several species possibly at risk.

Knowledge of the spatial and temporal scales necessary to quantify the transport, distribution, and concentration of particular contaminants accurately and precisely is vital in constructing exposure analyses in support of an ERA. The previous case studies emphasized hazardous waste sites of various sizes. Focusing on even larger spatial scales, Chapters 6, 7, and 8 address the usefulness of the risk assessment paradigm to regional aquatic monitoring programs for tributyltin (TBT). In Chapter 6, Long highlights 4 issues that appear critical to the validation and application of sediment bioassays in assessing TBT contamination and potential impacts. These issues include 1) quantifying the spatial extent of contamination in industrial harbors, 2) ascertaining the accuracy of sediment quality guideline values for predicting toxicity, 3) understanding the potential confounding effect of ammonia in determining sediment toxicity, and 4) recognizing the relative sensitivity of amphipods, compared to other taxa, in toxicity tests. Long examines these potentially controversial issues using data obtained from several sources including the National Oceanographic and Atmospheric Administration (NOAA) National Status and Trends Program's regional survey in the Hudson-Raritan estuary, which encompasses parts of New York and New Jersey. Matching chemical and toxicity data were also generated from sediment samples collected from Tampa Bay and Pensacola Bay in Florida and from San Pedro Bay, California.

In Chapter 7, the third monitoring case study, Valkirs and coauthors describe a multifaceted, long-term program that was designed to evaluate the impacts of TBT on organisms in San Diego Bay and Pearl Harbor. This study introduces and emphasizes the importance of considering several different (and independent) lines of evidence in evaluating the results of monitoring programs and ERAs. In this study, the set of possible indicators of TBT impacts included measures of the TBT concentration in water, tissue, and sediments; studies of the degradation of TBT; bioassays using caged mussels; portable microcosm studies; and life-cycle assays performed in the laboratory.

Salazar and Salazar (Chapter 8) describe the advantages of monitoring the in situ growth and bioaccumulation of TBT by mussels to assess exposure and effects of TBT in embayments. The authors advocate an exposure-dose-response triad approach using TBT in seawater (exposure), TBT bioaccumulation by mussels (dose), and in situ mussel growth (response) for assessing ecological risks in embayments such as San Diego Bay, California. This study underscores the strength of in situ field studies to minimize the uncertainties associated with analyzing site-specific spatial and temporal variability in exposure and effects of other stressors (e.g., temperature).

The following chapters are revisions of manuscripts developed from conference presentations. The editors appreciate the efforts of the contributing authors for providing and updating their manuscripts and responding to reviewer comments. The editors also wish to acknowledge the participation of the many peer reviewers who commented on earlier drafts.

References

Bartell, S.M. 1996. Ecological/environmental risk assessment: Principles and practices. In Kolluru, R., S,Bartell, R. Pitbladoand S. Stricoff (eds)., Risk assessment and management handbook for environmental, health, and safety professionals. New York: McGraw-Hill. 10-1 to 10-59 p.

Bartell SM, Gardner RH, O'Neill RV 1992. Ecological risk estimation. Chelsea MI: Lewis. 238 p.

Kolluru R, Bartell S, Pitblado R, Stricoff S. 1996. Risk assessment and management handbook for environmental, health, and safety professionals. New York: McGraw-Hill.

Merhle PM. 1993. Communicating science: a challenge for our next 15 years. *Environ Toxicol Chem* 12:1957–1958.

Moore DRJ, Biddinger GR. 1995. The interaction between risk assessors and risk managers during the problem formulation phase. *Environ Toxicol Chem* 14:2013–2014.

[NRC] National Research Council. 1983. Risk assessment in the federal government: managing the process. Washington DC: National Academy. 191 p.

[NRC] National Research Council. 1994. Science and judgement in risk assessment. Washington DC: National Academy. 762 p.

Suter II GW. 1993. Ecological risk assessment. Chelsea MI: Lewis. 505 p.

[USEPA] U.S. Environmental Protection Agency. 1992. Framework for ecological risk assessment. Washington DC: USEPA. EPA/630/R-92/001. 41 p.

[USEPA] U.S. Environmental Protection Agency. 1995. Draft proposed guidelines for ecological risk assessment. Washington DC: USEPA. EPA/630/R-95/002. 144 p.

Chapter 2

Ecological risk assessment guidance for Superfund sites

Clarence A. Callahan and B. Douglas Steele

Disclaimer - The guidance set out in this document is not final U.S. Environmental Protection (USEPA) action. It is not intended, nor can it be relied upon, to create any rights enforceable by any party in litigation with the United States. USEPA officials may decide to follow the guidance provided herein, or act at variance with the guidance, based on an analysis of specific circumstances. The USEPA also reserves the right to change this guidance at any time without public notice.

Background

This chapter describes guidance for the integration of information in planning and conducting ecological risk assessments (ERAs) at Superfund sites as required by Region 9 of the USEPA. Ecological risk assessments are conducted by Region 9 as part of its responsibility for enforcing the Superfund program under the Comprehensive Environmental Response, Compensation, and Liability Act (CERCLA), as amended by the Superfund Amendments and Reauthorization Act (SARA) and the National Oil and Hazardous Substances Pollution Contingency Plan (NCP) (Figure 2-1). An ecological assessment may parallel the human-health-assessment process in terms of timing, but the 2 efforts are quite different because the focus of the ecological assessment is "a qualitative and/or quantitative appraisal of the actual or potential effects prior to cleanup of a hazardous waste site on plants and animals other than people or domesticated species." (USEPA 1989a). Human-health risk assessments are limited to humans.

This discussion assumes some familiarity with USEPA Superfund risk-assessment guidance (USEPA 1989a) and the USEPA *Framework for Ecological Risk Assessment* (USEPA 1992a) (Figure 2-2). Region 9 guidance draws significantly from these and other USEPA documents. Individuals from the USEPA headquarters and state agencies (e.g., California Department of Toxic Substances Control) also made significant contributions to the Region 9 guidance. The overall approach and specific guidance statements of state agencies in Region 9 are similar in structure, phases, and overall purpose, so the process and final results are not expected to be significantly different if either guidance is used (e.g.,

9

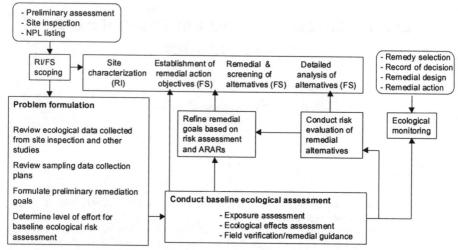

Figure 2-1   *ERA in the remedial investigation/feasibility study process. Reprinted from USEPA 1991*

the State of California Department of Toxic Substances Control or the Region 9 USEPA document). Any use of other guidance material in a risk assessment for Region 9 should be clearly documented.

As noted earlier, ERAs at Superfund sites are required under CERCLA, SARA, and NCP. However, little information from the USEPA was available for conducting an ERA until 1993 (USEPA 1989a, 1992a). Previously, several other documents provided information about how to

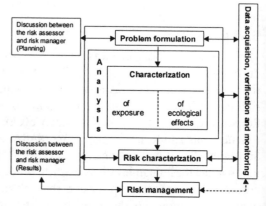

Figure 2-2   *ERA process as promoted and practiced by the USEPA. Reprinted from USEPA 1992a*

conduct remedial investigations and feasibility studies, but they provided only general approaches to risk assessments (Barnthouse, Suter et al. 1986; USEPA 1988; Norton et al. 1988; USEPA 1989b, 1991). The USEPA's *Framework for Ecological Risk Assessment* (USEPA 1992a) was intended to provide more comprehensive guidance for assessing risks to the environment. This framework can be utilized to evaluate the impact of stressors on the environment in situations other than risk assessments at hazardous waste sites (e.g., accidents involving chemical spills, proposed new construction in ecologically sensitive areas, or even more complex environmental phenomena like the impact of acid rain deposition and climate changes on a localized area of contamination). The USEPA framework document thereby serves many purposes and programs within the USEPA. The regional guidance described in this chapter is intended specifically to address Superfund sites within Region 9, although this phased approach is also appropriate for other programs such as the Resource Conservation and Recovery Act (RCRA).

Region 9 guidance, which is adapted from Agency material (USEPA 1988, 1989a, 1992a), follows a phased approach (Figure 2-3) whereby each phase increases the information base from which definitive answers to questions concerning chemical, biological, toxicological, or ecological stressors are formulated (USEPA 1992b, 1993). Box 2-1 shows the relationship between main components of the framework (USEPA 1992a) and the Region 9 guidance. The Region 9 document adds the Phase 2, Preliminary Impact Assessment Phase because the ERAs generally include only information that is best described as "preliminary estimates or predictions" of impact, rather than an exposure-response relationship for the chemicals of concern (COCs) and the site receptors. This work normally would occur in the Analysis Phase of the *Framework* document, where site-specific bioassay data would be presented; however, because modeling is routinely the only approach presented for this effort, the Region 9 document requires additional work in Phase 3, the validation phase, to confirm or verify these results.

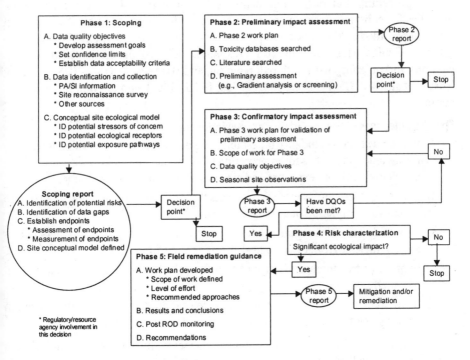

Figure 2-3   Phase approach to ERA as practiced at Superfund sites in USEPA Region 9

The remediation guidance phase is added in the Region 9 document to overcome the insufficient evaluations for the effects of the various remedial options on the resources being protected. Ecological risk assessment documents presented to Region 9 routinely present only the results of the hazard quotient (generally in tabular form) with little description of the overall impact to the measurement and assessment endpoints; therefore, a more comprehensive description is required.

The formalized and structured process integrates appropriate and relevant information in sequence to address the hazardous waste site remediation goals and, when necessary, the long-term monitoring effort. This phased approach allows for the synthesis of many different types of data into manageable and related elements that focus the ecological assessment on only the necessary information. This process permits both the regulatory agencies and the potentially responsible parties to evaluate the information for data sufficiency for the purpose of determining what level of effort is needed to complete the process.

Purpose of Region 9 guidance

The Region 9 guidance document is not meant to be a detailed step-by-step standard operating procedure, but rather a guideline for the principles and recommended approaches for conducting risk assessment at Region 9 Superfund sites. It is based on material provided by the Superfund program, Region 9's interpretation of the Risk Assessment Guidance for Superfund (USEPA 1989a), additional material presented in discussions and meetings with national, regional, and state risk assessors (USEPA 1988; Norton et al. 1988; USEPA 1989, 1991, 1992a, 1992b, 1993), and relevant published literature.

Specific objectives of these guidance are the following:

1) to provide general guidance for establishing data requirements, evaluation procedures, and approaches for interpreting relevant data for making decisions about problem definition, exposure and effects assessment, and risk characterization;

2) to highlight specific issues in this process that are deemed especially important to successful completion of a risk assessment;

3) to provide general recommendations for approaches for the measurement of biological, toxicological, or ecological effects at Superfund sites;

4) to promote the timely and efficient completion of the ERA based on sound scientific methods; and

5) to standardize and integrate the guidance used in Region 9 with those used in state agencies, other USEPA regions, and at the national level.

Superfund site risk assessments in Region 9 are reviewed by Region 9's Technical Support Section and will be compared to these recommendations prior to acceptance for use in the Superfund program. Site-specific discussions of the process by the Region 9 Biological Technical Assistance Group (BTAG) are promoted and generally occur at several points in the process (Figure 2-3). The goal of Region 9 is to use risk assessments that are reliable and within the framework of USEPA policy and the uncertainties of the risk-assessment process. The recommendations discussed in this chapter should be applied to all future Superfund risk assessments for Region 9 and any current projects where implementation of these recommendations will not unduly affect the scope of work or substantially delay the project's completion. Region 9's guidance is divided into 5 sections, with identified activities in each phase (see Box 2-1).

National guidance	Region 9 guidance
Problem formulation	Phase 1— Scoping Phase 2— Preliminary impact assessment
Analysis (characterization of exposure and ecological effects)	Phase 3— Confirmatory impact assessments
Risk characterization	Phase 4—Risk characterization Phase 5—Remediation guidance
Risk management	Risk management

Box 2-1 Relationship between framework (USEPA 1992) and Region 9 guidance

Although these 5 phases (Figure 2-3) can generally be separated into distinct units, the process should be considered a continuous one with an integration of the information and efforts moving through all of the phases. For example, selection of COCs, identification of potential receptors, and development of the site conceptual model may be developed simultaneously. At any 1 of the 5 phases, several activities may be in progress at the same time and eventually may be integrated into a comprehensive effort to guide the selection of a remedial action.

Phase 1—Scoping

Scoping is usually based on information resulting from the preliminary assessment/site investigation (PA/SI) activities. Available information is used to develop a site description including chemical contaminants as well as the fauna and flora known or expected to inhabit the site. It presents all of the available information about the site from all known sources (USEPA 1989b). The primary output from the Phase 1 scoping is a definition of the problem (i.e., problem formulation) and a clear description of the questions that must be addressed in subsequent phases of the risk assessment (USEPA 1992b, 1993). A listing of activities for the scoping phase is shown in Box 2-2:

> A. Developing a problem statement to define contaminant release, migration, and fate;
>
> B. Identifying COCs receptors, exposure pathways, known environmental effects;
>
> C. Defining data quality objectives (DQOs);
>
> D. Defining the site conceptual model;
>
> E. Selecting endpoints; and
>
> F. Summarizing site status.

Box 2-2 Activities for completing the scoping effort

Regulatory decision point 1

The purpose of the scoping phase is to gain some understanding of the site and identify the need for conducting a risk assessment. Scoping involves reaching a consensus among reviewing agencies regarding what resources are of concern and need to be addressed in development of the remedial action and the approach to be used in assessing the risk to those resources (Box 2-3). The need for a risk assessment is based, in part, on a consensus regarding the type and quality of habitat potentially impacted by the site. If a location within the site is determined to have 1 or more significant ecological habitats (e.g., wetlands, grasslands, forests, streams) with associated receptors exposed or potentially exposed to contaminants, the risk-assessment process proceeds to the next step where the scoping data are integrated, interpreted, and presented as the Phase 2 Preliminary Impact Assessment. The emphasis in the Scoping Phase is the description or status of the site by integrating all available background information in preparation for the decision of whether to proceed to Phase 2. In this scenario, the conceptual model clearly shows a completed pathway between a source and the site receptors for 1 or more of the contaminants.

> A. What is the relative amount of quality habitat available?
>
> B. What are the distributions and concentrations of the COCs?
>
> C. What are the appropriate assessments and measurement endpoints and site receptors?
>
> D. Is there quality habitat in the area (i.e., location) that is potentially impacted by COCs?

Box 2-3 Questions to be addressed in the scoping phase

If the site is described as having little quality habitat (e.g., an area covered with concrete [such as an airstrip or parking lot]), or it borders residential or industrial roadways, there is less justification for further efforts or more formal evaluation. In this situation, information about the site's habitat and receptors along with chemical contamination (i.e., a brief risk characterization) should be presented as summary information about the site with no further ecological assessment action proposed. This situation should be discussed with regulatory agencies. Supporting data descriptions and summaries could justify redirecting the process to the risk characterization phase for this location as shown in Figure 2-3.

The decision at this time is whether the particular location should be carried forward in the process (i.e., proceed to the preliminary impact phase), not whether a particular contaminant should be retained as a COC for the entire site. Locations with contaminants that are considered to be above the no-observed-effects concentration (NOEC) are moved forward to the risk-characterization and risk-management effort of the overall risk-assessment process. Although a particular location within a site may not proceed through the entire process for the reasons listed above, this decision has no bearing on the overall process for elimination of contaminants and other stressors found there.

Phase 2—Preliminary impact assessment

This is the phase in which a preliminary assessment of the potential impact of site contaminants is made. This phase utilizes the available data identified and synthesized during the scoping phase to estimate the range of potential effects of the contaminants at the known distribution and concentrations within the site. Using the measurement endpoints identified in the scoping activities, toxicity data are compared to evaluate the applicable receptors. The primary output of this activity is the identification of data gaps and the level of effort needed to confirm the predictions made about the impacts of contaminants on the receptors (USEPA 1992b).

Phase 2 is a pivotal step in the ecological impact assessment (see Box 2-4). The degree to which more relevant data can be obtained (e.g., determination of actual site receptors and relevant data about COCs) affects the degree of certainty with which the ERA can

---

A. Searching the literature for applicable toxicological, biological, and ecological data;

B. Searching the literature for relevant benchmarks;

C. Integrating the concentration distribution of the COCs with the predicted impacts of the biological/ecological resources;

D. Comparing site contaminant levels to literature benchmarks; calculating hazard quotients

E. Identifying data gaps and describing further work for the quantitative impact assessments; and

F. Summarizing the potential impacts and describing uncertainty for each assessment endpoint

---

Box 2-4 Activities for completing the preliminary impact-assessment phase

proceed. With site-specific data for the receptors and the COCs, a convincing and logical assessment of ecological impacts can be presented that provides a basis for the final evaluation of ecological risk for that particular location. The use of surrogate species and the substitution of similar or indicator chemicals for the COCs should be avoided whenever possible or used with caution because of the introduction of uncertainty in the ERA results. A primary output of Phase 2 activities includes the calculation of hazard quotients based on the data observed and the literature benchmarks identified for each COC, receptor, and endpoint.

Regulatory decision point 2

At this point in the process, the first screening has been completed and hazard quotients (USEPA 1986; Barnthouse, Breck et al. 1986) have been calculated for the assessment of ecological impacts with the associated comparisons of literature values and data that relate to the contaminants and receptors on the site. Those contaminants and locations where this preliminary impact-assessment phase indicates a high degree of uncertainty because of data gaps are carried forward to Phase 3 Confirmatory Impact Assessment. Because the preliminary assessment uses only the data that are collected during the site investigation to formulate the best estimate of the problem, all unacceptable levels of uncertainty indicate data gaps. This second regulatory decision point provides an opportunity for agency reviewers to discuss the findings from the preliminary impact screening and reach a consensus regarding the need to proceed in the risk assessment process. Some of the issues considered during this review phase are illustrated in Box 2-5. A decision to stop data collection after this phase is rare because assessors generally do not have sufficient site-specific data to directly assess the impact of the site COCs on the receptors with a very high degree of certainty. Therefore, this phase contributes to the formulation of the needed activities for Phase 3 where validation of the ERA process occurs. The summary report of Phase 2 is directed at the potential impact to receptors rather than at potential risk.

A. Do the distributions of COCs and receptors overlap?
B. Are COCs at significant concentrations relative to no observed effects concentrations (NOECs)?
C. Are COCs' measurement endpoints significantly impacted?
D. Are measurement endpoints significantly impacted?

Box 2-5   Questions to be addressed in the preliminary impact-assessment phase

Phase 3—confirmatory impact assessment

The primary purpose of this phase is to reduce or eliminate uncertainty and to provide assurances that the predictions and estimates stated in the risk assessment are based on accurate information (USEPA 1992b, 1993). Uncertainty may result from a number of sources including 1) lack of basic scientific information about the cause and effect of particular contaminants of concern; 2) the relationship between individual responses and higher levels of ecological organization (e.g., population and community levels) with respect to the site-specific contaminants; 3) seasonal and site-specific events in field situations that affect the relationship between the stressor and the receptor; and 4) imprecision in sampling, toxicological testing, and analysis (USEPA 1992c).

A number of tasks are undertaken as part of Phase 3, as presented in Box 2-6. This phase involves the measurement of contaminants in all identified affected media, and it incorporates information about pathways of exposure and the life history data for the animals identified as receptors in the conceptual site model. This is the phase that provides the "data quality check" or the quantification of any estimated values used in the preliminary impact assessment. Measurements are made to fill data gaps and verify all data obtained by modeling or estimates. Data are collected to establish the relationship between the receptor's exposure to the stressor and its response, which will be used to describe site-specific biological, toxicological, and ecological impacts.

A. Conduct the necessary tests, sampling, and/or measurements to confirm or verify the results of Phase 2;

B. Discuss the site-specific contaminant levels in relation to NOELs for toxicity tests performed in the laboratory and/or field;

C. Discuss the site-specific contaminant levels in relation to LOELs for toxicity tests performed in the field;

D. Discuss the assessment of biological/toxicological impact;

E. Discuss the existing criteria, standards, or benchmarks with respect to results obtained to describe to overall risk to the site resources;

F. Discuss the remaining level of uncertainty with respect to the results obtained;

G. Write a report defining the level of contamination from the COCs that result in a significant response in the receptors

---

Box 2-6 Activities for compiling the confirmatory impact-assessment effort

Regulatory decision point 3

Following reporting of the Phase 3 results, another review and consensus phase begins (regulatory decision 3). A number of key findings and issues, as illustrated in Box 2-7, are discussed with respect to what elements should be included in the next phase of the ERA (i.e., risk characterization). Because this phase of the ERA is designed to validate the estimates and predictions of potential impacts identified in the preliminary impact assessment phase, the results of the Phase 3 validation tests are weighed heavily by agency reviewers. All of the site locations indicating that significant impacts may occur are carried forward to the risk characterization phase (Box 2-8) in preparation for the remediation guidance phase (Box 2-9). For those locations where the testing did not show significant results, efforts are confined to risk-characterization evaluation in preparation for risk-management decisions.

A. Are the results of validation tests significantly different from the predictions made in Phase 2?

B. Are toxicity test results significant when compared to reference site test results, i.e., non-affected locations?

C. What is the distribution of toxicity results relative to site habitat conditions and receptors?

D. What lab and field tests are necessary to define the extent and distribution of impact to ecological/biological receptors (i.e., endpoints)?

Box 2-7　*Phase 3—questions to be addressed in the confirmatory impact-assessment phase*

Phase 4—risk characterization

The characterization of risk involves a description of the observed or potential impact to the ecological/biological resources at the site. This overall risk defines the potential impacts under the existing condition at the site and provides the perspective of how much of the site's resources are at risk of being permanently affected or lost because of the contamination. In the characterization of risk, there must be a description of 1) what resources (i.e., assessment endpoints) are potentially affected; 2) how much or at what level the impact is observed; and 3) over what portions of the total site are the impacts observed. This summary includes 1) a description of the contaminants, their concentrations, and their spatial and temporal distribution across the site; 2) a description of the overall severity of impacts to the biological/ecological resources of the site as a result of the contamination; and 3) identification of the potential impacts due to each of the remedial alternatives, including the "no-action" alternative (Box 2-8).

A. Describe the significance of the overall risks to the biological or ecological resources of the site as a result of the contaminants;

B. Describe the significance of the overall risks to endpoints for the site;

C. Describe the potential risks due to all of the options including the "no remedial action" option

---

Box 2-8　*Phase 4—risk characterization activities*

Phase 5—remediation guidance

This phase includes the sampling, testing, and evaluation that are necessary to define clearly the degree of remediation necessary to protect the selected receptors. The work performed during this task is directed at defining the limits and extent of the impact in order to define the limits and extent of cleanup. The primary goal of the remedial guidance phase is to define the extent of the contamination that is known to cause a significant impact, the areal extent of those impacts, and the magnitude of ecological impact. Box 2-9 lists the questions that must be addressed during the remedial guidance phase.

> A. What is the areal extent of the stressors that produce significant effects?
>
> B. What is the impact of the contaminants on the resident populations of receptors and ecological resources?
>
> C. What remedial alternative is best for the site based on ecological assessment?
>
> D. What are the significant effects on the assessment endpoints at the site?
>
> E. Will changes (such as habitat alterations) associated with the proposed remedial actions be more helpful or destructive to the ecological resources as compared to the no-action alternative at the present level of ecological impact?

Box 2-9 Questions to be addressed in the remediation guidance phase

This phase includes the following activities:

Task 1: The areal extent of the stressors must be determined through sampling. This effort must be planned and designed to address the specific assessment and measurement endpoints identified for the site in the original scope and assessed throughout the entire process. The specific choice of species for this task should be a resident species to make the assessment as site-specific as possible.

The level of effort during this phase is influenced, in part, by the possible remedial alternatives for the site, by the size of the site, by the number of samples previously taken, and by the detection limits for the COCs. All of the sampling efforts for this phase are directed towards the determination of the distribution of the chemical concentration that was shown to result in unacceptable risk (i.e., hazard quotient > criteria).

Task 2: If samples collected in certain areas during the confirmatory phase were shown to result in toxicity "hits" or significant differences in the measurement endpoints (e.g., a response in mortality, reproduction, and growth relative to reference or control endpoints), then a field effort would be defined to delimit the extent and intensity of the ecological impact. Field studies must include the locations on the site that have a range of contaminant concentration, which will result in significant impact to the site-specific receptors to produce data for the development of site-specific cleanup levels.

Task 3: The choice of a remedial alternative should consider input from both the human-health and ecological assessments. The ecological impact assessment during the remedial investigation phase of the Superfund process provides the evaluation of the no-action alternative, (i.e., the "leave it alone" decision). An important consideration is the comparison of the present ecological impacts from chemical contamination to the level of expected ecological impact from remediation, such that the least destructive course of action can be identified and selected. The results of the ERA must be weighed against the final choice of remedial alternative with regard to the tradeoffs in potential destruction of habitat and other ecological impacts. For example, loss (through remediation) of a site that may currently provide prime nesting and foraging habitat for either resident or migratory waterfowl may be more detrimental than the need to clean up moderate levels of contamination. The proposed remedial alternative is expected to eliminate or reduce the contamination, thereby removing the stressors to the ecological resources. An assessment of the net benefits of the proposed remedial alternative (i.e., habitat alterations) as compared to the no-action alternative, considering the present level of ecological impact, must be made. Therefore, the activities required in this phase of the ERA must provide definitive data to describe the level of impact on the assessment endpoints with the known contaminant level such that the impact of the remediation can be reasonably estimated.

Summary

This chapter provides guidance for the completion of an ERA that must include, at a minimum, a discussion of the following key topics:

1) the important biological and ecological resources at risk on the site;
2) the assessment and measurement endpoints that are identified and used in the evaluation;
3) the COCs;
4) the pathways of exposure;
5) the distribution and the concentrations of the COCs across the site and the COC-specific concentration that represents the NOELs for the receptors of concern;
6) the locations that have concentrations of COCs above and below the NOELs;
7) an estimate of the cleanup level for the COCs,
8) a description of observed and potential impacts;
9) an evaluation of uncertainty for each location relative to the final choice of remedial alternative; and
10) a description of the recommended remedy for the site and the rationale for the choice.

This chapter has established a background for understanding the overall process and steps involved in ERA at Superfund sites as mandated by Region 9 of the USEPA. Later chapters in this book will provide additional insight into other important regulatory and economic issues often facing risk assessors and risk managers including 1) recognizing and working with various approaches to ERA that may be encountered as other regional and state guidance evolves, with guidelines developed by the California Department of Toxic Substances Control presented as an example of requirements that must also be met in 1 state within Region 9; 2) coordinating efforts and communication among regulators, risk assessors and risk managers; and 3) balancing the goals of environmental protection through ERA and management with a need for sustained economic development.

Acknowledgments - We would like to thank our colleagues, the Remedial Project Managers in Region 9, who have added immeasurably to the development of the material in this document. Special appreciation is due to the Region 9 Biological Technical Assistance Group, including Laura Valoppi, Jim Polisini, Susan Gladstone, Bobbye Smith, Jim Hass, Mike Martin, and Denise Klimas, for the many hours of discussion of this topic. Thanks, also, to Harry Ohlendorf, Anne Sergeant, and Joe Greenblott, who provided many helpful comments at various stages of the preparation of this document. Any misunderstanding and misstatements, however, are the responsibility of the authors.

Afterword

The above paper describes ERA USEPA Region 9 as practiced in 1992 based on the best information available at that time and under a structure defined by early USEPA literature. During the last 5 years the process has become more formalized based on material from the USEPA Risk Assessment Forum and USEPA Office of Emergency and Remedial Response (i.e., ECO Updates). The official USEPA ERA guidance for Superfund is stated in *Ecological Risk Assessment Guidance for Superfund: Process for Designing and Conducting Ecological Risk Assessments*, EPA 540-R-97-006.

References

Barnthouse LW, Breck JE, Jones TD, Kraemer SR, Smith ED, Suter II GW. 1986. Development and demonstration of a hazard assessment rating methodology for phase II of the Installation Restoration Program. ORNL/TM-9857, Publication No. 2582. Environmental Sciences Division. Oak Ridge TN.

Barnthouse LW, Suter II GW, Bartell SM, Beauchamp JJ, Gardner RH, Linder E, O'Neill RV, Rosen AE. 1986. User's manual for ecological risk assessment. ORNL-6251, Publication No. 2679. Environmental Sciences Division. Oak Ridge TN.

Norton S, McVey M, Colt J, Durda J, Hegner R. 1988. Review of ecological risk assessment methods. Washington DC: Office of Policy Planning and Evaluation USEPA. EPA/230-10-88-041

Suter II GW. 1993. Ecological risk assessment. Chelsea MI: Lewis. 538 p.

[USEPA] U.S. Environmental Protection Agency. 1986. Urban DJ, Cook NJ. Hazard evaluation division standard evaluation procedure ecological risk assessment. Washington DC: USEPA Office of Pesticide Programs. EPA 540/9-85-001

[USEPA] U.S. Environmental Protection Agency. 1988. Guidance for conducting remedial investigations and feasibility studies under CERCLA. Interim final. OSWER Directive 9355.3-01. Washington DC: Office of Emergency and Remedial Response. EPA/540/G-89/004.

[USEPA] U.S. Environmental Protection Agency. 1989a. Risk assessment guidance for superfund Volume II: environmental evaluation manual. Washington DC: USEPA. EPA 540/1-89/001.

[USEPA] U.S. Environmental Protection Agency. 1989b. Ecological assessments of hazardous waste sites: a field and laboratory reference guide. Corvallis OR: Office of Research and Development. EPA 600/3-89/013.

[USEPA] U.S. Environmental Protection Agency. 1991. ECO update. Ecological assessment of superfund sites: an overview. Washington DC: Office of Solid Waste and Emergency Response. Volume 1, Number 2. 9345.0-051.

[USEPA] U.S. Environmental Protection Agency. 1992a. A framework for ecological risk assessment at the EPA. Washington DC: Risk Assessment Forum. EPA/630/R-92/001.

[USEPA] U.S. Environmental Protection Agency. 1992b. ECO update. Developing a work scope for ecological assessments. Washington DC: Office of Solid Waste and Emergency Response. Volume 1, Number 4. 9345.0-051.

[USEPA] U.S. Environmental Protection Agency. 1992c. An SAB report: review of the process and rationale for developing ecological risk assessment guidelines. Washington DC: Science Advisory Board (A-101). EPA-SAB-EPEC-92-023.

[USEPA] U.S. Environmental Protection Agency. 1993. Data quality objectives process for superfund workbook. Washington DC: Office of Solid Waste and Emergency Response. 9355.9-01A, EPA 540-R-93-078.

Chapter 3

Guidance for performing ecological risk assessments at hazardous waste sites and permitted facilities in California

James M. Polisini, James C. Carlisle, and Laura M. Valoppi

Disclaimer: This document was prepared by and represents the personal views of the authors. The methodology presented here is one approach to ecological risk assessments at hazardous waste sites and permitted facilities, but is not the only methodology which would be acceptable to the California Department of Toxic Substances Control.

The Office of Scientific Affairs in the California Department of Toxic Substances Control (DTSC) has developed a phased ecological risk assessment (ERA) paradigm to direct ERAs at sites that may pose a potential threat to ecological systems and direct the determination of the nature and degree of threat. Ecological risk assessments performed using this protocol proceed through 3 tiers of study, each more comprehensive than the preceding tier. The initial scoping assessment, which identifies potential receptors, contaminants, and potentially complete exposure pathways, would be performed at every site. Predictive assessment and validation studies follow for sites where the scoping assessment indicates a potential threat. The predictive assessment for terrestrial receptors consists of a more detailed assessment of multimedia exposure to ecological receptors, which is analogous to a human-health risk assessment. A validation study is required to verify the conclusions of the predictive assessment. Detailed field or laboratory studies are required for those sites where the predictive assessment and validation study indicate a significant threat to ecological receptors or where the responsible party chooses to proceed immediately to a detailed assessment from the scoping assessment. The detailed studies determine the extent of deleterious effects and define the extent of contamination.

The California Department of Toxic Substances Control (DTSC), a part of the California Environmental Protection Agency (CalEPA), has responsibility under California statutes (California Health and Safety Code, Section 25201, 25351, 25355, and 25358) for investigation of California and Federal Superfund sites, for permitting sites that treat, store, or dispose of hazardous wastes (California Health and Safety Code, Section 25120 and 25159.5), for corrective action at facilities that treat, store, or dispose of hazardous wastes (California Health and Safety Code, Section 25200.10) and closure of facilities that treat, store, or dispose of hazardous wastes (California Health and Safety Code, Section 25246). The DTSC is also the lead Department for all CalEPA involvement in remedial investiga-

23

tion and feasibility studies under the federal CERCLA (1980) as amended by the SARA (1986). The Human and Ecological Risk Section (HERS) in the DTSC Office of Scientific Affairs has developed a tiered approach for ERAs at hazardous waste sites and permitted facilities to assist responsible parties and their contractors in preparing ERAs that contain the information necessary for DTSC to discharge its public responsibility for mitigation or remediation of these sites.

The DTSC currently provides regulatory oversight and coordination of the CalEPA regulatory activities at more than 1200 sites throughout California. The sites vary in size from approximately 6000 square feet to more than 170 square miles and vary in complexity from sites capped with asphalt to sites containing the largest remaining contiguous sections of several types of habitat in California. The range of toxicity for materials released at these sites ranges from fairly innocuous materials (e.g., "weathered" straight-chain, aliphatic hydrocarbons of low environmental mobility and low or unmeasured toxicity to ecological receptors) to organochlorine compounds that are extremely toxic to some species receptors and bioaccumulate at higher levels in the food web.

Toxicologists and other scientists in HERS function as technical consultants to DTSC project managers. The approach developed by HERS stresses early involvement of technical specialists, from both the regulatory agencies and the potentially responsible parties (PRPs), in developing the work plan to investigate potential threats to ecological receptors. This ERA guidance was developed as a phased approach to conserve resources for investigation and mitigation or remediation of sites that present a significant threat to the environment. The methodology outlined in this guidance begins with a scoping assessment, which defines the potentially exposed biota, potential COCs, and potentially complete exposure pathways. Sites that proceed on in the process perform a predictive assessment, analogous to the human-health risk-assessment paradigm, with components of exposure assessment, toxicity assessment, and risk characterization expressed as a hazard quotient (HQ) and hazard index (HI). Field or laboratory studies in the validation study are designed to verify the predictive assessment. Sites that appear to be a threat, based on the predictive assessment and supported by the validation study, proceed to more detailed field or laboratory studies to quantify the magnitude of the effect on ecological receptors and delineate the lateral, and possibly vertical, extent of the contamination. Decision points are outlined in this guidance so that it is clear when no further investigations are required at a site and when more detailed investigations are called for to define the threat to ecological receptors. Finally, it should be stressed that HERS envisions this process as a truly cooperative effort among all parties. Development of the site-specific work plan and evaluation of the site-specific information gathered require frank and honest scientific discussion among all parties.

There are numerous names and terms applied to the incremental phases proposed and implemented during most ERAs. The names applied to the 3 phases in this guidance were developed in conjunction with the USEPA Region 9 Superfund Technical Support

Section to facilitate discussion between HERS and USEPA Region 9 staff coordinating site-specific review. The scoping assessment is purposely not designated as Phase 1 because the scoping assessment is an expansion of the existing guidance for ecological screening provided in the DTSC Preliminary Endangerment Assessment (PEA) Manual (DTSC 1994). The components of a complete ERA as defined in this guidance include the following:

- A scoping assessment that includes a characterization of site-related habitats, potential ecological receptors associated with these habitats, potential COCs to ecological receptors, and potentially complete exposure pathways

  A work plan for the Phase 1 predictive assessment is included as part of the scoping assessment for those sites or facilities that do not drop out and continue with the ERA process. A flowchart specifying the decision points and reports for the scoping assessment is contained in Figure 3-1.

- A Phase 1 predictive assessment followed by a Phase 2 validation study

  The Phase 1 predictive assessment utilizes a reference dose approach similar to a human-health risk assessment for most terrestrial receptors and a reference concentration approach for most aquatic receptors. The Phase 2 validation study focuses on the components of the Phase 1 predictive assessment that appear the most uncertain. For example, ecological transfer factors that predict the movement of a contaminant from soil to plant tissue to

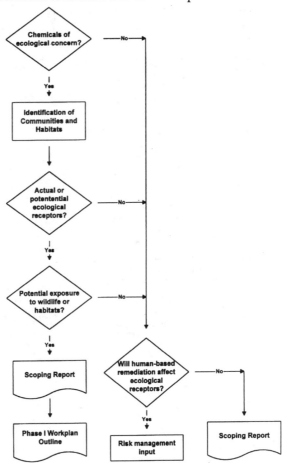

Figure 3-1   *Scoping assessment flow chart and decision criteria for tasks performed for all sites or facilities as the initial step in the ERA*

herbivore tissue or population studies of the species that appear to be the maximally affected receptors in the Phase 1 predictive assessment might be the focus of the Phase 2 validation study. The purpose of the Phase 2 validation study is to provide independent evidence that either supports or contradicts the conclusions of the Phase 1 predictive assessment. A flowchart specifying the decision points and reports for the Phase 1 predictive assessment and the Phase 2 validation study is contained in Figure 3-2.

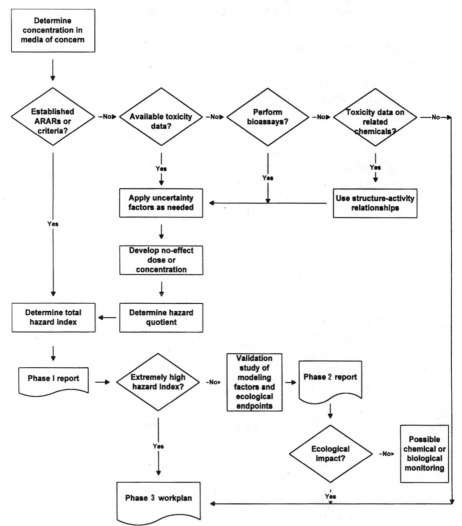

Figure 3-2   Phase 1 predictive assessment and Phase 2 validation study flow chart and decision criteria for sites or facilities proceeding to a Phase 1 predictive assessment based on the results of the scoping assessment

- A Phase 3 impact assessment that includes detailed site-specific field or laboratory evaluation of the degree and extent of the effect on ecological receptors at sites or facilities that appear to pose an ecological threat based on the Phase 1 predictive assessment and Phase 2 validation study. A flowchart specifying the decision points and reports for the Phase 3 impact assessment is contained in Figure 3-3.

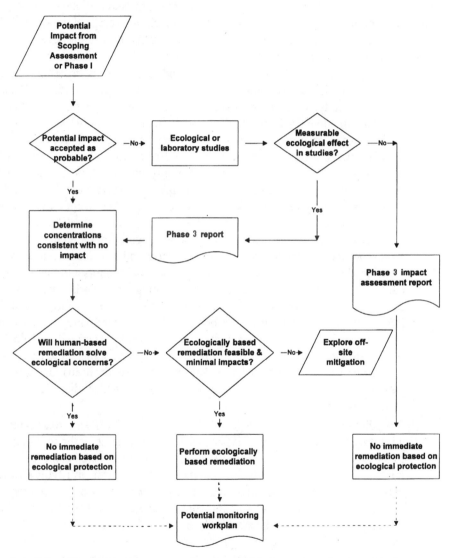

Figure 3-3   *Phase 3 impact assessment flow chart and decision criteria for sites of facilities proceeding to more detailed ERA based on the results of the Phase 1 predictive*

Rationale for methodology

The members of HERS developing this guidance have had numerous discussions with colleagues in other regulatory agencies and elsewhere who favor an ERA approach based more on field ecology or direct laboratory studies than on a predictive assessment analogous to the human-health paradigm, especially for evaluation of potential threats to terrestrial receptors. There has been a great deal of discussion in and outside of the scientific literature in support of both approaches. There are strengths and weaknesses associated with both approaches. This guidance is an attempt to take advantage of the strengths of each approach to support the other. The following strengths and weaknesses seem obvious to those developing this guidance:

1) A strength of ecological field or laboratory studies is that if an important component of the biological community is affected and the biological effect is of sufficient magnitude, the effect is measured directly with no need for extrapolation from an individual-level effect to the population or community level. Ecological field studies suffer from the weakness that there are many sources of variation in population and community parameters that frequently make interpretation of these studies difficult. Population or community effects related to contaminant exposure may not be observed by seasonal, positional, or meteorological differences, a fact that makes it impossible to demonstrate a significant difference. An additional weakness of ecological field studies is the difficulty in determining the important contaminant or exposure route when a significant difference is demonstrated between contaminated sites and treatment and control or reference sites. Identification of the significant contaminant or contaminants and the predominant routes of exposure can be crucial for evaluating the potential success or efficacy of remedial alternatives. Hazardous waste sites or permitted facilities frequently have elevated concentrations of multiple contaminants. The effects of each of these individual contaminants cannot be readily separated in ecological field studies. Severing a single exposure pathway may be sufficient to reduce the ecological threat to acceptable levels. The importance of the individual exposure pathways only rarely can be determined in ecological field studies at hazardous waste sites or permitted facilities.

2) A predictive assessment, analogous to the human-health HQ approach, has the advantage that 1) the toxic dose is fairly well-defined, at least for the species tested in the toxicological testing regime, 2) the toxic effect is fairly well-defined because it is the toxic endpoint determined from the toxicological test, and 3) the estimate of the contribution of each contaminant to the overall toxicity may help direct the remedial action to those contaminants contributing the greatest threat to ecological receptors. A predictive assessment based on a HQ has the weakness that a) the exposure rates and toxicity of many contaminants are not well known for many species of ecological concern, although the existing exposure-rate database is becoming more readily accessible (USEPA 1993a, 1993b) and b) extrapolation is

necessary to draw conclusions on ecological impacts based on toxic endpoints demonstrated in a small group of exposed individuals.

This guidance seeks to capture the strengths of each approach into an integrated approach that allows an informed decision for hazardous waste sties and permitted facilities. Sites or facilities can proceed from relatively rapid, inexpensive evaluations, which may allow a site or facility to exit the ERA process, to more detailed, expensive evaluations, or directly to mitigation or remediation for sites that appear to pose an ecological threat. Despite some of the methodological weaknesses, the HQ approach remains the most widely used model for risk characterization (Suter et al. 1993; Cockerham and Shane 1994). The HQ approach is used in this methodology as a screening step prior to more detailed analyses (USEPA 1988, 1994), and this approach compares an exposure with an effect level to evaluate whether adverse effects are expected. If the representative species and the toxicity data are appropriate and the ratio is less than 1, there is some confidence that there will be no significant ecological effect.

Scoping assessment

A scoping assessment is performed for all sites. The scoping assessment is not designed to determine definitely whether there is a problem with the site, but whether there is a potential ecological problem associated with the site. The scoping assessment provides the receptor, habitat, potential suite of contaminants, and exposure-pathway analysis necessary to produce the conceptual site model for those sites or facilities that proceed to more detailed levels of ERA. In order to reduce the labor required to perform this preliminary evaluation of the potential for ecological impacts, a habitat approach rather than a species census approach is specified to identify potential receptors. The habitat enumeration includes habitats in the immediate vicinity of the site at a distance that potential off-site receptors might reasonably make use of on-site habitats and come in contact with site-related contaminants, or that site-related contaminants may be transported to habitats in the immediate vicinity of the site. The habitat enumeration should extend to a distance at least 1 mile from the site boundary unless justification is provided that receptors associated with habitats on site and in the nearby area are unlikely to travel the 1 mile to on-site habitats. The scoping assessment also requires consideration of the potential impact associated with mitigation or remediation measures based on the human-health risk assessment. In certain cases, human health and ecological receptors may be more fully protected by implementation of risk-management measures, such as fencing to exclude humans, rather than immediate removal of contaminated soils and associated biota to a hazardous waste landfill. This is particularly true if natural biodegradation or physical processes such as photolysis will reduce soil contaminants to a no-effect concentration in a reasonable period of time.

The basis for the scoping assessment guidance is the DTSC PEA Manual (DTSC 1994). Assessments completed prior to the release of the scoping assessment guidance using the approach outlined in the PEA Manual will be accepted as equivalent to a scoping assessment report.

Identification of habitats

The biological characterization of the site should result in development of a conceptual site model that can focus investigation of any potential threat toward the species and habitats most likely to experience site-related effects. In lieu of an extensive site-specific biological survey conducted over an extended period of time to identify species occupying each distinct habitat, the species expected to occupy each habitat can be identified. A qualified field biologist should first identify each distinct habitat occupying the site and the surrounding area within 1 mile (including identification of locations where contaminants may be transported). The site survey should allow identification and determination of the extent of coverage of site-specific habitats. Off-site habitats that may be affected by site-related contamination must also be evaluated. Aquatic habitats should be evaluated in terms of both water and sediment components. All natural terrestrial habitats, as well as disturbed agricultural or landscape habitats, should be evaluated and characterized as to types of terrestrial vegetation communities. Transition zone habitats such as freshwater wetlands, saltwater wetlands, brackish water wetlands, marine intertidal zones and mudflats of rivers, lakes, or streams should be evaluated and characterized. The location of all wildlife areas, preserves, reserves, sanctuaries, parks, natural areas, conservation areas, or other protected areas within 1 mile of the site must be identified. Depending on regional habitat characteristics, it may be appropriate to identify these areas within a larger radius such as 5 miles. Seasonal variation should be considered for habitats with strong seasonal changes when scheduling site visits.

Identification of potential receptors

Particular emphasis should be placed on identification of plants and animals listed as "special species" and their habitats that occur on or within a 1-mile radius of the site or would be expected to occur based on habitat identification. Special species include

1) California species of special concern;

2) state and federally listed rare, threatened, or endangered species; and

3) species that are proposed or recommended for state or federal listing.

The California Department of Fish and Game's (DFG) Natural Heritage Division should be contacted for the current special animal and plant lists. The DFG's Natural Diversity Data Base (NDDB) can be a starting point for location information on special species that have been found near the site, although the NDDB is not an all-inclusive listing. (For more information on special plant and animal lists and the NDDB, contact: Information Services Coordinator, Information Services, Natural Heritage Division, California Dept. of Fish and Game, 1416 9th St., 12th Floor, Sacramento, CA , USA 95814, (916) 324-3812 or (916) 327-5960.)

In addition to the rare, threatened, or endangered species, the initial list of potential receptors includes those species that can be expected to occupy the habitats identified for the site based on the available literature. Examples of useful literature sources include Airola 1988, Mayer and Laudenslayer 1988, Zeiner et al. 1988, and Zeiner et al. 1990a. These references are available for purchase from Wildlife Habitat Relationship Coordinator, California Department of Fish and Game (916) 657-3933. These references also provide summary information on food items, life history, and habitat requirements for many species found in California.

A field biologist should visit the site to note the species, or signs of species activity, at the site. Observations should be made at dawn, in midday, and at dusk. The species present, or signs of activity, should be presented for comparison with the list of potential species based on the habitat evaluation. Advance notice of the date and time of the site survey to concerned regulatory agencies should be considered when appropriate.

Identification of potential contaminants of concern

The identification of contaminants of potential concern to ecological receptors is a separate process from any human-health screening evaluation, since a chemical not generally considered a threat to human health may be a potential chemical of concern for biota. For example, the chronic ambient water quality criteria (AWQC) for Cu is 6.5 g/L while the maximum contaminant level goal (MCLG) for drinking water is 1300 g/L. The chronic AWQC for Zn is 1.1 g/L while the secondary maximum contaminant level (SMCL) for drinking water is 5000 g/L (USEPA 1995). In contrast to aquatic organisms, individual exposure pathways for terrestrial organisms can be evaluated more easily. It is, therefore, difficult to offer similar media-specific comparisons for terrestrial organisms because toxicity can differ significantly depending on the route of exposure. However, for example, organophosphate pesticides such as diazinon (Eisler 1986a), carbamate pesticides such as carbofuran (Eisler 1985a), organochlorine pesticides such as mirex (Eisler 1985b), herbicides such as atrazine (Eisler 1989), and polychlorinated biphenyls (PCBs) (Eisler 1986b) may be of concern for terrestrial organisms at lower concentrations than for humans.

The list of potential contaminants of concern (COCs) may be developed based either on site-specific history of use or laboratory testing of environmental media. The history of site-specific use is more typically the source of potential COCs in the scoping assessment phase of work. A table should be prepared listing the potential COCs (whether historical use or laboratory results were the basis for inclusion) the contaminated or potentially contaminated environmental media, and the potentially affected habitat. Potential COCs that are included based on chemical analysis must include the number of samples analyzed, the minimum concentration, the maximum concentration, and the mean concentration for each contaminated medium.

Identification of potentially complete exposure pathways

Once potential species and habitats are identified, a pathway assessment is conducted. Pathway assessment identifies the potential for contact between biota and chemicals of concern in any medium and by any route. Media to be considered include soil, sediments, air, water, and biota. In particular, off-site transport of contaminants such as surface water drainage pathways must be evaluated. Physical and chemical characteristics that influence environmental fate and transport must be considered. Persistent chemicals should receive particular consideration.

Pathways may be direct, e.g., inhalation of air, or indirect, e.g., movement through the food web. Direct exposure routes to be considered include inhalation, ingestion, and dermal contact. Indirect exposure via consumption of food items also should be evaluated for those chemicals of concern with physical parameters that indicate a potential for persistence, bioaccumulation, and toxicity. Both bioconcentration from environmental media and biomagnification at successive trophic levels should be included in evaluation of bioaccumulation. Inorganic contaminants, e.g., Hg, Pb, Cd, and Se, which are known to bioaccumulate, should be included in the assessment of bioaccumulation. Trophic transfer of inorganic contaminants may contribute significantly to hazard in wildlife species. Organic compounds that have a log octanol/water partition coefficient (log K_{ow}) > 2.0 should be evaluated for inclusion in the bioaccumulation assessment based on toxicity and persistence. Exposure via food web transfers must be evaluated for organic compounds that have a log K_{ow} > 3.5 (Garten and Trabalka 1983). Highly bioaccumulative organic compounds that have a log K_{ow} greater than 5.0 can be expected to have the food-intake pathway as the dominant exposure pathway contributing to a hazard.

The scoping assessment should include evaluation of the potential threat associated with direct exposure pathways in addition to potential threat associated with food-web transfers. Pathways shall be considered complete unless the chemical will not enter the medium or the receptor will not contact the medium, either directly or indirectly. Realistic future conditions should also be considered also so that potential future exposure enters into the determination of complete exposure pathways.

A conceptual site model must be prepared for the site or permitted facility as part of the analysis. The conceptual site model describes a series of working hypotheses of how the stressors interact with 1 or more biological components (USEPA 1994). Conceptual site models describe the potentially threatened ecosystem, the relationship between assessment and measurement endpoints, and the applicable exposure scenarios. Conceptual site models are frequently presented as a figure showing the direct and food-chain exposure of components of the biological community to site-related chemicals.

A qualitative description of the magnitude, duration, and frequency of exposure to the various biological receptors, representing multiple trophic levels, for each contaminant or area of contamination should be provided. Restricted site use, seasonally restricted use, and daily activity patterns are factors that may limit exposure. A tabular summary of the exposure pathways for each habitat type should be provided. The most significant exposure pathways should be identified along with the potential COCs and the potential ecological receptors. This exposure-pathway analysis is an expansion of the site conceptual model.

Findings of the scoping assessment

A qualitative statement should be provided that summarizes the findings of the scoping assessment. If the conclusion is that no further investigation is required because the site and areas actually or potentially affected by the site are not utilized by biota and do not contain wildlife habitats, or because there are no actually or potentially complete exposure pathways, this conclusion must be clearly stated and justified. If potentially toxic chemicals have contaminated (or may reasonably be expected to contaminate) media that may contact wildlife or wildlife habitats, either on-site or off-site, directly or indirectly, the potential for exposure is considered to exist, and further investigation and assessment may be warranted.

In the event that no further ecological assessment is required for the site or permitted facility, the listing of habitats and potential receptors contained in the scoping assessment should then be used to evaluate any potential impact associated with mitigation or remediation actions that are based on protection of human health. An evaluation of potential damage to ecological systems may be a critical factor in selecting an appropriate remedial alternative.

Maps and figures

A site-wide habitat map is required as part of the scoping assessment. All major habitats should be displayed on a map equivalent to a 7.5' U.S. Geological Survey (USGS) quadrangle map. Separate indication of the coverage of tree canopy, shrubs, or dominant herbaceous plants may be appropriate depending on the coverage of the tree canopy. A site-wide map of similar dimension should indicate historical land-use patterns, particularly those land uses that may have resulted in release of hazardous substances. All areas where potential releases may have occurred should be noted even if no release has been documented. Where there is significant change in elevation, land-use and potential release sites should be presented on a topographic map to aid in identification of contaminant transport pathways such as surface drainages. Current land use that differs from historical land use must be indicated. Location of former landfills, waste piles, material stockpiles, burn pits, surface impoundments, firing ranges, strafing or bombing ranges, hazardous waste storage areas, and reutilization areas are especially important. Both the habitat coverage and the land use may be displayed on the same map if the degree of detail is not confusing. Additional smaller scale maps of portions of the site may be necessary, as appropriate, to adequately portray habitat-specific information. Sites where future land use is industrial or commercial may not require smaller habitat-specific maps.

Phase 1 work plan

An outline of the Phase 1 work plan is required as part of the scoping assessment report for those sites that will proceed to a more detailed ERA. This outline should include a list of the potential representative species to be evaluated in the Phase 1 predictive assessment. The potential receptor listing and the conceptual site model should guide selection of the representative species. A preliminary list of the pathways proposed for evaluation should be included. The field survey methods proposed to validate the preliminary habitat maps should be listed. The assessment and measurement endpoints should be clearly stated and justified. The proposed data-quality objectives should be clearly stated. The preliminary conceptual site model should be presented as support for the proposed assessment and measurement endpoints. The hypotheses for any proposed statistical testing, as well as the proposed statistical method, must be presented.

Contents of scoping report

At a minimum the scoping report must contain the following materials or their equivalents:

1) A facility-wide habitat map showing all major habitat types and equivalent to a 7.5' USGS quadrangle map scale is needed. A qualitative habitat map that outlines the general boundaries and extent of all major habitat types (e.g., canopies, shrubs, dominant herbs) will fulfill this requirement. A formal plant-community, field-mapping effort is not required for the scoping report.

2) A facility-wide, land-use-history map showing current and historical land use (e.g., landfills, waste piles, firing ranges, strafing areas, burn pits, explosives areas, hazardous waste storage areas, pesticide storage and wash areas, scrap yards, motor pools, gasoline stations, and fuel farms) is required. A topographic map presentation should be used where appropriate.

3) An overlay or combination of the facility-wide habitat map and the facility-wide, land-use map is needed if significant to the findings of the scoping study.

4) A site-specific habitat map should be available if significant to the findings of the scoping study. Alter the scale of the site-specific habitat map to suit each site, habitat, and density of ecological receptors. For sites where future land use is industrial, commercial, or residential, smaller site-scale maps may not be necessary.

5) A summary table of potential COCs and range of concentrations, similar to Table 3-1, is needed. The detail will vary with facility and site and how much is known at the time of the scoping assessment, but all available site-contaminant information should be provided.

6) Current and historical land-use information is required. This table may accompany and more fully explain the land-use-history map.

7) A summary table of potential receptors, similar to Table 3-2, should be provided, including the following additional information using known species lists as a base: species name; seasons in which it is expected to be found on the facility; presence

noted during the site walk (visual sighting [provide photograph], tracks [provide photograph], nest [provide photograph], call, and scat); and nocturnal or diurnal activity patterns. Indicate whether the species was observed during the morning or evening site visit. Also indicate whether the species are rare, threatened, or endangered (RTE).

8) A summary table of potentially complete exposure pathways similar to Table 3-3 is needed. This table should include receptors from each significant habitat including terrestrial receptors, e.g., piscivorous birds or waterfowl, which may have significant exposure to contaminants present in both terrestrial and aquatic habitats.

9) Copies of data logs used during the site walk to generate tables of observed species are required.

10) Copies of photographs used to document presence of ecological receptors are needed.

Contents of the Phase 1 work plan outline

An outline of the proposed Phase 1 predictive assessment work plan is required for those sites or facilities that will proceed with a more detailed ERA based on the conclusions of the scoping assessment. A fully developed Phase 1 predictive assessment work plan will be prepared in consultation with regulatory agencies, based on the proposals contained in this outline. The outline must contain the following items:

1) a preliminary list of potential receptors to be evaluated in detail,

2) a preliminary list of potential pathways for each receptor to be evaluated,

3) field validation of preliminary facility-specific habitat maps,

4) assessment endpoints to be evaluated,

5) measurement endpoints to be measured,

6) proposed data-quality objectives,

7) preliminary conceptual site model, and

8) proposed hypotheses for any statistical testing.

Further detail is provided in the following section.

Alternatives to Phase 1 predictive assessment

A responsible party may, with concurrence of regulatory agencies, proceed directly from the scoping assessment to the more detailed field or laboratory analysis identified as Phase 3 impact assessment. Determination of the lateral and vertical extent of contamination without performing a predictive assessment or the validation study may be appropriate when coupled with subsequent removal or treatment actions for small areas of contamination or extremely toxic contaminants. Extensive field or laboratory testing is part of Phase 3 in the tiered structure outlined in this guidance. Progression to detailed toxicity testing or extensive ecological field studies directly from the scoping phase im-

Table 3-1   *Potential chemicals of concern, media, site history and chemical analysis indication, number of detects in the number of samples, detection limits, and minimum, mean and maximum detected concentration*

Chemical	Medium	Site history	Analysis	Detects/ samples	Limit of detection	Mini- mum	Mean	Maxi- mum
2,4,5-T	Soil	X						
Beryllium	Soil	X	X	0/5	100 μg/kg	ND	ND	ND
DDT	Soil	X	X	3/5	100 μg/kg	1 mg/kg	20 mg/kg	10,000 mg/kg
Mercury	Sediment		X	4/5	.01 μg/kg	0.5μg/kg	4 μg/kg	6 μg/kg
Beryllium	Water		X	3/5	.5 μg/L	1 μg/L	5 μg/L	100μg/L

Table 3-2   *Site habitat summary and potential ecological receptors listing the habitat types, acreage and percent of cover, species name; whether the species was observed during the morning (a.m.) or evening (p.m.) site visit. Also indicate whether the species are RTE*

Habitat type	Acres (% site)	Expected species	Observed species	Relative occurence	RTE
Chaparral				Common	No
Oak woodland	10 (50%)	Scrub jay	a.m. x p.m. x	Common	No
Vernal pool	1 (5%)	Fairy shrimp	a.m. x p.m. x	Common	No
Oak/willow riparian	9 (45%)	Least bell's vireo	a.m. x p.m.	Rare	Yes

Table 3-3   *Assessment of potentially complete exposure pathways listing the habitat type, potential contaminant, potentially contaminated media, potential exposure route, specifics of food web exposure, and whether the pathway is judged complete*

Habitat type	Potential contaminants	Contaminated media	Direct exposure	Food web exposure	Complete exposure pathway
Chaparral	DDT	Soil	Soil ingestion		Yes
Chaparral	DDT	Soil	Ingestion of prey	Soil invertebrates to mouse	Yes
Stream	DDT	Sediment	Ingestion of prey	Stream invertebrates to fish	Yes
Chaparral	Chloroform	Groundwater	Inhalation of soil gases		Yes
Chaparral	Chloroform	Groundwater	Ingestion		No

plies agreement that the findings of the scoping assessment indicate a potential threat of sufficient magnitude that the Phase 1 predictive assessment and the Phase 2 validation study are unnecessary.

Phase 1 predictive assessment and Phase 2 validation study

A Phase 1 predictive assessment coupled with a Phase 2 validation study is required for those sites where the scoping assessment demonstrates that releases are occurring (or have occurred in the past), potential receptors are present on or near the site, and that exposure pathways are potentially complete. The Phase 1 predictive assessment and Phase 2 validation study are not required for sites that have minimal terrestrial or aquatic habitats, wherein the habitat is not provided regulatory protection, the habitat is not utilized by special species, or the site is shown in the scoping assessment to have no potentially complete exposure pathways. The magnitude of the Phase 1 and Phase 2 study will vary with the nature of the site and the list of potential COCs developed in the scoping assessment. Development of the Phase 1 and Phase 2 work plan should, therefore, be a cooperative endeavor with regulatory agencies.

The Phase 1 and Phase 2 studies under this guidance are conducted to provide an estimate of the magnitude of the potential risk to ecological receptors. Determination of the temporal, lateral, and vertical extent of any contaminated media identified in the Phase 1 and Phase 2 studies is performed in Phase 3. It is appropriate, therefore, to concentrate the Phase 1 and Phase 2 studies on areas or locations expected to be maximally contaminated. Terrestrial systems are frequently evaluated using a HQ approach based on a reference dose (RfD) while aquatic systems are routinely evaluated using a reference concentration (RfC) approach. Guidance for the 2 ecosystem types are separated for clarity. The Phase 1 predictive assessment contains components analogous to a human-health risk assessment (USEPA 1989): data collection and data evaluation; toxicity assessment; exposure assessment; and risk characterization. The suite of contaminants of ecological concern (COECs) is developed as part of the data evaluation. Potential exposure pathways to be evaluated are identified, exposure concentration estimates are developed, and chemical intakes are estimated in the exposure assessment. Toxicity information is gathered for the COECs, and toxicity values are developed from the representative species during toxicity assessment. The threat to the representative species is quantified for individual COECs and the threat from multiple COECs is estimated during risk characterization.

A Phase 1 predictive assessment for terrestrial biota, like human-health risk assessments, uses an RfD and associated methodology to predict the threat associated with a dose. An RfD approach is used because the exposure of terrestrial species can be separated into multiple separate exposure pathways. Uncertainty factors are used to provide additional protection when extrapolation of toxicity data is necessary, providing protection for species that may be more sensitive than those tested and evaluated.

Terrestrial receptors

In this guidance, functional groupings (ecological guilds) are used to represent diverse taxa that may be exposed to contamination at or near a site or facility because it is generally recognized that it would be impractical to individually evaluate the effects of the chemicals of concern on every potentially affected species. Rooted macrophytes, carnivorous birds, and small omnivorous mammals are examples of ecological guilds. As it would be impossible to evaluate all members of an ecological guild, representative species are chosen to typify the response of the guilds based on the potential species identified in the scoping assessment. Representative species need not actually occupy the habitat at the site, but they are used to represent a group which potentially or actually does. Representative species selected should include a primary producer, a primary consumer, higher level consumers, and may include decomposers. Representative species chosen also should be those species potentially maximally affected by contaminants at the site. The choice among several members of an ecological guild also may be influenced by the availability of toxicity information in the literature. Selection criteria for the representative species should include: sensitivity of the representative species relative to other members of the ecological guild; availability of data for the representative species; relationship of the representative species to the species or ecological guild being evaluated; consistency of exposure scenarios with the species or ecological guild being evaluated; and practical issues such as availability of suitable test protocols in the event testing is proposed in the Phase 2 validation study. Any special species that are known or expected to occur on or near the site should be considered as candidates for inclusion as representative species. If special species are not chosen as representative species, their ecological guild must be adequately protected by the representative species. Groups to be considered in the ERA are those that occupy or could potentially occupy habitats that are affected or potentially affected by contamination related to the site or facility. Species are considered potential users of a habitat based on their historical presence or their presence in similar habitats in the ecoregion.

Contaminants of concern

Reduction in the number of chemicals of concern is included as an option for human-health risk assessments (USEPA 1989). The criteria defined may be used to eliminate potential COECs detected at the site if the number of potential COECs is excessive. In general, given the use of electronic spreadsheets for hazard calculation, reduction of the number of COECs should not be performed unless the number of potential COECs exceeds 50. These criteria, if employed, are meant to be employed in an integrated manner. The risk assessment guidelines (RAGS) for Superfund criteria are (DTSC 1994)

1) Consultation with the remedial project manager (RPM) is necessary. Approval of the RPM must be obtained prior to eliminating potential COECs.

2) Documentation of the rationale for eliminating potential COECs is required. If a continuing need to justify elimination of potential COECs is anticipated, it may be preferable to retain all potential COECs.

3) Consideration of the historical site-specific information is needed. Potential COECs reliably associated with site use should not be removed from the analysis.

4) Evaluation of concentration and toxicity is necessary. Highly toxic potential COECs should be retained even if present at low concentration or low frequency of detection. The conceptual site model developed as part of the scoping assessment is critical for this decision.

5) Mobility, persistence, and bioaccumulation should be considered. Highly volatile potential COECs may be critical if inhalation appears to be a significant exposure pathway. Highly bioaccumulative potential COECs should not be eliminated.

6) Potential COECs that are difficult to treat may drive the selection of remedial alternatives and should remain in the full analysis.

7) Potential COECs for which ARARs have been promulgated usually are not candidates for elimination.

8) Potential COECs that are infrequently detected may be artifacts of sampling or analytical procedures. However, the detection limit should be evaluated against appropriate ecological effect concentrations to determine whether the analytical technique is sufficiently sensitive. Any detection frequency criterion must be approved by the RPM prior to implementation. No potential COEC that is reliably reported as being used at the site should be removed based on this criterion.

Sequential evaluation of each criterion with exclusion of contaminants at each stage is inappropriate. For example the "5% detect" level (RAGS,Chapter 5) is stated as an example of a level at which contaminants might be excluded from further consideration. Sequential evaluation of the 5% detect criterion followed by exclusion of common laboratory contaminants could unreasonably remove contaminants that should be carried forward in the risk assessment. For example, eliminating dichlorodiphenyl-dichloroethylene (DDE) from further consideration based on a low frequency of detection and then eliminating dichlorodiphenyltrichloroethane (DDT) and dichlorodiphenylethane (DDD) based on low media concentrations would be inappropriate.

Selection and use of toxicity data

Toxicity data for the representative species and members of the same order should be considered in estimating toxicity to representative species. If data from the representative species and members of the same taxonomic order are unavailable, of questionable quality, or are known to be inappropriate because of physiological differences, then a wider range of taxa should be considered. Data for structurally related chemicals also should be considered if data for the chemical in question are inadequate. Selection of appropriate data should be based on a balance of taxonomic and physiological similarity, quality of the data, and expected mode of toxic action. The dataset selection should be fully justified, and summaries of the data used should be provided. The data should be used to estimate the no-observed-adverse-effect level (NOAEL) in the representative species. Adverse effects include acute, chronic, lethal, and sublethal toxicity, including, but not limited to, behavioral, reproductive, and some biochemical effects. Other possible adverse effects include excess stimulation of growth or reproduction that may lead to population imbalances.

Standardized toxicity tests may be performed to assess the hazard to plants, decomposers, and the soil invertebrate community if insufficient toxicity data are available for the site-specific COECs to evaluate the threat to these receptors.

Uncertainty factors

When appropriate, the NOAEL should be divided by one or more uncertainty factors (UF) to determine the RfD. Uncertainty factors are multiplicative, such that the UF denominator is 25 for 2 single UFs of 5. The magnitude and number of UFs are based on the number, quality, duration, and sensitivity of the studies used in the assessment and taxonomic extrapolation from the tested organism to the representative species used in the risk assessment. Development of the UFs should be clearly described and, when possible, supported by a range of toxicity values within a taxonomic group. Uncertainty factors of 1 are required to compensate for each of the following:

1) A study duration of less than 1 full life cycle when the most sensitive stages of the life cycle were not tested. Use an UF of 1 (for tests over the full life cycle or testing on the most sensitive life stages) to 10 (for acute tests).

2) A study that does not address sensitive indicators of toxicity such as reproduction, behavior, or pathology. Use an UF of 1 (for tests measuring sensitive endpoints such as reproduction, behavior, or pathology) to 5 (for insensitive endpoints such as death or immobilization). Where the toxicity data are insufficient to develop UFs for species-specific endpoints and test exposure period, use the following default UFs. In the absence of toxicity testing that indicates different UFs should be used, the default UFs for endpoint and exposure period extrapolation are the following:

	UF	Example
a) To adjust from less sensitive endpoints such as mortality to more sensitive endpoints	5	$LD50$ to $LOAEL_{Acute}$
b) To adjust from less than chronic to chronic exposure	5	$LOAEL_{Acute}$ to $LOAEL_{Chronic}$
c) To adjust from observable effect to NOEC levels	5	$LOAEL_{Chronic}$ to $NOAEL_{Chronic}$

3) Interspecies extrapolation when the extrapolation is between taxonomically distant species (e.g., different family or order). When the range of species tested is narrow, making it impossible to base the UF on the toxicity data, use the following default UFs. No detailed review of toxicity data was performed by HERS to de-

velop these default UFs for interspecies extrapolation of toxicity data. They are a reasonable compromise between using no UFs and using a UF of 10 at every level of extrapolation. These UFs are in the range of the geometric mean of 4 for interspecies chronic and subchronic NOAEL comparisons in studies of UFs currently in preparation (USEPA in prep.).

a) Toxicity extrapolation within the Class Mammalia.

	UF	Example
i. Within the same taxonomic family	1	Beagle to fox (canidae to canidae)
ii. Within the same taxonomic order	2	Laboratory mouse to ground squirrel (muridae to sciuridae)
iii. Between taxonomic orders	5	Laboratory mouse to fox (rodent to carnivore)
b) Toxicity extrapolation from Class Mammalia to Class Aves	10	Laboratory rat to red-tailed hawk

4) The best studies available have deficiencies that result in uncertainty about the results.

5) Study duration is insufficient to obtain maximum tissue concentration and toxic effect.

6) Bodyweight extrapolation is necessary. Scale the RfD on the basis of body weight to the ¾ power where body weights of terrestrial test species differ from the representative species by 2 orders of magnitude.

Terrestrial exposure assessment

All complete direct and indirect exposure pathways should be included in the Phase 1 predictive assessment. Exposure pathways that must be considered include the following:

- ingestion of contaminated soil or sediment;
- dermal contact with contaminated soil, sediment, or water;
- inhalation of contaminated airborne particles;
- inhalation of vapors (surface and subsurface locations);
- ingestion of contaminated water; and
- ingestion of contaminated food.

Bioaccumulation, which includes both tissue concentration increases from environmental media (bioconcentration) and tissue concentration increases with successive food web transfers (biomagnification), must be evaluated unless sufficient justification is provided that the COCs do not bioaccumulate. Indirect exposure via consumption of food items should be evaluated for those chemicals of concern with physical parameters that indicate a potential for persistence, bioaccumulation, and toxicity. Both bioconcentration from environmental media and biomagnification at successive trophic levels should be included in evaluation of bioaccumulation. Inorganic contaminants, e.g., Hg, Pb, Cd and Se, that are known to bioaccumulate should be included in the assessment of bioaccumulation. Trophic transfer of inorganic contaminants may contribute significantly to hazard in wildlife species. Organic compounds that have a log K_{ow} > 2.0 should be evaluated for inclusion in the bioaccumulation assessment based on toxicity and persistence. Exposure via food web transfers must be evaluated for organic compounds that have a log K_{ow} > 3.5 (Garten and Trabalka 1983). Highly bioaccumulative organic compounds that have a log K_{ow} > 5.0 can be expected to contribute significantly to ecological hazard. Any exposure pathways not evaluated must be clearly indicated with appropriate justification for no further evaluation. Separate exposure pathway analysis by dose need not be completed for those pathways that are evaluated simultaneously by comparison with reference concentrations. This is typically the approach employed for many aquatic species.

A series of equations are used to estimate the uptake via the various pathways. All parameters must be supported by literature citations or a detailed justification explaining the exposure parameter development. Intake equations are of the form

$$\text{Daily intake} = \frac{\text{CM} * \text{CR} * \text{FI} * \text{AF}}{\text{BW}}$$

Equation 3-1

where

Daily Intake = the intake rate or dose per body weight (mass of chemical per body weight per unit time, usually mg $_{chemical}$ /kg $_{body\,weight}$ -d)

CM = Concentrations of potentially toxic chemicals in media of concern (usually as mg $_{chemical}$ / kg $_{media}$). These are typically determined by a combination of measurement and modeling. A source should be characterized by analysis, whereas movement into other media might be measured or modeled. In either case, spatial and temporal variation should be addressed. All computer models must be models published in peer-reviewed journals and readily available.

CR = contact rates. These should be determined or estimated for each medium and pathway of concern for each representative species, except as noted above for Phase 1 predictive assessments using reference concentrations typical of aquatic risk assessments. Contact rates are expressed in terms of quantity of the medium (weight or volume) per day, usually as mg/d. When contact rates for the representative species are not available, they may be estimated using data from related species. In selecting surrogate species, taxonomic, anatomic, physiologic, and behavioral relationships should be considered, along with the quality of the studies. The selection of surrogate data must be fully justified.

FI = fractional intake. This is the fraction of time spent in contact with contaminated media at the hazardous waste site or permitted facility. For example, the fractional intake for a carnivore with a home range 10 x the area of a site would be 0.1 unless there are resources such as available water or cover that would increase the time spent at the site and therefore increase the value for fractional intake.

AF = absorption fraction. This term may be used if there are data to show that absorption by the route in question is a fraction of that by the route for which the RfD was determined. An absorption fraction is most often proposed for conversion of an ingestion RfD an inhalation RfD. Use of an absorption fraction different from 1 requires that the absorption fraction be determined for the original route of exposure.

BW = body weight of the animal. The most health-protective body weight, i.e., the lowest body weight, should be used for those representative species with sufficient life-history data. For most species, the spring body weight is the lowest and therefore the most protective.

Terrestrial risk characterization

A HQ should be calculated for each COEC for each species under evaluation. The HQ for each representative species and COEC is the total dose from all exposure routes divided by the toxicity RfD. The duration of the exposure and the toxicity criterion should match as closely as possible (i.e., chronic exposures should be compared with chronic toxicity endpoints). If this is not possible, UFs may be required to adjust for differences. Hazard quotients in excess of 1 indicate a potential COEC-specific threat. For a screening-level evaluation of potential additive effects from multiple COECs, the HQs for all COECs are added to arrive at a (HI) for each representative species. An HI for all COECs < 1, is a reasonably good indication that adverse effects on the species under assessment are unlikely. If the HI for all COECs exceeds 1, the HQs should be summed by 1) mechanism of toxic action or 2) target organ to provide a more realistic assessment of potential threat. Hazard indexes are intended to be conservative estimators of potential additive threat and potential hazard. Hazard indices < 1 for each mode of toxic action or target organ provide a reasonably good indication that adverse effects on the species under assessment are unlikely. The conclusion of little or no threat requires that sensitive indicators of chronic toxicity have been measured in appropriate test species and that environmental concentrations have not been underestimated.

Nonetheless, field and/or laboratory verification of key facets of the Phase 1 predictive assessment is usually required. The extent of this Phase 2 validation study will be determined in conjunction with DTSC project manager and other regulatory agencies.

Terrestrial Phase 2 validation

A Phase 2 validation study usually will be required unless the results of the Phase 1 predictive study indicate an incredibly high HI and the responsible party agrees to proceed directly to the Phase 3 impact assessment or proceed with immediate remediation. A

Phase 2 validation study is required where the results of the Phase 1 investigation indicate an unacceptable threat to ecological receptors (HI > 1) or the results are ambiguous. A Phase 2 validation study may not be required if the threat to ecological receptors is considered minimal (HI << 1) in the judgment of the regulatory agencies. The scope of the Phase 2 validation study should be developed in conjunction with regulatory agencies. The purpose of the Phase 2 validation study is to provide support for the predictive estimate of threat to ecological receptors developed in Phase 1. The Phase 2 validation study may provide evidence to evaluate a Phase 1 predictive assessment of little potential threat or a Phase 1 predictive study indicative of some degree of threat. Depending on the results of the Phase 1 study, the Phase 2 validation may focus either on 1) assessing biological population or community parameters or 2) demonstrating that an estimated or derived transfer factor used in Phase 1 predictive assessment is a valid transfer factor. It is impossible to exactly define the Phase 2 validation study because each will be tailored to investigate the assumptions and conclusions of the Phase 1 predictive assessment. For example, the Phase 2 validation study for a terrestrial system might focus on a demonstration that populations of the receptor most likely to display some toxic effect are similar to populations from a control area in density, age structure, and reproductive rate. Alternately, the Phase 2 validation study for a terrestrial system might measure soil concentration and the uptake of a COEC into plant tissue to demonstrate that the plant uptake factor used in the Phase 1 predictive assessment was appropriate. Toxicity tests of species, e.g., earthworms and plants, or community analysis of the soil microarthropod community are 2 other examples of relatively simple methods of assessing the threat to terrestrial ecological receptors that would be appropriate for a Phase 2 validation study.

Aquatic introduction
The Phase 1 predictive assessment of the risk to aquatic ecological receptors includes selection of representative species for the aquatic habitats that are potentially impacted by contaminants and comparison of reference concentrations with measured or projected media concentrations.

Aquatic representative species
Aquatic representative species should be chosen from those present at the site or facility (or closely related species) to limit the magnitude and number of UFs necessary to derive the toxicity criterion. In the absence of site-specific representative species with adequate toxicity datasets, the following species or groups are recommended (Table 3-4):

- Freshwater habitats—water soluble contaminants

    The alga, *Selenastrum capricornutum* or an equivalent unicellular primary producer, a microcrustacean, e.g., *Ceriodaphnia dubia*, and a relatively sensitive carnivorous fish, e.g., the rainbow trout, should be evaluated as default representative species.

Table 3-4   Default representative species or species groups to be evaluated for aquatic predictive assessments, in the absence of site-specific representative species, in addition to comparison with applicable regulatory guidance concentrations

	Primary producer	Consumer	Consumer
Freshwater - water soluble	*Selenastrum capricornutum*	*Ceriodaphnia dubia*	*Oncorhynchus mykiss*
Freshwater - sediment-bound	Alga or rooted macrophyte	*Hyallella azteca*	*Chironomus* sp.
Estuarine/marine - water soluble	Marine alga	Invertebrate	Larval fish
Estuarine/marine - sediment-bound	Marine alga	Amphipod	Polychaete worm

- Freshwater habitats—sediment-bound contaminants

  A rooted macrophyte or a freshwater amphipod, e.g., *Hyallella azteca* and a freshwater insect larva, e.g., a chironomid midge, should be evaluated.

- Estuarine or marine habitat—water column contaminants

  The potential response of a marine alga e.g., Skeletonema costatum *or* Macrocystis pyrifera, an estuarine or marine larval fish e.g., the inland silverside (*Menidia beryllina*) or the sand dab *(Pleuronectes platessa),* and an invertebrate, e.g., *Mysidopsis bahia* or *Holmesimysis costata,* should be evaluated.

- Estuarine or marine habitat—sediment-bound contaminants

  The potential response of a rooted macrophyte or a marine alga, e.g., kelp, to the porewater concentration should be evaluated. In addition, the response of a marine amphipod, e.g., *Repoxynius abronius, Eohaustorius estuarius,* or *Grandidierella japonica,* and of a marine polychaete worm, e.g, *Neanthes* sp., should be evaluated.

Aquatic reference concentrations

Two types of reference concentration data should be reviewed, and the most protective reference concentration should be used in the predictive assessment. In addition to reference concentration data for the site-specific representative species or the default species listed above, an additional source of reference concentrations should be multiple-species reference concentrations developed by state, federal or regional regulatory agencies. Federal Aquatic Water Quality Criteria (AWQC), California Regional Water Quality Control Board Basin Plan Water Quality Objectives (WQO), National Oceanic and Atmospheric Administration (NOAA), effect range-lows (ER-Ls), and apparent effect thresholds (AETs) are examples of multiple-species reference concentrations. In addition, recent literature should be reviewed for toxicity data relevant to the site-specific representative species. Reference concentrations that are developed as guidance rather than regulation are available from many sources. Examples of various sources for reference concentrations are

- The potential for biological effects of sediment-sorbed contaminants tested in the national status and trends program. March 1990. NOAA Technical Memorandum NOS OMA 52.
- California enclosed bays and estuaries plan. Water quality control plan for enclosed bays and estuaries of California. California Water Resources Control Board, April 1991, 91-13 WQ.
- Devillers J, Exbrayat JM. 1992. Ecotoxicity of chemicals to amphibians. Volume 1. Philadelphia PA: Gordon and Breach Science. 338 p.
- Peterle TJ. Wildlife toxicology. 1991. New York: Van Nostrand Reinhold. 322 p.
- USEPA ambient water quality criteria (chemical-specific documents).
- U.S. Fish and Wildlife Service Contaminant Hazard Review Series (Biological Report 85(1.xx). Ronald Eisler, USFWS Patuxent Wildlife Research Center, Laurel, Maryland.
- Handbook of toxicity of pesticides to wildlife, 1970. U.S. Dept. of Interior, Fish and Wildlife Service, Resource Publication 153.
- USEPA AQUIRE data system. Scientific Outreach Program. USEPA Duluth, Minnesota.
- USEPA ECOTOX data system. Scientific Outreach Program. USEPA Duluth, Minnesota.

The USEPA AQUIRE data system was searched on 30 Oct 1995 as an example of the volume of toxicity testing performed on the proposed default aquatic representative species. Searches on the taxonomic groups of the representative species produced indicated a sufficient number of chemicals for most ERAs (Table 3-5).

Table 3-5   Number of records and approximate number of chemicals tested by taxonomic group (USEPA AQUIRE October 1995).

Taxonomic group	AQUIRE entries	Chemicals
green alga	6177	1035
amphipod	2656	356
Daphnia sp.	9449	1282
mysids	705	130
polychaete	1258	111
rainbow trout [1]	18026	

[1] Toxicity records for rainbow trout so numerous that AQUIRE would not allow download to determine number of chemicals

Aquatic risk characterization

An HQ should be calculated for each representative species and each COEC (see earlier Terrestrial Risk Characterization section for discussion of HQs and HIs). Hazard quotients are added to arrive at a chemical-specific HI. Hazard indexes are additive when the chemicals have a common mechanism of action or target organ. For example, HQs for all divalent heavy metals (i.e., Cd, Cu, Pb, Ni, and Zn) should be added to produce an HI. Hazard indexes are intended to be conservative estimators of potential hazard. Hazard indexes less than 1 for each chemical mode of action or target organ are reasonably good indications that adverse effects on the species under assessment are unlikely, provided that sensitive indicators of chronic toxicity have been measured in appropriate test species and environmental concentrations have not been underestimated. Nonetheless, field and/or laboratory verification of key facets of the Phase 1 predictive assessment is usually required in the Phase 2 validation study.

Phase 2 validation study

The Phase 2 validation study should address the portion of the predictive assessment that contains the most uncertainty. The scope of the Phase 2 validation study should be developed in consultation with DTSC project manager and other regulatory agencies. Phase 2 validation studies for terrestrial Phase 1 predictive assessments that contain a large body of toxicity data for the representative species might seek to validate the projected media concentrations with field tests or measurements of surface water input, dry deposition, or water concentration of sediment-bound contaminants. Phase 2 validation studies for terrestrial sites that performed toxicity tests of plants, decomposers of the soil invertebrate community in the predictive assessment might incorporate tests on different species. An aquatic Phase 2 validation study should include testing of either the representative species used in the Phase 1 predictive assessment or species closely related to that representative species. Toxicity testing should focus on sensitive endpoints for the most sensitive species identified in the Phase 1 predictive assessment, unless the COCs include a variety of contaminants that may exhibit variable toxicity depending on the species tested. Sites where the COCs include both metals and pesticides, for example, might be candidates for Phase 2 validation testing of more than 1 species where the Phase 1 predictive assessment indicates a marked difference in response of the representative species. Bioaccumulation must be addressed in addition to direct toxicity where COCs include substances that have been demonstrated to bioaccumulate or have the potential to bioaccumulate based on physical parameters such as persistence, K_{ow}, and water solubility.

Report contents

The Phase 1 predictive assessment and Phase 2 validation study report should present the potential receptors identified at and near the site, the representative species chosen for the predictive assessment, the exposure pathways evaluated in the predictive assessment, the exposure parameters for each representative species, the reference doses for each representative species and their source, the COEC-specific HQ and HI for each exposure pathway for each representative species, the total HI for each representative species, and a statement of the potential risk to ecological receptors. An uncertainty section should be included identifying the most probable sources of uncertainty.

A separate section of the report should outline the development of the Phase 2 validation study, including the justification for selection of the species used for validation or the transfer factors validated. The Phase 2 validation study section should also contain a clear statement of the degree to which the Phase 2 validation study strengthens or weakens the conclusions of the Phase 1 predictive study. The following descriptive figures and tables, or their functional equivalents, must be included:

1) A map of scale appropriate to identify the media sampled and the media concentrations is required. A facility-wide map must be supplied indicating the location of the individual investigation sites if it is necessary to provide separate investigation site maps due to the number of sites, number of samples, or the amount of chemical concentration data.

2) A map of scale appropriate to identify the terrestrial and aquatic habitats present both on-site and in the surrounding area is needed. The property line is not necessarily the point at which habitat identification should end if significant habitat exists near the site.

3) A table of species identified in the scoping report listed by habitat, indicating the species chosen as representative species and feeding guild identification, is required.

4) A table of representative species and feeding guilds chosen for assessment in Phase 1 predictive assessment with contact parameters and reference similar to Table 3-6 should be included.

5) A table of exposure parameters with complete reference to literature source for representative species, similar to Table 3-7, is needed.

6) A table listing the RfD and factors used in development of the reference dose for each representative species, similar to Table 3-8, should be provided.

7) A table listing calculation of the HQ for each exposure route and total HI for each representative species, similar to Table 3-9, is required.

Phase 3 impact assessment

Phase 3 investigations will be extremely site-specific. The goal of Phase 3 investigation is to more completely determine the critical ecological effect concentration and identify the lateral and vertical extent of contamination that poses an ecological threat so that remedial measures can be designed and evaluated. Detailed guidance for the Phase 3 impact assessment is currently in preparation. A modified triad approach (Chapman 1986, 1990), which includes initial paired chemical analysis and toxicity testing, is recommended for aquatic habitats. If the results of the chemical analysis and toxicity testing indicate a potential threat to ecological receptors, aquatic community analysis is performed on a range of locations.

The Phase 3 impact assessment is not required if the responsible party agrees to proceed directly to mitigation or remediation based on the results of the Phase 1 predictive assessment and Phase 2 validation study. The Phase 3 impact assessment should focus on the ecological endpoints developed in the prior site investigations unless more sensitive endpoints and ecological effects are discovered as a result of those investigations. The

Table 3-6 Listing of representative species, guild identification, physiological exposure parameter values, and citation for values used in the predictive assessment

Receptor	Guild	Parameter	Value	Reference
Vulpes vulpes Red fox	omnivore	Bodyweight Male Female Juvenile	 4.82 kg 3.94 kg 0.7 kg	Storm et al. 1976
		Skin surface Male Female	 3220 cm² 2760 cm²	Estimated from Stahl 1967
		Water Ingestion	0.084 g/g-d	Estimated from Calder and Braun 1983
		Food Ingestion	0.075 g/g-d	Estimated from Stahl 1967
		Inhalation Male Female	 2.0 m³/d 1.7 m³/d	Estimated from Stahl 1967.
Callipepla californica California quail	granivore	Bodyweight Male Female	 154 g 157 g	Guhery et al. 1988
		Skin surface Male Female	 298 g 320 g	Estimated from Meeh 1879 cited in Walsberg and King 1978
		Water Ingestion	0.11 g/g-d	Koerth and Guthery 1990
		Food Ingestion	0.079 g/g-d	Koerth and Guthery 1990
		Inhalation Male Female	 0.10 m³/d 0.11 m³/d	Estimated from Lasiewski and Calder 1971

ecological impact of mitigation or remediation based on protection of human health should be explicitly evaluated, including the potential impact to off-site receptors utilizing on-site habitats. Continued monitoring may be required for permitted facilities.

Future developments

The Department of Toxic Substances Control's guidance was developed to provide a common framework for ERAs at all sites as an attempt to make ERAs less labor-intensive and more cost-effective. One possibility for further development is that DTSC could serve as a central repository for the exposure factors and toxicity data used in ERAs and

Table 3-7   *Listing of representative species, guild identification, exposure media, exposure pathway, exposure pathway parameter value and citation for exposure values used in the predictive assessment*

Receptor	Guild	Media	Pathway	Exposure parameter	Reference
Vulpes vulpes Red fox	omnivore	Soil	Ingestion	2.8% of food	Beyer et al. 1991
		Water	Ingestion	0.53 liters/d	From Calder and Braun 1983 for male bodyweight.
		Food	Ingestion	37.1% mammals 43.2% birds 11.6% arthropods 6.3% plants 1.8% other items	Knable 1974 (summer diet)
		Air	Inhalation	10 ug/m^3 in 2 m^3/d	Sacramento AQMD 1992
		Soil	Dermal	25% of 3220 cm^2	Best estimate

Table 3-8   *Listing of representative species, contaminant, derived reference dose, tested species, toxicological endpoint, study reference dose, each UFs applied to derive reference dose and citation from the predictive assessment*

Representative species	Contaminant	Derived reference dose	Exposed species	Endpoint	Study reference dose	UF	Reference
Red fox	Cd	1 mg/kg-d	Laboratory rat	Devel. NOAEL	1 mg/kg-d	Interspecies = 10 NOAEL = 1	Sutou et al. 1980
California quail	Cd	.2 mg/kg-d	Mallard duck	Repro. NOAEL	2 mg/kg-d	Interspecies = 10 NOAEL = 1	White and Finley 1978

Table 3-9   *Listing of representative species, exposure pathway, contaminant, media concentration, total dose, derived reference dose, chemical-specific HQ, and total hazard index*

Receptor	Pathway	Contaminant	Concentration (mg/kg)	Dose (mg/kg-d)	Reference dose (mg/kg-d)	HQ	Total HI
Red Fox	Ingestion	Cd	Soil = 82	0.17	.1	1.7	
			Water = 0.2	0.022	.1	.22	
			Food = 13	0.97	.1	9.7	
	Inhalation	Cd	Air = 82	3.4E-07	.1	3.4E-06	
	Dermal	Cd	Soil = 82	8.2E-05	.1	8.2E-04	
							11.68

make the data available via electronic means to parties preparing risk assessments. Access to an expanding database of exposure and toxicity information should significantly decrease the labor required to prepare custom ERAs. Ecological risk assessments could be finalized more quickly, and more resources could then be focused on site-specific investigations required for sites that pose the greatest threat.

Addendum

This chapter is based upon draft guidance for conducting an ERA that the California DTSC circulated for public comment in July and August of 1994. After reviewing public comments, changes were made in the guidance document, and a final version was published in July 1996. For example, some changes in the final guidance document were made to the default UFs listed in this manuscript (see Uncertainty Factors section).

Currently, 2 documents have been finalized: 1) Part A: Overview, 2) Part B: Scoping Assessment. Part A consists of an overview of the entire ERA process (scoping assessment, Phase 1, Phase 2, and Phase 3). Part A also contains flow charts of the entire ERA process, a summary of the public comments received, and the DTSC response with changes made in the final document noted. Part B consists of more detailed guidance for conducting a scoping assessment and includes several sample tables and diagrams to assist the preparer in completing a scoping assessment. It is anticipated that more detailed guidance for conducting Phase 1, 2, and 3 assessments will be released in the future.

Subsequent to presentation of this paper at the SETAC meetings, several federal agencies, including the USEPA (Superfund Program), the Department of Defense (Tri-Services Committee), the U.S. Army Corps of Engineers, and others have published detailed guidance for conducting an ERA. All of these guidance documents adopted a phased or tiered approach to conducting an ERA. A phased approach is consistent with the USEPA's *Framework for Ecological Risk Assessment* (1992), in that data acquisition, verification, and monitoring are explicit activities that provide input to and validation of each phase of the ERA.

These authors wish to continue to emphasize the need for data acquisition, verification, and monitoring in ERAs conducted for hazardous waste sites and permitted facilities. Our experience to date is that validation of predictive assessments and monitoring of sites after removal or remedial action are often given cursory attention or ignored completely by decision makers. We believe validation and monitoring are integral components of sound application of scientific principles to ERA and acknowledge that complex and interrelated ecological systems are not adequately described by simplistic or empirical models.

Acknowledgments - The authors would like to thank the many scientists who participated in the frank discussions which led to development of this guidance package. The number of contributors is too large to list individually, but we particularly thank Clarence Callahan of the USEPA Region 9, James Haas of the U.S. Fish and Wildlife Service, Denise Klimas of NOAA, Michael Martin of the California Department of Fish and Game, Harry Ohlendorf of CH2M Hill, and Barbara Smith formerly of the San Francisco Regional Water Quality Control Board and currently in USEPA Region 9.

Special thanks are due Jeffrey J. Wong, Science Advisor in the Department of Toxic Substances Control, and the members of the Office of Scientific Affairs for encouraging, assisting, and supporting development of this guidance.

References

Airola DA. 1988. Guide to the California wildlife habitat relationships system. California Department of Fish and Game. Sacramento CA. 74 p.

Calder WA , Braun JE. 1983. Scaling of osmotic regulation in mammals and birds. *Am J Physiol* 244:R601–R606.

Chapman PM. 1986. Sediment quality criteria from the sediment quality triad: An example. *Environ Toxicol Chem* 11:637–644.

Chapman PM. 1990. The sediment quality triad approach to determining pollution-induced degradation. *Sci Total Environ* 97/8:815–825.

Cockerham LG, Shane BS. 1994. Basic environmental toxicology. Boca Raton FL: CRC.

[DTSC] California Department of Toxic Substances Control. 1994. Preliminary endangerment assessment manual. Sacramento CA.

Eisler R. 1985a. Carbofuran hazards to fish, wildlife, and invertebrates: A synoptic review. U.S. Fish and Wildlife Service , Contaminant Hazard Reviews. Report No. 3, Biological Report 85(1.3).

Eisler R. 1985b. Mirex hazards to fish, wildlife, and invertebrates: A synoptic review. U.S. Fish and Wildlife Service , Contaminant Hazard Reviews. Report No. 1, Biological Report 85(1.1).

Eisler R. 1986a. Diazinon hazards to fish, wildlife, and invertebrates: A synoptic review. U.S. Fish and Wildlife Service, Contaminant Hazard Reviews. Report No. 9, Biological Report 85(1.9).

Eisler R. 1986b. Polychlorinated biphenyl hazards to fish, wildlife, and invertebrates: A synoptic review. U.S. Fish and Wildlife Service, Contaminant Hazard Reviews. Report No. 7, Biological Report 85(1.7).

Eisler R. 1989. Atrazine hazards to fish, wildlife, and invertebrates: A synoptic review. U.S. Fish and Wildlife Service, Contaminant Hazard Reviews. Report No. 18, Biological Report 85(1.18).

Garten Jr CT, Trabalka JR. 1983. Evaluation of models for predicting terrestrial food chain behavior of xenobiotics. *Environ Sci Echnol* 17:590–595.

Guthery FS, Koerth NE, Smith DS. 1988. Reproduction of northern bobwhites in semiarid environments. *J Wildl Manage* 52:144–149.

Koerth NE, Guthery FS. 1990. Water requirements of captive northern bobwhites under subtropical seasons. *J Wildl Manage* 54:667–672.

Lasiewski RC, Calder WA. 1971. A preliminary allometric analysis of respiratory variables in resting birds. *Resp Phys* 11:152–166.

Mayer KE, Laudenslayer Jr WF. 1988. A guide to wildlife habitats of California. California Department of Forestry and Fire Protection. Sacramento CA. 166 p.

Stahl WR. 1967. Scaling of respiratory variables in mammals. *J Appl Physiol* 22:453–460.

Storm GL, Andrews RD, Phillips RL. 1976. Morphology, reproduction, dispersal and mortality of midwestern red fox populations. *Wildlife Monogr* 49:1–82.

Suter GW, Barnthouse L, Bartell SM, Mill T, Mackay D, Peterson S. 1993. Ecological risk assessment. Boca Raton, FL: Lewis Publishers.

[USEPA] U.S. Environmental Protection Agency. 1988. Review of ecological risk assessment methods. Prepared for Office of Policy Planning and Evaluation, Washington, DC. PB89-134357.

[USEPA] U.S. Environmental Protection Agency. 1989. Risk assessment guidance for Superfund, Volume I, human health evaluation manual (Part A), Interim Final. Washington DC:Office of Emergency and Remedial Response. EPA/540/1-89/002.

[USEPA] U.S. Environmental Protection Agency. 1992. Framework for ecological risk assessment. USEPA Risk Assessment Forum, Washington DC. EPA/630/R-92/001.

[USEPA] U.S. Environmental Protection Agency. 1993a. Wildlife Exposure Factors Handbook. Volume I of II. Washington DC: Office of Research and Development. EPA/600/R-93/187a.

[USEPA] U.S. Environmental Protection Agency. 1993b. Wildlife Exposure Factors Handbook. Volume II of II. Washington DC: Office of Research and Development. EPA/600/R-93/187b.

[USEPA] U.S. Environmental Protection Agency. 1994. A review of ecological assessment case studies from a risk assessment perspective. Volume II. Washington DC: Risk Assessment Forum. EPA/630/R-94/003.

[USEPA] U.S. Environmental Protection Agency. 1995. Integrated risk information system for microcomputers (IRIS2), October 1995 update.

[USEPA] U.S. Environmental Protection Agency. (In Preparation). Review and analysis of toxicity data to support the development of uncertainty factors for use in estimating risk of contaminant stressors to wildlife. Office of Water, Washington, DC.

Walsberg GE and King Jr. 1978. The relationshp of the external surface area of birds to skin surface and body mass. *J Exp Biol* 76:185–189.

Zeiner DC, Laudenslayer Jr WF, Mayer KE. 1988. California's wildlife, Volume I, amphibians and reptiles. California Department of Fish and Game. Sacramento CA. 2 May 1988. 272 p.

Zeiner DC, Laudenslayer Jr WF, Mayer KE, White M. 1990a. California's wildlife, Volume II, birds. California Department of Fish and Game. Sacramento CA. November 1990. 732 p.

Zeiner DC, Laudenslayer Jr WF, Mayer KE, White M. 1990b. California's wildlife, Volume III, mammals. California Department of Fish and Game. Sacramento CA. April 1990. 407 p.

Chapter 4

Managing ecological risks: what information do regulators need and want?

Bruce A. Macler

Disclaimer - The views expressed in this chapter are those of the author and may not necessarily be those of the U.S. Environmental Protection Agency.

Ecological risk assessments (ERAs) are required at Superfund sites and may provide the site manager and other decision-makers with useful information to make appropriate legal, social, and ecological decisions in the management of the site. However, these ecological assessments will always be only one of several elements in these decisions and may play only a limited role. Therefore, they need not always be extensive or detailed. The degree of effort for an assessment of a particular site is dependent on a variety of site-specific characteristics and on the applicable or relevant and appropriate requirements that must be satisfied in the development and implementation of any actions at the site. Thus, the site manager, Natural Resource Trustees, and other parties must determine at the earliest stages of an investigation the goals and scope of the ERA.

This approach has been taken with the Montrose Chemical Corporation Superfund site. Using ARARs, the realities of the site location and possible management options, specific assessment goals, and a work plan were developed within U.S. Environmental Protection Agency's ERA framework. A problem formulation step gathered available information, characterized ecological risks, and identified data gaps. This led to development of more detailed scientific questions necessary to characterize the exposures of organisms to dichlorodiphenyltrichloroethane and related contaminants from this site. A sampling and analysis plan evolved to provide the necessary data and the required fieldwork subsequently undertaken. While a formal risk characterization has not yet been completed, the resulting data will be combined with existing toxicity information to estimate risks to specific organisms and the affected ecosystems.

Ecological risk assessment as a tool for decision-making

An ecological risk assessment (ERA) may provide valuable information to the regulatory manager required to make decisions affecting ecological systems. The practical application of ERAs in this decision-making process requires not only providing a credible scientific description of the problem, but also considering the specific risk information needs of the regulator in the context of the relevant statutory requirements, precedence, available resources, time constraints, and social/political situation. The risk assessor must understand that management decisions are unlikely to rest solely upon the risk assessment. Therefore, an ERA useful to the manager may not be one structured along a purely scientific approach or directed by purely scientific questions. A useful product may not necessarily be complete, unambiguous, or have the minimum possible uncertainty. Because of this, the risk assessor's approaches to ERA should be flexible and developed only after careful discussion with the risk manager. As appropriate, the management and nonscientific considerations brought forward should be used to direct the risk assessment effort.

Ecological risk assessments may be used in 2 broad ways. National regulatory development efforts can use ERAs in the formulation of ecological criteria or standards that are widely or generally applicable. These assessments must use exposure information that is relevant to the large areas or generic ecosystems covered by these regulations. Examples of these are pesticide registrations under the Federal Insecticide, Fungicide and Rodenticide Act 1947 and ambient water quality criteria for aquatic organisms under the Clean Water Act 1972. More frequently, however, ERAs for regulatory management purposes are performed on a limited, site-specific basis. These assessments typically are required to support a judgment on whether specific contaminants or situations at the site have affected and/or are affecting the species and ecosystems there. These situations arise primarily under the Comprehensive Environmental Response, Compensation and Liability Act (Superfund) 1980.

Early guidance from the U.S. Environmental Protection Agency (USEPA) (1989) was specific to Superfund site evaluations and generally was not useful for developing risk assessments to address other regulatory situations. This guidance was also limited in its approach to ecological assessments and was frequently used in a narrow, formalistic way that did not provide the risk manager with usable information. Ecological risk assessments frequently appeared as afterthoughts to Superfund human-health risk assessments. The typical product was long on measurements of contaminant levels in environmental and biological samples, but short on careful description of ecosystems, analysis of effects, and discussion of significance.

The USEPA has recently developed a framework for ERAs that addresses the need for flexibility and provides guidance to achieve a more complete description of ecological risks at a site (USEPA 1992). This framework (Figure 4-1) considers the risk assessment as a scientific problem based on the specific questions of the risk manager. As with any good scientific study, it begins with an assessment of what is currently known about the situation. A problem formulation step is used to gather available data on contaminants and their toxicities, receptors and ecosystems, site characteristics, and ecological effects. Starting from this information, the risk assessor and risk manager determine what questions need to be answered and what information needs to be acquired in order to develop satisfactory answers to these questions. The specific objectives and scope of the assessment are laid out in a form that will allow formulation of appropriate endpoints for the study. This process is iterative—i.e., after the overall goals of the ERA are established, the investigations necessary to achieve these goals are taken in an order that will allow for comment, consideration, and possible redirection of these efforts based on the data as they become available.

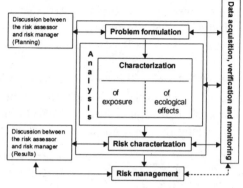

This process is key to the success of the assessment and requires careful and full discussion between assessor and manager over an extended period of time.

Figure 4-1   USEPA's framework for ecological risk assessment (USEPA 1992)

The assessor must be aware of the regulatory context of the study and must understand the needs of the manager in order to provide the most useful information. The assessor must be able to communicate the results of the assessment in a user-friendly form. The manager should be able to describe the role the ERA will serve in the risk-management process such that the necessary questions are asked and the appropriate answers result from the study. It must be recognized that risk assessors (and risk assessments) are seldom revered, and are more often abused, by risk managers. Developing a functional relationship between assessor and manager is a necessary first step for success.

Once the scientific questions are established, data acquisition typically focuses on describing in sufficient detail the affected ecosystems, assessing exposures, and determining ecological effects. From the resulting information, a characterization of risk, description of uncertainties, and discussion of significance can be developed.

Table 4-1   Examples of ecological ARARs for Superfund considered for the Montrose site

Under Superfund, ERAs are concerned with current and future risks. The assessment must be able to address any "applicable and/or relevant and appropriate regulations" (Table 4-1). An ERA under Superfund need not be limited by applicable or relevant and appropriate requirements (ARARs), but must be useful in answering questions about their applicability and impact. The Natural Resource Trustees, made up of the various federal and state agencies with responsibilities for ecological protection, participate in the development of ERAs under Superfund.

Clean Air Act
Clean Water Act
Coastal Zone Management Act
Endangered Species Act
Federal Insecticide, Fungicide and Rodenticide Act
Fish and Wildlife Conservation Act
Fish and Wildlife Coordination Act
Marine Mammal Protection Act
Marine Protection, Research and Sanctuaries Act
Migratory Bird Treaty Act
National Environmental Policy Act
Toxic Substances Control Act
Titles 22 and 26, California Code of Regulations
California Endangered Species Act
California Fish and Game Code

The Trustees represent the interests of their respective agencies and also serve as technical advisors. The site manager and risk assessment team should discuss with and get agreement from the Trustees on the details of the assessment.

The Montrose Chemical Corporation Superfund site

An example of utilizing this approach is the ongoing ERA of the Montrose Chemical Corporation Superfund site. From 1947 to 1982, Montrose owned and operated a DDT manufacturing facility on about 13 acres in Torrance, California (Figure 4-2).

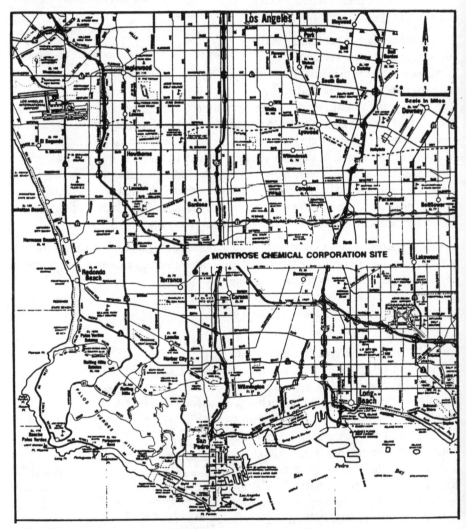

Figure 4-2   Regional area map. Montrose superfund site (CH2M Hill 1993)

Dichlorodiphenyltrichloroethane is a chlorinated insecticide known to be persistent in the environment. In aquatic ecosystems, DDT and its metabolites, dichlorodiphenyl-dichloroethylene (DDE) and dichlorodiphenylethane (DDD), associate primarily with sediments, water, and aquatic life. They are concentrated in marine organisms and are transferred through the aquatic foodchain. Adverse biological effects of DDT and its metabolites occur at all trophic levels (CH2M Hill 1992).

The Montrose facility consisted of the DDT processing building and adjacent processing equipment, a formulation and grinding plant, transfer station areas, warehouse, filtration area, waste recycling ponds, acid recovery area, waste pits, and several underground storage tanks. Production was reported as approximately 1 to 7 million pounds per month throughout the 35 years of plant operations. When production of DDT was banned in 1982, operation of the Montrose plant was discontinued. Montrose removed the buildings and materials, regraded the property, and capped most of it with asphalt to prevent movement of remaining contamination.

Prior to the 1940s, the principal land use in the area was agricultural. During and following World War II, a variety of industrial operations began, including aircraft manufacturing, oil refining, and chemical production. The area has been substantially affected by these activities and has several other federal and state hazardous waste site investigations currently underway. In recent years, residential and commercial areas have been heavily developed near the facility.

During the years of operation, reagent materials, product, and wastes were stored on-site, both above and below ground. Some of this material was dispersed off-site by wind or stormwater. Stormwater runoff from the property runs into ditches surrounding the property, then to a catchbasin, and then into the stormwater drainage system serving the area. This system follows natural drainage contours to the former Dominguez Creek. The pathway currently consists of the underground Kenwood Drain, discharging into the open, concrete-lined Torrance Lateral, which discharges into the clay-lined Dominguez Channel, which finally flows into the Consolidated Slip portion of Los Angeles Harbor (Figure 4-3). Prior to the 1970s, much of this pathway was open and unlined. In addition to stormwater, it currently receives industrial waste discharges from other facilities in the area. The Torrance Lateral, Dominguez Channel and Consolidated Slip are tidally influenced and have occasional flooding events. They also have been dredged infrequently over the years.

Montrose site ecological risk assessment

The USEPA and the Los Angeles Regional Water Quality Control Board first brought action against Montrose in 1982, based on the results of sampling conducted the previous year. Chlorobenzene, chloroform, DDT, DDD, DDE, and a number of other organic chemicals were found at significant levels in soils and groundwater at the site. In 1984, the site was proposed for the Superfund National Priority List. The listing of the

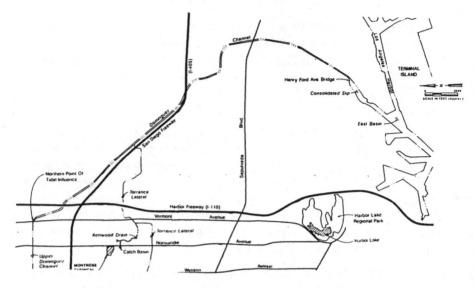

Figure 4-3   Montrose site and stormwater pathway (CH2M Hill 1992)

Montrose facility by USEPA required human-health assessments and ERAs for the facility site itself and for adjacent areas affected by the facility. Substantial additional monitoring was undertaken. An ecological site assessment performed by Montrose contractors using this data was rejected as inadequate by the USEPA in 1991. The USEPA determined at that time to conduct another assessment using the framework approach.

To initiate this effort, members of the federal and California state agencies responsible for the site were identified and formed a Natural Resource Trustees workgroup in early 1992 to discuss ecological goals and priorities for the site and to develop an ERA plan. These agencies included California EPA, California Fish and Game, National Oceanic and Atmospheric Administration (NOAA), U.S. Department of Interior, U.S. Department of Justice, USEPA, and U.S. Fish and Wildlife Service (USFWS). The first activity of the Trustees was to determine the scope and goals of the investigation. It was agreed that the property where the facility had been located, being mostly paved, was of limited ecological interest and importance (Metcalf and Eddy 1986; CH2M Hill 1992). For the same reason, the airborne exposure pathway, while likely to have had historical significance in the distribution of contaminants to soils in the nearby areas, was not considered to be a current exposure route. Additionally, remediation of the many square miles of area likely to have been affected by airborne contamination was not perceived as feasible. Attention was then focused on contaminants carried away from the site by stormwater runoff. The Trustees considered that the aquatic ecosystems were those most likely to be both affected by Montrose contamination and amenable to remediation. Terrestrial areas adjacent to the waterways were also considered suitable for study. Therefore, the area of ecological interest to the Trustees and site managers was not the facility site proper, but the watercourses from the site down to Los Angeles Harbor. It was agreed to limit the investigation to drainages down through the Consolidated Slip, but not beyond, since a related investigation of the Harbor and Los Angeles Bight was then being conducted under the direction of NOAA.

The Trustees selected goals of the overall risk assessment to determine 1) if there was a current adverse ecological risk from DDT or its metabolites in the waterways or associated terrestrial areas from the facility through the Consolidated Slip and 2) whether a plausible remediation (dredging) would improve the situation or make it worse than doing nothing at all. This restricted the investigation both geographically and with respect to the contaminants of concern. While general ARARs were identified to support these efforts (Table 4-1), they were not specifically used to limit the investigation, since it was unknown what organisms in the area might have been exposed to contamination.

CH2M Hill was contracted by the USEPA to perform the initial problem formulation step of the framework approach under the guidance of the USEPA and the Trustees. Specific objectives and work plans were developed in scoping meetings held between these groups. These meetings were also used to uncover available occurrence, exposure, and toxicity information and to discuss data quality objectives. A substantial amount of information was found to be readily available to different Trustees and was consolidated.

As part of this effort, a reconnaissance group of experts surveyed the site, surrounding terrestrial areas, and drainage waterways from the site through the Consolidated Slip. Habitats were described and limited faunal counts were made. Sites in the Torrance Lateral, Dominguez Channel, and Consolidated Slip were selected as promising locations for subsequent sampling. An aerial survey was done and proved useful in placing the Montrose site and drainage zone in a context of the surrounding industries, communities, parklands, and other geographical features.

The problem formulation activity considered all readily available data. The resulting report (CH2M Hill 1992) described the site and surrounding areas; provided known information on the nature and extent of contamination; described likely ecological receptors, exposure mechanisms, foodwebs, and exposure pathways; and described available toxicity information. Data gaps were determined. From this, a preliminary risk characterization was performed; this characterization was limited by inadequate exposure data. Little of the available exposure information was found to be valid or relevant. Besides methodological problems in sampling and analysis, it was noted that much of the data had been collected prior to a major flooding event that was judged to have significantly altered the sediments in the area. Toxicity information on DDT and its metabolites in the literature was found to be extensive and adequate for the purposes of the characterization.

The conclusions of the report include findings that 1) the property where the Montrose facility was located was most likely a source of DDT and its metabolites downstream from the site, 2) DDT and its metabolites are the primary chemicals of concern for the downstream aquatic ecosystems, 3) a variety of receptor organisms sensitive to DDT and its metabolites occur downstream, 4) historical concentrations of DDT, DDE, and DDD in some of the sediments exceeded levels associated with reported adverse effects in biota, and 5) if these levels were maintained, bioaccumulation of DDT and metabolites by aquatic invertebrates and fish could be expected to reach levels causing adverse effects in fish and birds consuming them.

The major areas where inadequate data existed were for levels of DDT and metabolite contamination in the sediments, tissue levels of these contaminants in benthic inverte-brates and fish, and descriptions and population levels of the aquatic communities. Rec-ommendations were made by the contractor on approaches to acquire this information.

Another conclusion was that direct toxic effects of DDT and metabolites on fish or benthic invertebrates in the Dominguez Channel or the adjacent Consolidated Slip area of Los Angeles Harbor were judged impossible to gauge due to the heavy influence of other contaminant discharges into the waterways from other facilities in the area. Pos-sible damage to organisms or ecosystems from these other contaminants could mask effects from DDT. The risk assessors therefore recommended that the risk characteriza-tion compare site-specific exposures to literature toxicity values.

Because of the exposure data gaps, the risk characterization was not considered adequate by itself for management purposes. It could not support a determination of current eco-logical damage or assess the ecological pros and cons of remediation by dredging. How-ever, this information was considered adequate for the USEPA and the other Trustees to agree to go forward with additional data collection efforts to support a full risk character-ization. The information from the problem formulation was used by the USEPA, the Trustees, and CH2M Hill to develop a second work plan (CH2M Hill 1993) to address the indicated data gaps and outstanding questions. Since adequate toxicity information was available from the literature, toxicity studies were not indicated. This second effort was focused primarily on acquiring data to assess or estimate exposures to DDT and its me-tabolites to higher trophic level organisms in the aquatic ecosystems of interest. Study sites were selected and sampling protocols were developed based on the results of the reconnaissance to maximize the likelihood of useful data while minimizing unnecessary sampling.

The sampling activities specified in the work plan were performed in April 1994. These included determination of contaminant levels in sediment and water at key locations and measurement of contaminant levels in fish and invertebrate tissues.

When the information from the second study becomes available, exposures to the con-taminants can be estimated for individual species. The USEPA will specifically examine the foodchains for the ecosystems at the site. We anticipate the use of one or more food-chain models, appropriate transfer and bioaccumulation factors, measured water, sedi-ment and tissue levels, and a Monte Carlo simulation to estimate a distribution of expo-sures to key species. The risk characterization will be developed to combine the existing toxicity information with the calculated exposures. A ratio approach between estimated exposure levels and known adverse effect levels for individual species will be used. An overall judgement of the significance of these exposures for species and the ecosystems in their entirety will be made. The USEPA and the Trustees will consider the adequacy of this characterization in light of the goals and management needs to determine if additional work will be necessary.

Conclusions

This approach, while not yet resulting in a completed ERA for the Montrose site, has already been successful in several ways. The close communication and interaction of the USEPA, the other Natural Resource Trustees, and the contractor conducting the work have resulted in a clear understanding of the nature, goals, and limits of this risk assessment and of the relationship of the risk assessment to management decisions. This team work has provided the risk managers with information that has already been useful in planning and decision-making with respect to possible remediation approaches. By careful up-front planning and successive iterations of plans and products, the important ecological issues were uncovered and focused upon. This has saved unnecessary effort and expense and is approaching the goal in the USEPA's framework guidance that the "phased approach ensures that only the necessary work will be done and all the necessary work will be done."

Acknowledgment - The author wishes to thank Nancy Woo for her advice and helpful comments on the draft manuscript.

References

CH2M Hill. 1992. Ecological risk assessment. Montrose Chemical Corporation, Los Angeles, California. Draft report. CH2M Hill, Emeryville, CA, for USEPA Region 9.

CH2M Hill. 1993. Sampling and analysis plan for sediment, surface water and biological sampling. Montrose superfund site, Los Angeles, California. Emeryville CA: CH2M Hill. EPA WA #31-28-9P26. CH2M Hill #SFO69132.04.04.

Metcalf and Eddy. 1986. Draft Preliminary Report. Remedial Investigation, Part I. Montrose Facility Site, Los Angeles. Redwood City CA.

[USEPA] U.S. Environmental Protection Agency. 1989. Risk assessment guidance for Superfund. Volume II. Environmental evaluation manual. Washington DC: USEPA. EPA/540/1-89/001.

[USEPA] U.S. Environmental Protection Agency. 1992. Framework for ecological risk assessment. Washington DC: USEPA. EPA/630/R-92/001

Chapter 5

Evaluating bioaccumulation in wildlife food chains

Harry M. Ohlendorf

Animals can be exposed to environmental contaminants through various media and exposure routes. This exposure can be measured by analyzing their food, water, air, or body tissues. Some contaminants are bioaccumulated from soil, sediment, or water by food-chain organisms that may be eaten by wildlife at higher trophic levels. Food-chain exposure is best evaluated through a phased approach to help ensure that appropriate evaluations are performed and that they address risk-management decisions needed for the site in a cost-effective way. Approaches for measuring exposure that are discussed include field sampling or monitoring, bioassays, and modeling. The ecological significance of contaminant concentrations found in food-chain organisms or in wildlife tissues can be evaluated through comparison to concurrently sampled reference areas, background or normal levels elsewhere, and benchmark concentrations. Three case studies are described in which these various methods were applied to determine whether contaminants may adversely affect wildlife.

Animals can be exposed to environmental contaminants through various media and exposure routes. This exposure can be measured by analyzing their food, water, air, or body tissues (Ohlendorf et al. 1978; Ohlendorf 1993; Maughan 1993; Suter 1993; USEPA 1993). However, in most ecological risk assessments (ERAs) it is possible to assume that one route of exposure is dominant and other routes are negligible. The relative importance of food-chain transfer depends on the contaminants of concern (COCs) and the potential receptors, among other factors. This chapter describes some of the approaches used in evaluating the food-chain route of exposure under different conditions.

Bioaccumulation is defined as the net accumulation of a chemical by an organism as a result of uptake from all routes of exposure (Suter 1993). Food-chain organisms were considered to represent the primary exposure medium for wildlife in the 3 case studies described later. Contaminants found in the soil, sediment, water, or air would tend to be ingested or inhaled in much smaller quantities than those in the main components of the diet. The food-chain organisms, in turn, would have accumulated contaminants through an integration of their exposures to abiotic media (e.g., soil/sediment, water, or air) to which they were exposed, along with their own dietary exposures.

Food-chain exposure analysis is 1 component of the analysis phase in conducting an ERA, as described in *Framework for Ecological Risk Assessment* (USEPA 1992a) and other references (e.g., Maughan 1993; Suter 1993) and illustrated in Figures 5-1 and 5-2. The analysis phase and other aspects of the overall ERA process, including agency guidance, also are discussed in more detail in other chapters of this volume.

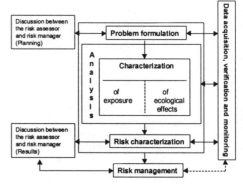

The main focus of this chapter is evaluation of food-chain transfer as a source of exposure to wildlife, with an emphasis on the methods used to measure contaminant concentrations in potential foods of animals inhabiting the study sites. The approaches used in measuring food-chain exposure and methods used for evaluating ecological significance of concentrations found in the study sites are described first. Three case studies then are described to illustrate how these procedures were applied in recent studies.

Figure 5-1   Framework for ecological risk assessment (USEPA 1992a)

Approaches to measuring food-chain exposure

A critical first element in determining the approach to be used in ERAs is to establish communication between the risk assessors (those conducting the scientific evaluation) and risk managers (those making management decisions) (Figure 5-1). Discussion among these individuals will help ensure that the risk assessment will ultimately provide information that is relevant to making decisions on the issues under consideration, while the risk assessor can ensure that the risk assessment addresses all relevant ecological concerns (USEPA 1992a).

Involvement of the risk managers during problem formulation, the initial planning phase of an ERA, helps to develop the assessment and measurement endpoints and the conceptual model that will serve to guide other phases of the risk assessment (i.e., analysis and risk characterization).

Phased approach

The most cost-effective approach to conducting an ERA is to phase the work so that all necessary work is done, but only the necessary work is done (USEPA 1991a, 1992b, 1993). In relation to measuring food-chain exposure, this means that all relevant available data for the site are first evaluated to determine whether more information is needed and, if so, what the best methods are for obtaining the information. The first critical question is whether exposure pathways are potentially complete (i.e., whether contami-

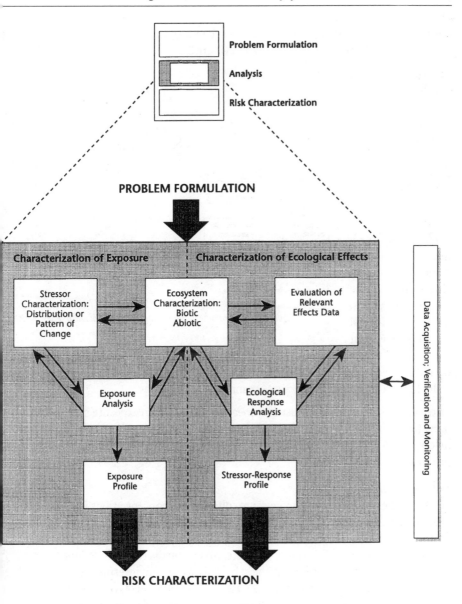

Figure 5-2   Analysis phase of an ecological risk assessment (USEPA 1992a)

nants are present in habitats where sensitive plants or animals may occur). An example of such a phased approach is illustrated in Figure 5-3.

Biological sampling may have been conducted previously at the study site, and contaminant concentrations in those samples are usually the most meaningful (i.e., easily interpreted) in identifying COCs in relation to food-chain exposure. However, the analytes measured in the biological samples may not

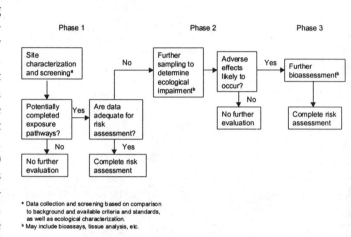

Figure 5-3   Example of phased approach to ecological assessment

include all of the potential COCs, or no biological sampling may have occurred. In addition, it may sometimes be necessary to estimate future contaminant concentrations in order for risk managers to make site-management decisions.

Three approaches that can be used for measuring food-chain exposure include field sampling (or monitoring), bioassays, and modeling. These approaches are briefly described below, and 3 case studies are then described to illustrate the application of these approaches.

Field sampling/monitoring

Field sampling or monitoring to measure contaminant concentrations in common food-chain organisms (including plants, invertebrates, and small vertebrate animals) or in the receptor species (i.e., herbivores and various other trophic levels of consumers) provides the most direct means of assessing exposure. Abiotic media (i.e., soil, sediment, or water) may be collected along with food-chain organisms to help interpret the relationships between biota and their exposure media. However, evaluation of contaminant concentrations in abiotic media in relation to higher trophic levels has many uncertainties unless food-chain organisms are sampled also.

Field sampling of food-chain organisms or receptor species is often the next logical step to be conducted after available data have been evaluated. Sampling of the foodchain is especially important when the receptor species cannot be sampled because of their endangered status, low population size on the site, or for other reasons. Sampling of the receptor species must take into account the potential effects of seasonal migration, for aging range while present on the site, and other factors that may complicate interpretation of contaminant concentrations in their tissues. Bird eggs can be good indicators of previous or current exposure of the female that laid them to some inorganics (such as Hg and Se) and to organochlorines (Ohlendorf et al. 1978; Ohlendorf 1993). However, for some chemicals of potential concern (such as Cd and Pb), there is little relationship between the female's dietary exposure and the concentrations found in the eggs. Furthermore, some chemicals (including Hg and organochlorines) that are passed on to eggs may represent body burdens accumulated by the female over long periods, including exposure in previous years and in overwintering locations.

Bioassays

Bioassays have been developed to evaluate the toxicity of soil, sediment, or water to terrestrial and aquatic organisms (e.g., USEPA 1991b; Linder et al. 1992). In addition to measuring the toxicity of contaminants to test organisms, chronic exposure bioassays can be used to measure bioaccumulation of contaminants in the surviving plants or animals. Although such measurements are not appropriate for all chemicals or all test organisms, they do provide a good measure of food-chain bioaccumulation for many settings. The results of these measurements can be used in conjunction with field sampling to compare and evaluate food-chain bioaccumulation in the risk assessment.

Another aspect of using bioassays is that they can be used to determine the degree of bioaccumulation when potential food-chain organisms cannot be collected in the field, e.g., when the soil, sediment, or water is toxic to food-chain organisms. By using a dilution series of site medium mixed with clean soil, sediment, or water, it is possible to determine the no-observed-adverse-effect level (NOAEL) for toxicity as well as the soil, sediment, or water concentration for a contaminant that does not result in bioaccumulation above levels that may affect wildlife consuming the test organisms.

Laboratory bioassays include collection of exposure medium (soil, sediment, or water), homogenization and subsampling for contaminant analysis and bioassays (using organisms such as earthworms or plants), and analysis of plant or invertebrate tissues following the chronic exposure period (either 28 or 45 d, depending on test species).

Modeling

Modeling can be a useful approach to measuring food-chain exposure when it is not possible or necessary to measure contaminant concentrations directly. Food-chain contaminant levels can be estimated by using literature-derived bioconcentration factors (BCFs) or bioaccumulation factors (BAFs) and procedures described in more detail elsewhere (e.g., Maughan 1993; Opresko et al. 1994; Suter 1993; USEPA 1993). This level of analysis may be suitable for some situations, but in others it may be necessary to estimate future concentrations of COCs on the basis of current concentrations in abiotic media and in concurrently sampled food-chain organisms. With an adequate baseline of monitoring data for abiotic media and biota from the site, it may be possible to make reasonable estimates of future conditions and evaluate the potential significance of food-chain exposure.

Uncertainty factors are an important component of modeling estimates, and sources of uncertainty should be described qualitatively or estimated quantitatively.

Evaluating ecological significance

The ecological significance of contaminant concentrations in food-chain organisms or in the tissues of receptor species can be evaluated in various ways. Three approaches of evaluation include comparisons to similar organisms collected concurrently at reference areas not having similar sources of contaminant exposure, comparisons to background or normal levels found elsewhere (i.e., comparison to literature-derived values), and comparisons to various benchmark values (e.g., NOAELs and lowest-observed-adverse-effect levels [LOAELs]).

Concurrent reference areas

Sampling of food-chain organisms and receptor species concurrently at a site known or suspected to be contaminated and at a reference site provides a good method for comparing and evaluating the contaminant concentrations that are found (Hothem and Ohlendorf 1989; Ohlendorf et al. 1989, 1990; Ohlendorf and Hothem 1995). Concurrent sampling eliminates the uncertainties that may be caused by temporal variations, and it reduces spatial variation if the reference area is located in proximity to the site being investigated. Concurrent sampling also allows for qualitative and quantitative comparison of habitat conditions, ecosystem composition (e.g., presence or absence of sensitive species, species diversity), or other factors that may be important for the evaluation. Because some of those measurements are more time-consuming and costly to perform, they may occur only in later phases of an ERA. Initial sampling may be limited to a "snapshot" that compares contaminant concentrations in the food-chain organisms or in the tissues of wildlife receptors at only one time or over a short period.

Background/normal levels elsewhere

Comparison of contaminant concentrations found at the study site to background or normal levels found elsewhere is also useful in evaluating the relative degree of contamination. Such comparisons are especially useful when no reference area was sampled concurrently with the study site or when further comparisons to background are needed.

Various sources of information are available for contaminant concentrations in biota. Examples include the Contaminant Hazard Reviews published by the U.S. Fish and Wildlife Service (Eisler 1985–1993), the National Contaminant Biomonitoring Program (Schmitt and Brumbaugh 1990; Schmitt et al. 1990), various databases, regional contaminant monitoring programs, and general literature sources. In evaluating background or normal levels for inorganics found in tissues, it is important to be aware of natural regional differences for some elements (such as Hg) that may be elevated regionally in comparison to national or worldwide averages.

Benchmark comparisons

Toxic effect levels have been determined for many organic or inorganic contaminants that may be found at contaminated sites. These contaminant concentrations can be found by conducting literature searches that include published values or by checking available databases. Summary publications such as the Contaminant Hazard Reviews (Eisler 1985–1993) provide a good start for many chemicals, but no such reviews (or even published values) are available for some of the less well-studied chemicals.

Although comparison to LD50 or other toxic levels may be of interest, the most meaningful comparisons are usually to NOAELs or LOAELs because the goal of site remediation or site management is usually to achieve or maintain exposures below the effect level. In some other instances, however, dose-response functions for other levels of effect may be useful.

Case studies

Naval Weapons Station Seal Beach

Results of a study of contaminants in wildlife food chains at Naval Weapons Station (NWS) Seal Beach are presented in a final report by the Southwest Division Naval Facilities Engineering Command (SWDIV 1995a), but methods used in conducting this study are the main focus of this section.

Background

NWS Seal Beach occupies about 5,000 acres adjacent to Anaheim Bay, 26 miles south of the Los Angeles urban center (Figure 5-4). The 911-acre Seal Beach National Wildlife Refuge (NWR), which is managed by the USFWS, is located within the boundaries of NWS Seal Beach.

The NWR encompasses most of the remaining tidal saltmarsh of the once larger Anaheim Bay system (SWDIV 1995a). The tidal saltmarsh in the NWR is composed of 3 main tidal channels, their tributaries, and the tidal flats that are several feet higher in elevation than the adjacent tidal channels (Figure 5-5). The tidal flats are densely vegetated by a variety of saltmarsh plant species and are inundated by only the highest tides, which occur several times each year. These tidal flats provide nesting habitats for an array of bird species that occupy the NWR and habitat for a variety of invertebrate species upon which birds and other vertebrates feed. In 1990, the Port of Long Beach (POLB) built 4 ponds at the landward ends of the east and west tidal channels in the NWR. The POLB ponds are hydraulically connected to the tidal saltmarsh and are part of the NWR. The ponds were constructed as mitigation for POLB operations off-site and were intended to expand the tidal saltmarsh to provide habitat for endangered species and other biota in the NWR.

As part of the Navy's Installation Restoration Program, an initial assessment study (USN 1985) and a remedial investigation (RI) (USN 1989) identified potential past hazardous waste disposal sites and contaminated areas on NWS Seal Beach that could pose a threat to the biota in the NWR. An environmental impact statement (EIS) for the NWR was prepared by the USFWS and the Navy (USFWS/USN 1990) on the Endangered Species Management and Protection Plan. Among other management issues, the EIS addressed the potential for operations at NWS Seal Beach to contribute contaminants to the NWR that could adversely affect the health of the tidal saltmarsh ecosystem and several endangered species that occupy the NWR. The record of decision (ROD) for that EIS (dated 27 February 1991) identified, among other actions, the need to assess the impacts of operations at NWS Seal Beach on the biota of the tidal saltmarsh in the NWR. The Seal Beach NWR Study was initiated by the Navy in response to that ROD. The development of the final work plan (SWDIV 1992) for the NWR Study included the Navy and the USFWS.

Several special-status species occupy the NWR (SWDIV 1995a). In particular, the NWR provides essential breeding habitat for the California least tern *(Sterna antillarum browni)*, and the light-footed clapper rail *(Rallus longirostris levipes)*, both of which are listed as endan-

Figure 5-4   *Locations of Kesterson Reservoir, NWS Seal Beach, and MCB Camp Pendleton study sites*

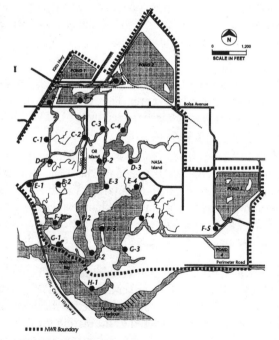

Figure 5-5   *Seal Beach NWR sediment and biota sampling locations*

gered by USFWS and the California Department of Fish and Game (CDFG). The California brown pelican *(Pelecanus occidentalis californicus)* and American peregrine falcon *(Falco peregrinus)*, both listed as endangered by the USFWS and the CDFG, occasionally feed at the NWR. The CDFG-listed endangered and USFWS Category 2 candidate (species for which sufficient evidence for listing as threatened or endangered is not yet available), Belding's savannah sparrow *(Passerculus sandwichensis beldingi)*, is resident at the edges of the tidal saltmarsh.

The clapper rail is a permanent resident of the NWR, nesting in saltmarsh vegetation throughout the NWR and obtaining the crabs and snails that are its primary food items in the NWR (SWDIV 1995a). The least tern occupies and forages for fish in the NWR only during the breeding season from March through late August. Adult least terns forage up to 2 miles away from the nesting colony (USFWS and USN 1990) on NASA Island in the NWR, but most food for adults and chicks is collected in POLB ponds and tidal channels in the NWR. The direct contact of the food species of the clapper rail and least tern with potentially contaminated sediments and water makes the clapper rail and least tern the most likely of the special-status species in the NWR to be exposed to potentially harmful concentrations of contaminants in their food. The primary focus of the NWR study, therefore, was on the possible impacts of potential contaminants in the food chain on these 2 species.

General approach and objectives

For the purposes of the NWR study, the final work plan (SWDIV 1992) defined background as those levels of chemicals that would exist in the NWR without the presence of the NWS Seal Beach. That is, background levels would be those attributable to regionally ubiquitous chemicals or those contributed to the NWR from the surrounding Anaheim Bay watershed, with the exception of NWS Seal Beach (SWDIV 1995a).

The approach chosen to evaluate background contaminants in the NWR was a phased study that combined assessing existing chemicals in sediments and biota in the NWR, coupled with an investigation of the physical processes in the tidal saltmarsh (which determine sediment transport mechanisms and contaminant patterns), along with an evaluation of potential contaminant effects on clapper rails and least terns. Under ideal conditions, the results of this study would be compared to contaminant levels in sediments and biota at a location that is physically and ecologically comparable to the tidal saltmarsh in the NWR and its watershed, but the NWR lacks a military installation that could be a contaminant source similar to NWS Seal Beach (SWDIV 1995a). If the locations were strictly comparable, the differences in chemicals and their concentrations would identify those chemicals likely to be attributable to operations of NWS Seal Beach.

The Phase 1 investigation was designed to collect sufficient information to assess the following (SWDIV 1995a):

1) Do elevated levels of chemicals exist in the sediments and/or selected biota in the NWR tidal saltmarsh?

2) What are the types and distributions of chemicals in sediments and selected biota in the NWR? Are contamination gradients identifiable?

3) What are the dynamics of contamination problems in the NWR? Do the existing conditions in the NWR result from previous transport of contaminants or is transport ongoing?

4) Did the contamination likely originate from NWS Seal Beach, other sources, or both?

5) What are the potential effects of COCs identified in the NWR on endangered species and other biota?

6) Are data analyses beyond those included in Phase 1 required to further define the types and extent of contamination or to recommend action?

The amounts and types of data collected and analyses performed in the Phase 1 study were intended to provide sufficient information to assess whether a contaminant problem exists in the NWR, as well as to design Phase 2 studies as deemed necessary based on the results of Phase 1 (SWDIV 1995a). This phased approach was considered cost-effective because it would contain the overall cost of the study if no contaminant problems were identified in Phase 1, and warranted because there was no evidence that endangered species at the NWR were being affected by contaminants.

Phase 1 of the NWR Study included an evaluation of the dynamics of physical processes and the status of physical and biological components of the tidal saltmarsh (SWDIV 1995a). Assessment of the contaminant status of these components and the physical processes that affect them was necessary to evaluate the existing conditions in the NWR and to project how conditions may change and affect the NWR biota. However, only the biota sampling plan and evaluation methods are presented in this chapter.

In the Seal Beach NWR Study (SWDIV 1995a), the focus was on the foods of the endangered species because many of the chemicals of potential concern were known to bioaccumulate in plants and animals. The primary foods of clapper rails include snails and crabs, whereas the least terns eat almost exclusively fish. The snails, in turn, feed on algae and detritus, whereas the crabs also eat smaller invertebrates. The fish sampled in the NWR Study feed on various small plants (phytoplankton) and animals (zooplankton, insects, etc.) that may have accumulated chemicals through ingestion or direct uptake from the water or sediment.

Information collected to evaluate the physical and biological components of the NWR for Phase 1 included assessment of chemical concentrations in sediments in the NWR because contact with food-chain species could cause bioaccumulation of chemicals; assessment of chemical concentrations in the food-chain species (invertebrates and fish) most frequently consumed by the 2 species of greatest concern in the NWR, the clapper rail and the least tern; and assessment of chemical concentrations in benthic invertebrates to evaluate potential effects on other aquatic bird species that feed in the NWR, as well as other measures of physical processes or factors affecting distribution or toxicity of contaminants (SWDIV 1995a).

The chemicals selected for analysis were those that were expected to occur as a result of NWS Seal Beach activities for which information on wildlife toxicology was available (SWDIV 1992, 1995a). In general, the emphasis was on inorganic and organic chemicals that could be expected to have adverse effects on species of concern, if the chemicals occurred in the food chain at elevated concentrations.

Exposure assessment

The purpose of biological chemical evaluation in the NWR was to identify chemical levels in invertebrate and fish species ingested by the clapper rail and the least tern, as well as by other bird species that forage in the NWR (SWDIV 1992, 1995a). Invertebrate species eaten by the clapper rail (snails, crabs, and benthic species) and fish species eaten by the least tern were chosen for sampling because these food species potentially bioaccumulate chemicals, making the birds more likely to be exposed to harmful levels of chemicals in food rather than in other media (air, water, or sediment). Sampling events were scheduled for the breeding season during which exposure to chemicals is of greatest concern because chemical exposure during egg-laying could subsequently affect developing embryos in the eggs and because adult birds feed chicks food items collected in the NWR.

Sample collection - Samples of invertebrates and fish were collected by biologists from CH2M HILL (with assistance on some occasions from Navy, USFWS, and California Department of Toxic Substances Control personnel) using an inflatable boat to gain access to most of the sample locations (SWDIV 1992, 1995a). Invertebrates were collected at 22 sample locations in the NWR and 1 sample location at the mouth of Huntington Harbour, near the southern boundary of the NWR (Figure 5-5).

Fish were collected in the 4 POLB ponds and at 4 locations in tidal channels in the NWR (SWDIV 1995a). Fish collection occurred twice during the breeding season in 1992 and 3 times during the breeding season in 1993 so that all size classes of fish fed to least tern chicks would be analyzed for contaminants. The most frequently sampled species included topsmelt (*Atherinops affinis*), deepbody anchovy (*Anchoa campressa*), northern anchovy (*Engraulis mordax*), and California killifish (*Fundulus parvipinnis*). Fish (primarily topsmelt and deepbody anchovy) were sampled in the 4 POLB mitigation ponds located within the NWR. During each sampling event, fish also were collected at 4 locations in NWR tidal channels where least terns were observed feeding and where it was possible to sample with the available equipment.

Crabs and snails were collected once during the 1992 breeding season and then were resampled over 2 sampling events following the 1992 breeding season in October 1992 and during the 1993 breeding season (SWDIV 1995a). Horned snails (*Certhidea californica*), saltmarsh snails (*Melampus olivaceous*), and striped shore crabs (*Pachygrapsus crassipes*) were the main species sampled. Striped shore crabs, saltmarsh snails, and horned snails were collected at each of the 23 sample locations shown in Figure 5-5. The USFWS requested the collection and analysis of benthic infauna samples to evaluate the potential contaminants in the food items of birds other than the clapper rail and least tern that forage in the NWR. Benthic invertebrates (polychaetes and mollusks) were collected at sample locations where they were sufficiently abundant to obtain adequate biomass for analysis.

Sampling was coordinated with the USFWS to ensure that disturbance to nesting birds (especially the clapper rails that nest throughout the NWR) would be minimized (SWDIV 1995a). Fish sampling was also coordinated with investigators monitoring the POLB mitigation ponds to minimize impacts of the NWR sampling on their ongoing monitoring of biotic colonization of the ponds.

Least tern eggs that failed to hatch in the breeding colony at NASA Island in the NWR were collected by the USFWS in 1991 and 1993 and were analyzed for inorganic and organic contaminants as part of the NWR study (SWDIV 1995a). These samples included 5 single eggs and 6 composites composed of 3 eggs each.

Chemical analysis - Samples of invertebrates (including exoskeleton and shells) and fish were analyzed as whole-body-composited samples for inorganic and organic contaminants by the Geochemical and Environmental Research Group (GERG) at Texas A&M University, College Station (SWDIV 1995a). Least tern eggs were analyzed for inorganic and organic contaminants if adequate sample biomass was available. However, the sample biomass for single eggs was not always sufficient for all analyses; therefore, the following analyses were performed: 6 composites and 3 single eggs were analyzed for all chemicals, and 2 single eggs were analyzed only for organics. The GERG was under contract to USFWS to perform analyses of sediment and biological samples for the NWR Study. The choice of a USFWS contract laboratory to conduct the analyses was made because of the role of the USFWS in managing the NWR and to help ensure the acceptability of the data. The GERG was selected from among the USFWS-contracted laboratories because it was the only laboratory that could perform the full suite of analyses required. Quality assurance/quality control (QA/QC) for the chemical analyses was provided by the USFWS in accordance with that agency's existing contract with GERG.

Statistical methods - The NWR biological analysis results required log transformation to normalize data distributions before statistical analysis, as is common for environmental analytical data (SWDIV 1995a). Means were computed (as geometric means) if detected values occurred in at least 50% of the samples. For cases where chemicals were detected in more than 50% of the samples, means were computed using ½ of the method detection limit for the "nondetected" values. This procedure is commonly used when contaminant concentrations in biological samples are not normally distributed and when the chemicals are not measurable in all samples (e.g., Schmitt and Brumbaugh 1990; Schmitt et al. 1990).

Effects assessment

Chemicals of potential concern - Exposure of birds to environmental contaminants was assessed by comparison of concentrations in food-chain organisms to applicable values for dietary exposure that are summarized in the USFWS Contaminant Hazard Reviews published by Eisler (1985–1993) (SWDIV 1995a). Assessment values for inorganics available from that source, as well as those provided for waterfowl or poultry by Puls (1988) and the National Academy of Sciences (NAS) (1980), were used to evaluate potential effects via the food chain. Whenever available, values for wild birds were used instead of using those for poultry.

Effect levels in wild birds for many chemicals, and especially in environmentally realistic chemical forms and concentrations, have not been clearly established. For example, Eisler (1985a) states for Cd that "until other data become available, wildlife dietary levels exceeding 100 µg Cd/kg fresh weight on a sustained basis should be viewed with caution." However, feeding studies with mallards (*Anas platyrhynchos*) indicated that diets containing 200 mg Cd/kg produced no obvious deleterious effects after 13 weeks, although Cd had accumulated to high levels in the ducks' kidneys. Species differences in sensitivity to various chemicals measured in the NWR study are unknown. Therefore, the values used for assessment of analytical results were generally the more conservative ones.

Organochlorine contaminants such as dichlorodiphenyltricloroethane (DDT) and its metabolites (primarily dichlorodiphenyldichloroethylene [DDE] and dichlorodiphenylethane [DDD]), polychlorinated biphenyls (PCBs), and chlordane have a tendency to bioaccumulate to high levels in birds that consume contaminated organisms (Stickel 1973; Ohlendorf et al. 1978; Eisler 1986b, 1990b). In contrast, polycyclic aromatic hydrocarbons (PAHs) generally show little tendency to bioaccumulate in foodchains, despite their high lipid solubility, probably because most PAHs are rapidly metabolized (Eisler 1987b). The organic chemicals considered most likely to cause potential effects in birds at the NWR were selected on the basis of their frequency of occurrence, maximum and mean concentrations, potential to bioaccumulate, and known effects in birds (SWDIV 1995a).

Dietary concentrations used for assessment of some organic contaminants are provided by Eisler (1986b, 1990b) and by other reviews (Stickel 1973; Ohlendorf et al. 1978), although effect levels in clapper rails and least terns are not known (SWDIV 1995a). In general, dietary concentrations of 3 mg/kg (fresh weight) of either DDE or PCBs are considered to cause adverse effects in birds. Dietary concentrations up to 0.3 mg/kg (fresh weight) total chlordane are considered acceptable. Acute and chronic toxicity effects on birds exposed to PAHs in their diet are very limited (Eisler 1987b). When mallards were fed diets containing 4,000 mg PAHs/kg (mostly as naphthalenes, naphthenes, and phenanthrene) for a period of 7 months, no mortality or visible signs of toxicity were observed, but the birds did show physiological responses (including 25% larger livers than controls).

The USFWS has periodically determined concentrations of selected inorganic and organochlorine chemicals in freshwater fish collected from a nationwide network of stations as part of the National Contaminant Biomonitoring Program (NCBP) (Schmitt and Brumbaugh 1990; Schmitt et al. 1990). Chemical concentrations in the NCBP are typically reported on a wet-weight basis. Average moisture content of the fish is about 75%; thus, wet-weight concentrations can be converted to approximate dry-weight concentrations with a multiplier of 4. Results of the most recently published NCBP survey were compared with results from the NWR (SWDIV 1995a).

The NAS has established recommended maximum concentrations of certain toxic substances in freshwater fish and marine fish tissue to protect the fish containing those chemicals, as well as to protect animals that consume the contaminated fish (NAS/NAE 1973). Contaminant concentrations in fish from the NWR were compared with these recommended guidelines (SWDIV 1995a).

Contaminant concentrations in fish and in mussels from California waters are measured periodically through the Toxic Substances Monitoring Program (TSMP) or the California State Mussel Watch (CSMW) (Phillips 1988; Rasmussen 1992). Those programs use "elevated data levels" (EDLs) as internal comparative measures that rank a given concentration of a particular substance with previous data from the TSMP or CSMW. The EDLs are calculated by ranking all of the results for a given chemical from the highest concentration to the lowest concentration measured (including those not detected). From this, a cumulative distribution is constructed and percentile rankings are calculated. The 85th percentile (EDL 85) is used as an indication that a chemical is elevated from the median. Although species sampled at the NWR are different from those sampled in the TSMP and CSMW, the available EDL 85 values were used for evaluating results from the NWR (SWDIV 1995a).

The State of California (1993) also has developed maximum tissue residue levels (MTRLs) for evaluating contaminant concentration in organisms as an element of the Bay Protection and Toxic Cleanup Program (BPTCP). The MTRLs are calculated by multiplying the human-health water-quality objective in the appropriate statewide plan by the chemical's bioconcentration factor. Exceedance of MTRLs by toxic chemicals in tissues of resident organisms is given in the BPTCP as one of the conditions that may indicate the site is a "potential hot spot" (as defined by State of California 1993). Contaminants found in the biological samples from the NWR were compared with these MTRLs (SWDIV 1995a).

Chemicals that occurred in invertebrates or fish from the NWR at concentrations exceeding these various benchmarks were identified as being of concern for possible effects in clapper rails and least terns at the NWR (SWDIV 1995a).

Spatial patterns - Overall patterns in the occurrence of various COCs (6 inorganics, 2 organics) were examined by comparing the locations where they occurred at highest concentrations in the most widely collected species (SWDIV 1995a). Those species included horned snails, saltmarsh snails, striped shore crabs, and topsmelt. Although topsmelt was not collected at each of the 23 sample locations, it was collected at least once at 9 sample locations and at least 3 times in each of the POLB mitigation ponds. Topsmelt also is more mobile than are the invertebrates sampled in this study, so it may not be as reliable an indicator of locations-specific exposure as are the invertebrates. Nevertheless, the evaluation did indicate that topsmelt often had the highest concentrations of contaminants at the same general locations where some of the invertebrates had the highest levels.

Although the highest and second-highest concentrations of inorganics within a particular species sometimes occurred at adjacent or nearby sample locations, this event was unusual (SWDIV 1995a). Most often, the spatial patterns within species were unclear, and it was more useful to consider the patterns for all invertebrate species combined with topsmelt. In doing so, concentrations for each metal appeared to be generally higher at several areas (invertebrates and fish often were not collected at the same sample locations, so ponds were combined with adjacent sample locations).

Bird eggs - Taking various factors concerning the usefulness of bird eggs into consideration, contaminant concentrations in tern eggs were compared with inorganics for which interpretive guidelines are available, DDE levels associated with impaired reproduction in sensitive species (although effect levels in least terns are not well known), and concentrations of PCBs in eggs recommended by Eisler (1986b) as a proposed criterion for protection of birds (SWDIV 1995a). Other organochlorines (e.g., *trans*-nonachlor and PCBs), as well as PAHs (e.g., pyrene and phenanthrene), occurred only at concentrations lower than 0.5 mg/kg and 0.1 mg/kg, respectively.

Conclusions and recommendations
Although the detailed findings of this study cannot be presented here, it is possible to state that the patterns of elevated levels of contaminants in sediment at the NWR sometimes were reproduced in potential effect-level concentrations found in invertebrate and fish tissue in several areas of the Anaheim Bay saltmarsh system (SWDIV 1995a). However, the spatial patterns of contamination for inorganic and organic chemicals were somewhat different and probably reflect different sources. In addition, some chemicals showed no consistent pattern of distribution in the biota that would relate to source areas at the NWS Seal Beach. Inorganic and organic contaminants are not expected to cause lethal effects on clapper rails or least terns at the concentrations found in food-chain components at the NWR. Similarly, the contaminants found in least tern eggs do not indicate likely lethal effects in nesting birds.

The observed levels of invertebrate and fish contamination in the NWR were not considered sufficient to warrant a concern for immediate remediation (SWDIV 1995a). However, because of the potential for sediment transport in the NWR resulting from construction of the POLB ponds, several follow-up actions were recommended. These included further monitoring of contaminant levels in food-chain organisms and sediments in identified areas of contamination that are subject to erosion or deposition. To track the potential occurrence of sublethal effects of identified contaminants on the clapper rail and the least tern, continued coordination with the USFWS was advised in order to have access to analyses on addled eggs that they may collect, as well as any population information they may have for these species.

Marine Corps Base Camp Pendleton

Background

An RI report for Group A sites at the Marine Corps Base (MCB) Camp Pendleton, California, was prepared in accordance with the MCB Camp Pendleton Federal Facility Agreement (FFA), as amended (SWDIV 1993c). The RI Report for Group A sites at MCB Camp Pendleton was prepared within the context of the Navy's Installation Restoration Program (IRP). The IRP is designed, in part, to evaluate and remediate, if necessary, contamination caused by hazardous substances, pollutants, or contaminants, pursuant to the Comprehensive Environmental Response, Compensation, and Liability Act of 1980, as amended by the Superfund Amendments and Reauthorization Act of 1986.

Marine Corps Base Camp Pendleton is located between the cities of Los Angeles to the north and San Diego to the south (Figure 5-4). Camp Pendleton covers about 125,000 acres of land, almost entirely in San Diego County, and is bordered on the west by the Pacific Ocean. The westernmost portion of the base encompasses about 17 miles of undisturbed coastal area, from which rolling hills and valleys range inland an average of 10 to 12 miles.

Several ecosystems dominate the specific sites addressed in the work plan. These include coastal sage scrub, oak woodland, riparian woodland, chaparral, native grassland, nonnative grassland, freshwater marsh, and disturbed habitat. An estuarine ecosystem occurs along the coast, outside the area of the Group A sites but receiving drainage from them. Some of these habitats can also be divided into subassociations. All Group A sites are below 300 feet in elevation. The distribution and composition of plants are largely predicated on soil type, water, slope, temperature, and degree of soil disturbance. Fires are common, but mainly as a result of military activities. The general characteristics of these ecosystems are described in the RI Report (SWDIV 1993c).

A total of 26 RI sites were identified in the FFA (USEPA 1990). Additional sites were identified as a result of the Resource Conservation and Recovery Act facility assessment conducted at the base and were subsequently added to the FFA (USEPA 1992c). The sites were divided into 4 groups for RI purposes. The locations of the Group A sites are shown in Figure 5-6, and they are briefly described below.

- Site 3–Pest Control Wash Rack

The concrete wash rack reportedly was used from the 1950s until 1980 for washing pest control vehicles, rinsing application tanks and other equipment, mixing pesticide solutions, and disposing of leftover insecticide or herbicide solutions. The wash rack is sloped to drain into a corrugated steel culvert that runs about 170 feet to an approximately 10-foot-wide unlined ditch. The ditch cuts into the alluvium of the Santa Margarita River basin and follows a southwesterly course for about 1,000 feet before emptying into the floodplain of the Santa Margarita River.

- Sites 4 and 4A–Marine Corps Air Station Drainage Ditch and Concrete-Lined Surface Impoundment

  Liquid wastes generated by flight-line operations at the Marine Corps Air Station reportedly were discharged to this ditch prior to 1982. The concrete-lined surface impoundment is located adjacent to the ditch. The hangar deluge system for fire suppression discharges into this impoundment after flowing through an oil/water separator.

- Site 5–Firefighter Drill Field

  This area was used until about 1981 to train firefighters in the suppression of fuel and oil fires. The unlined burn pit was also used until the mid- to late-1970s to store fuels and other flammable liquids between burns.

- Site 6–Defense Property Disposal Office (Defense Reutilization and Marketing Office) Scrap Yard

  The Defense Property Disposal Office (Defense Reutilization and Marketing Office) scrap yard operated from the early 1950s to 1979 as a storage, processing, and disposal area for scrap metals, salvage items, hazardous materials, and PCB transformer fluids. The yard was divided into 4 separate areas for investigation including a PCB spreading area, a wood burning area, a battery electrolyte disposal area, and a hazardous waste drum storage area.

- Site 9-41 area–Stuart Mesa Waste Stabilization Pond

  This site was part of an active sewage treatment plant until 1974 or 1975. Since that time, the pond reportedly has been used for stockpiling contaminated soils and for disposal of mess hall grease-trap wastes.

- Site 24-26 area–Morale, Welfare, and Recreation Maintenance Facility

  This facility provides maintenance services for approximately 200 buildings on the base. From the 1940s to about 1970, the facility was used to perform maintenance on vehicles. Previous practices reportedly saturated the soil with waste oil and other vehicle fluids.

Figure 5-6 also shows expanded views of Sites 3, 4 and 4A, 5, and 6 because of their proximity to the Santa Margarita River and the following discussion. The remaining RI/FS sites have been divided into Groups B, C, and D and are being evaluated separately. The Group B sites include landfills and surface impoundments. The Group C sites include the

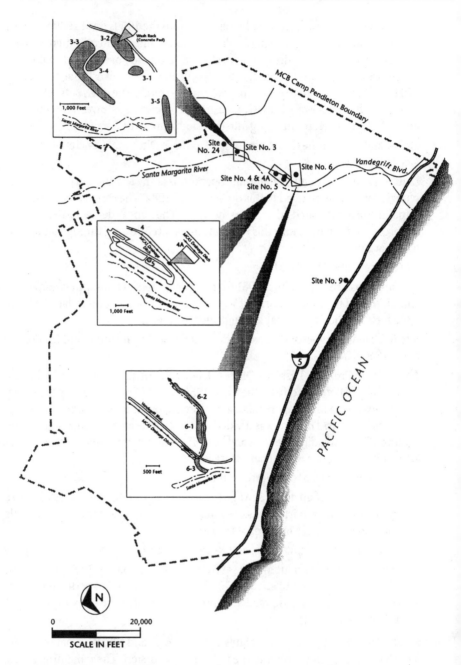

Figure 5-6   Locations of MCB Camp Pendleton Group A RI/FS sites, including subareas within Sites 3 and 6.

remaining sites in the Santa Margarita River Basin, and Group D sites are those outside the Santa Margarita Basin.

General approach and objectives

A sampling and analysis plan (SAP) (SWDIV 1993b) was prepared to support the ERA work plan for MCB Camp Pendleton (SWDIV 1993a). The Draft Final Work Plan proposed that the ERA for MCB Camp Pendleton be conducted following the phased approach recommended by the USEPA (1991a, 1992b). The phased approach for MCB Camp Pendleton (which is similar to that illustrated in Figure 5-3) involved 3 major tasks or phases, during which the data and observations from one phase were used to determine whether further studies were needed to meet the objectives of the assessment. The SAP presents the field sampling procedures, bioassay methods, analytical requirements, and quality assurance measures necessary to support the baseline ERA. The SAP was based on decisions reached through discussions with the federal and state regulatory and resource agencies that are providing oversight for the MCB Camp Pendleton ERA.

The ERA work plan (SWDIV 1993a) summarizes the nature and extent of contamination and the potential ecological receptors and provides a comparison of contaminant concentrations to screening levels for the chemicals detected at Group A sites. Screening levels were used for general comparisons and to complement other factors in selecting the sites that warranted further sampling and bioassays. Final decisions regarding the toxicity of detected chemicals of concern to ecological receptors at each site were made after complete ecological toxicity reviews for those chemicals during the ERA as described in the work plan. Further information regarding the rationale for additional soils sampling also is contained in the work plan and SAP for the RI (SWDIV 1991a, 1991b).

The Draft Final ERA Work Plan (SWDIV 1993a) identifies the general objectives of the work to be performed in support of the RI/FS investigation as follows:

1) to reduce ecological risks to an acceptable level,
2) to protect food chain integrity,
3) to protect water quality,
4) to maintain biotic diversity, and
5) to protect ecosystem structure.

The measurement endpoints include the following:

1) assessment of "ecosystem health," as shown by contaminant impacts on plants and animals (both actual and potential), through quantitative comparisons with reported effect levels, calculated effect levels, and ARARs (effect levels include those for terrestrial plants and animals [invertebrates and vertebrates] and for aquatic invertebrates and fish),
2) assessment of bioaccumulation potential of contaminants to secondary receptors (birds) through quantitative comparisons with calculated soil criteria based on food-chain bioaccumulation, and

3) assessment of toxicity and bioaccumulation potential of contaminants to primary receptors (plants and soil invertebrates) through bioassays conducted using site soils collected from selected locations.

The SAP (SWDIV 1993b) describes the field and laboratory sampling and analyses that were conducted at Sites 3, 4, 6, and 9. Findings from selected sampling locations at these sites were applied to existing data from other Group A sites to characterize likely risks to ecological receptors during the risk assessment.

The work plan reviewed the available information, identified potential ecological receptors and exposure pathways, presented methods for characterizing risk, and outlined additional data needs for each site. The results of RI sampling at the Group A sites were reviewed and summarized to define the needs for further assessment of ecological effects at each site. The phased approach for studies at the sites is summarized below.

Phase 1 - Site characterization and screening
This phase involved identifying the presence and levels of contaminants at the sites and evaluating whether exposure pathways to ecological receptors exist. This stage also involved comparing contaminant concentrations at various locations to available criteria, standards, and reference values. Much of the work for this phase was completed as part of the Phase 1 RI sampling or in the development of the work plan.

Phase 2 - Initial determination of ecological impairment
This phase involved conducting ecological comparisons between potentially impacted and non-impacted areas. The work plan provided qualitative ecological characterization of habitats and ecological receptors (including plants, vertebrate animals, and soil macroinvertebrates) in the vicinity of the Group A sites. The SAP does not include plans for determining in more detail the presence or absence of terrestrial species, health of plants and animals, or community structure, in part because those studies are best conducted outside the time period available for work under the SAP (February–March 1993). Assessment of these parameters was left as a part of follow-up work to the sampling and analyses described in the SAP if the results of the tissue analysis or toxicity studies conducted as part of Phase 3 indicated potential for ecological impacts and the need for further studies. Ecological characterization of aquatic communities in the Santa Margarita River near the Group A was included in the SAP. This phase also included evaluation of the potential bioaccumulation of contaminants into plants and animals, which was considered in selection of sampling locations for Phase 3 work.

Phase 3 - Bioassessment
This phase involved laboratory studies to determine what level of contamination resulted in measurable effects. Information collected as part of this phase was used to help make decisions about potential remediation. The SAP describes plant and animal bioassay procedures (and associated chemical analyses of exposure media) to determine the

toxicity of contamination at each site and the levels of contamination that result in no observed effect and in measurable effects.

Exposure assessment

Each of the Group A sites was characterized during the field study to obtain general descriptive accounts of wetlands, vegetation, wildlife (including soil invertebrates), and wildlife habitat. General habitat maps were produced at scales of 1 inch = 200 feet and 1 inch = 400 feet using U.S. Geological Survey topographic maps and MCB Camp Pendleton base maps. Visual methods were used to define on-the-ground changes in wildlife habitat. Areas for which the habitats were mapped were considered to constitute the site vicinity in which ecological receptors could be exposed to contaminants originating at the site. Mapping was ground-truthed during a field visit, and written plant community/habitat descriptions were prepared to accompany the maps. In accordance with the phased approach of the overall project, wildlife studies were conducted on a reconnaissance level and focused on identifying species that could be documented during the preliminary surveys.

The following groups of chemicals were analyzed in sediment and soil samples from MCB Camp Pendleton:

- volatile organics,
- total petroleum hydrocarbons (TPH) as gasoline, aviation fuel (JP-5), or diesel,
- semivolatile organics,
- dioxins/furans,
- pesticides and PCBs,
- chlorinated herbicides,
- organophosphate pesticides,
- carbamates and urea pesticides,
- triazine pesticides, and
- metals.

Comparison with screening levels - Screening levels were used to provide a preliminary determination of whether measured contaminant concentrations were above or below levels that are likely to cause adverse effects. Screening levels were based on applicable criteria and standards established by regulatory agencies, effect levels available from published literature, or comparison with MCB Camp Pendleton background data.

Applicable criteria and standards represent regulatory values that are considered protective of most environmental receptors. These included the USEPA water-quality criteria for the protection of aquatic life (USEPA 1992d) and the California water-quality control plan for inland surface waters (CSWRCB 1992). Because U.S. soil criteria based on environmental effects are not available, professional judgment was used in screening data from each of the Group A sites against reference levels, which included interim Canadian environmental quality criteria for contaminated sites (CCME 1991), background soils concentrations for inorganics measured in soils throughout the western U.S. (Shacklette and Boerngen 1984), and concentrations of inorganics measured at apparently uncontaminated locations on MCB Camp Pendleton during the RI sampling in 1992.

Other concentrations presented in the published toxicological literature as no-effect or toxic levels in water or soils and sediments were also considered during the risk assessment.

Data for soils and sediments from the sampling locations for Group A sites were compared with these criteria and reference values as one factor during the screening process for selecting locations that warrant further studies. The history of chemical use and exposure at the site was also considered in the screening process.

Follow-up sampling - A description of the overall decision strategy and a summary of the sampling plans for each of the Group A sites follows. Phase 1 RI sampling results were used in conjunction with the site-specific habitat information to select subareas and COCs for toxicity assessments (SWDIV 1993a). (A subarea was defined as a subdivision of the site vicinity where RI sampling was conducted and the available data indicated a general profile of contamination that differed qualitatively or quantitatively from other subareas. Habitat characteristics also are considered in the designation of subareas.) The basic sampling plan objective was to characterize contamination, toxicity, and possible bioaccumulation of contaminants within subareas at selected MCB Camp Pendleton sites. Several metals (e.g., As, Cd, Cr, Cu, Pb, Hg, molybdenum, Ni, and Zn) exceeded screening criteria at Sites 3, 6, or 9. Thus, the primary focus for inorganics was those specific metals identified above; for organic compounds, the focus was those compounds detected at a particular site. Sampling for bioaccumulation in biota depended on the potential for bioaccumulation of the contaminants detected at any given site.

Sampling locations - Evaluation of results from the Phase 1 RI sampling of soil, sediment, and surface water during the spring and summer of 1992 at the Group A sites revealed a wide range of concentrations of a number of contaminants. In the Draft Final ERA Work Plan (SWDIV 1993a), subareas were defined on the basis of habitat homogeneity and the grouping of samples with similar contamination patterns. The RI sampling results were used as an indication of the contaminants (and their concentrations) that were expected during the follow-up work.

Shallow soil boring (top 5 feet of soil) and sediment sampling and analysis for organic and inorganic constituents allowed sites to be categorized into general groups according to type of contamination. Major groups of contaminants such as fuel hydrocarbons, solvents, organochlorines and other pesticides, and heavy metals occur at various locations in different sites, as shown by the soil and sediment sample results. An important goal of further sampling for the ERA was to choose sampling locations at sites so that they included all of the major types of contaminants and the range of concentrations detected during the Phase 1 RI (SWDIV 1993b). Individual soil or sediment samples were ranked within sites by the concentrations of key contaminants and were grouped into subareas having similar contamination patterns. The subareas exhibiting the highest contamination for any given compound or group of compounds within sites were chosen for further soil, sediment, and biota testing and for toxicity bioassays. Contaminant heterogeneity was used to determine the number of sampling locations within subareas. Subareas characterized by 1 group of contaminants had 1 sampling location; more variable subareas required 2 or more sampling locations. For some sites, certain subareas were eliminated from further sampling because lower contaminant concentrations there could be assessed on the basis of sampling in other subareas having higher concentrations. The use of dilution series in bioassays for each of the collected samples makes this possible. Subarea maps for Sites 3 and 6 are shown in Figure 5-6.

Based on the ranking of locations and the profiles of contaminants present, 11 terrestrial locations were selected for further sampling of surface soil/sediment. These locations, the rationale for their selection, and the anticipated uses of the data are listed in Table 5-1. A reference location from near Site 3 (3SD34), where RI sampling results showed background levels of contaminants, was included in tests for toxicity. Results from this location were expected to provide a useful comparison for toxicity results from more contaminated sites. Toxicity testing was conducted in a dilution series using clean laboratory soil or sediment to define the relationship between concentration and toxicity for given types of contaminants. In this way, it was expected that known soil or sediment to define the relationship between concentration and toxicity for given types of contaminants. In this way, it was expected that known soil or sediment toxicity and accumulation in biota could be assigned to the 11 selected sites, and cleanup goals could be set for contaminants at all of the Group A sites.

In addition to sampling at the identified RI sites, sampling locations in the Santa Margarita River channel were selected as ecologically sensitive areas above and below known drainage from 3 Group A sites (Sites 3, 4, and 6). The Santa Margarita River sites were sampled for sediment chemistry (including constituents identified at the sites draining to the river, plus total organic carbon), aquatic macroinvertebrate contaminant body burden (if sufficient biomass could be collected for analysis), and sediment toxicity (to amphipods and to nutsedge as representative aquatic plants) without previous knowledge of the level of contaminant exposure. Aquatic macroinvertebrate abundance and diversity also were assessed at those location. Because of extensive flooding just prior to the sampling conducted during early February 1993, ecological sampling in the Santa Margarita River channel was deferred until it could be performed as part of the Phase 2 RI at Site 6 in July 1993.

Chemical analyses - All sampling locations were characterized for soil or sediment chemistry to aid in the interpretation of toxicity testing results. Chemicals of concern were identified in the Draft Final ERA Work Plan (SWDIV 1993a) on the basis of the history of the site and available contaminant concentration data. Contaminant analysis at most locations was limited to those groups of chemicals previously identified in the Phase 1 RI soil and sediment sampling from that subarea.

Table 5-1   *Rationale for and uses of data from terrestrial locations selected for further sampling MCB Camp Pendleton*

Subarea	Site location	Rationale	Uses of data
Site 3			
3-2	3B18	Highest or near-highest concentrations of several organics plus arsenic; potential toxicity to plants and invertebrates and potential bioaccumulation in them	Determine toxicity and bioaccumulation at this site and range of lower concentrations
3-3	3SD34	Reference location with low contamination concentrations	Compare toxicity and bioaccumulation with other locations
3-4	3SD31	High concentration of azinphosmethyl; moderate levels of DDT and metabolites	Determine toxicity and bioaccumulation, including DDT and metabolites in absence of other organochlorines
	3B19	Moderate concentrations of endrin and other organics	Determine toxicity and bioaccumulation
Site 4			
--	None	No contaminants sufficiently elevated to warrant further sampling except at 6SD7 (see below)	--
Site 6			
6-1	6B15	Highest or near-highest concentrations of numerous organics and inorganics, with Cu, Pb, Hg, Ni, and Zn above background	Determine toxicity and bioaccumulation at this site and range of lower concentration
	6B16	Highest or near-highest concentrations of numerous contaminants (including PCB1260), with several inorganics far above background	Determine toxicity and bioaccumulation at this site and range of lower concentrations
	6B21	Highest or near-highest concentrations of several organics (including DDT) and inorganics (including Cu, Pb, Zn will above background)	Determine toxicity and bioaccumulation at this site and range of lower concentrations
6-3	6SD7	Downstream area near combined Sites 4 and 6 discharge to river; moderate contaminant concentrations	Verify no significant toxicity or bioaccumulation

Table 5-2 Continued

Subarea	Site location	Rationale	Uses of data
Site 9			
9-1	9B11	High concentrations of fuel hydrocarbons; elevated inorganics (e.g., Cu, Zn); different profile than most other locations	Determine toxicity and bioaccumulation at this site and range of lower concentrations
	9B16	High concentrations of fuel hydrocarbons; lead elevated with other inorganics near background	Determine toxicity and bioaccumulation at this site and range of lower concentrations
Site 24			
--	None	No contaminants sufficiently elevated to warrant further sampling; generally covered through dilution series at other locations	--

[a]In addition, aquatic sediments and algae were sampled at 2 locations for combined Sites 4 and 6 (upstream and downstream of the discharge to the Santa Margarita River).

Bioassays and bioaccumulation assessment - All sampling locations were tested for soil or sediment toxicity using whole soil or sediment and a dilution series of 75, 50, and 25% test soil or sediment mixed with clean laboratory media. Because all the earthworms in sample 3B18 died in less than 7 d at each of those dilutions, the soil was diluted to 5% to ensure survival of adequate numbers of earthworms for chemical analyses. Detailed methods for the bioassays are described in the Draft Final ERA SAP (SWDIV 1993b). Surface soils and areas of sediment accumulation in terrestrial habitats were examined for toxicity using earthworm toxicity tests, lettuce seed germination tests, and lettuce seedling growth tests. A standard laboratory soil was used as a control in earthworm tests, and fertilized silica sand was used as the lettuce control medium. Bioaccumulation was measured following the toxicity testing if the biomass of surviving test organisms was adequate for chemical analysis.

The presence of bioaccumulating chemicals such as organochlorines and heavy metals was the criterion for sampling of biota for chemical body burdens. During the follow-up sampling, sampling locations previously characterized by high levels of organochlorine or metals contamination were searched for an adequate biomass of soil- or sediment-dwelling macroinvertebrates for chemical analysis. Earthworms were found at only 1 location (3SD43) in sufficient quantity for analysis.

The second type of bioaccumulation testing involved analyzing accumulation in laboratory test organisms following toxicity tests from sites with bioaccumulating chemicals. Earthworm tests were continued for 28 d, and surviving earthworms were analyzed for organochlorines and metals (if appropriate). In addition, for sites tested because of potential metals toxicity, above-ground portions of surviving lettuce seedlings were analyzed for metals at the end of the 28-d early seedling growth tests. Plants are not expected to accumulate organochlorines as readily as are earthworms; thus, they were not analyzed for those chemicals.

When biota could not be analyzed for organochlorines and metals because available biomass was insufficient, potential bioaccumulation of those chemicals was determined during the ERA. That determination was based on available data concerning bioaccumulation of organochlorines and metals by plants and invertebrates from soil or sediment in which they live.

Effects assessment

Bioaccumulation - The lettuce and earthworms that survived the 28-d bioassay and the nutsedge that survived the 45-d bioassay were assessed for bioaccumulation of contaminants. Only those lettuce plants or earthworms from the highest site soil concentrations with adequate biomass for analysis were used. Nutsedge was analyzed at 100% sediment concentrations only. The above-ground portions of lettuce plants and nutsedge and the whole earthworms were analyzed for tissue concentrations of contaminants. These concentrations were compared with concentrations in control populations grown in uncontaminated laboratory soil and with concentrations in the Site 3 reference location (3SD34) soil. These data were used to approximate potential plant or terrestrial invertebrate bioaccumulation of contaminants at sublethal concentrations that might be experienced in or near the MCB Camp Pendleton sampling locations. Lettuce plants and nutsedge were analyzed for uptake of metals. Earthworms were analyzed for uptake of metals and organochlorine pesticides. Maximum observed tissue concentrations in the bioaccumulation tests were compared with literature values for dietary toxic effect levels for terrestrial animals (potential consumers), along with data on field-collected earthworms from Site 3 and filamentous algae from the Santa Margarita River.

The lettuce plants showed bioaccumulation of Al, Cd, Cu, Fe, Pb, V, and Zn in soils from Sites 3, 6, and 9 at dilutions ranging from 100 to 25% site soil. Bioaccumulation of those elements was at least twice that of the control concentration. Of the bioaccumulating elements, Pb and Al showed the greatest increase over control concentrations (5- to 10-fold increases). An identical list of bioaccumulating metals with a similar emphasis on Pb and Al was determined when bioaccumulation was assessed via comparison between contaminated locations and the Site 3 reference location. Analytical results for nutsedge from the bioassays showed similar, relatively low levels of inorganics from all 3 sediment samples tested for bioaccumulation.

The earthworms yielded an expanded list of bioaccumulating metals. Compared with earthworms grown in control soil, experimental animals demonstrated bioaccumulation (at least twice the control concentrations) for Al, As, Ba, Cd, Co, Cu, Fe, Hg, Mn, and Pb. In the same manner as for lettuce, only Al and Pb showed concentration increases as much as 5- to 10-fold over controls. Compared with earthworms from the Site 3 reference location, test animals from other locations demonstrated a reduced list of bioaccumulating metals, consisting of Al, Ba, Cu, Fe, Hg, and Pb. In the reference location comparison, only Pb showed bioaccumulation greater than 5- to 10-fold. Al, Cd, Cu, Fe, and Pb showed bioaccumulation in both earthworms and lettuce plants. A list of bioaccumulating organic chemicals was developed by comparing earthworms in control and reference location bioassay tests with tests from other locations at Sites 3, 6, and 9.

Earthworms in control and site reference bioassay tests were compared to identify organic chemicals that were bioaccumulated. Organic chemicals that were bioaccumulated in site reference earthworms consisted of *alpha*-chlordane, *gamma*-chlordane, DDD, DDE, DDT, gamma-BHC, and dieldrin.

Lettuce plants grown in the laboratory bioassay experiments for Site 3 had tissue concentrations of Al, Cu, Fe, Pb, V, and Zn exceeding criteria protective of herbivores. Lettuce grown in Site 9 soil showed bioaccumulation of Zn.

Earthworms grown in laboratory bioassay experiments for Site 3 had tissue concentrations of Al, As, Cd, Fe, Hg, *alpha*-chlordane, *gamma*-chlordane, DDT, and dieldrin exceeding criteria protective of carnivores and birds.

Earthworms collected from the Site 3 field location (3SD43) had tissue concentrations of Al, Cd, Fe, Pb, Hg, and V exceeding criteria protective of carnivores and birds. However, because these elements were present at background levels in the soil from the field collection location, the bioaccumulation by earthworms may be normal. As such, the results for this sample should be considered when evaluating other bioaccumulation results.

Risk characterization
The COC selection process for the ERA is depicted in Figure 5-7. All chemicals detected (inorganic and organic) were considered in the COC selection process. Final ecological COCs were selected using the following screening processes:

1) comparison of inorganic chemicals detected in soil with background concentrations at MCB Camp Pendleton,

2) comparison with toxic effect levels and calculated criteria for primary receptors (soil invertebrates, plants, terrestrial vertebrates, and aquatic organisms), and

3) assessment of bioaccumulation potential in primary receptors and through the food chain.

To be conservative, the site-wide maximum concentration of chemicals detected in soil, surface water, and sediment was used as the exposure point concentration for each COC screening process. The remainder of this section focuses on bioaccumulation assessment.

Indirect exposure to consumer organisms (herbivores, carnivores, and omnivores) was addressed by analyzing bioaccumulation and bioconcentration potential (where applicable). In addition, the potential effects to herbivores and omnivores were addressed by comparing earthworm and lettuce bioassay results with toxic effect levels, and physical and chemical parameters that characterize the bioaccumulative potential of a chemical

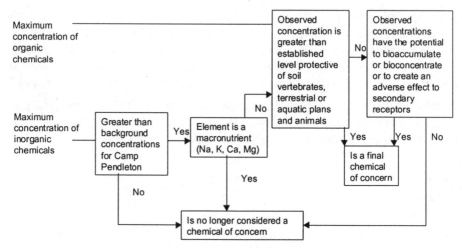

Figure 5-7   Screening process for COCs at MCB Camp Pendleton

were compiled for the toxicity assessment. If a chemical was documented as bioaccumulating at significant levels within foodchains similar to those observed within MCB Camp Pendleton, the chemical was retained as a COC.

A standard technique for reporting the potential of a given chemical to bioconcentrate within an aquatic organism is the bioconcentration (BCF). The steady-state BCF is defined as the ratio of the concentration of a chemical in the tissues of an aquatic organism to the concentration of that chemical in water. The potential of many highly water-insoluble compounds (such as DDT and its metabolites) to bioaccumulate and become toxic is greatly affected by chemicals and physical parameters, including soil adsorption coefficient (K_d), octanol/water partition coefficient (K_{ow}), BCF, and Henry's Law constant (H). These parameters and potential bioaccumulation were evaluated and then applied to the uptake of contaminants by organisms of interest for the Group A sites. The BCF was used to provide a relative measure of the potential of a specific chemical to accumulate within an organism and its hazard to that and other exposed organisms.

Most chemicals detected at MCB Camp Pendleton reside within the soils. Therefore, the receptors of particular concern included soil-dwelling organisms such as invertebrates. Earthworms can accumulate chemicals as they tunnel through the soil, either through ingestion or dermal absorption. These chemicals can be stored within the tissues of the organisms and accumulate to levels greater than those in the soil (e.g., concentrations of Cd in earthworm tissues can be as much as 20 x greater than ambient soil concentrations) (Beyer 1990). These concentrations can then be passed on to birds or other consumers that depend on earthworms as a food source.

The risk characterization for MCB Camp Pendleton evaluated a number of exposure routes, including potential bioaccumulation from soil to earthworms, earthworms to consumers, soil to plants, plants to herbivores, and water to aquatic organisms. Chemicals of concern were then selected on the basis of bioaccumulation as well as other factors mentioned above.

Results of bioaccumulation studies on Site 3 soils indicate that several chemicals are bioaccumulated in lettuce and earthworms at levels exceeding toxic effect levels and calculated criteria protective of herbivores, small mammals, and birds. Lettuce bioassay samples were analyzed only for metals accumulation, whereas earthworms were analyzed for metals, pesticides, and PCBs. Metals and organochlorines (especially 4,4'-DDT and its metabolites) were bioaccumulated in earthworms. Earthworms grown in laboratory bioassay experiments bioaccumulated metals and herbicides, whereas field-collected earthworms bioaccumulated only metals and a low concentration of 4,4'-DDE.

The potential for higher trophic organisms to become exposed at Site 4 to chemicals through bioaccumulation appears to be negligible. Many of the chemicals detected in soil do not bioaccumulate because of their chemical and physical properties. However, some of the metals detected in surface water and sediment may bioconcentrate in aquatic organisms. Although the bioconcentration potential of the metals depends on bioavailability, potential risk to higher trophic organisms could occur. Evidence was found of Mn bioaccumulation in filamentous algae immediately downstream from the confluence of the Site 4 drainage ditch with the Santa Margarita River, although the algae did not contain toxic levels of Mn. Based on the analyses of toxicity to aquatic and terrestrial organisms, the concentrations of chemicals in soil, sediment, and surface water were not considered to pose ecological risks to terrestrial or aquatic organisms.

At Site 5, the potential for bioaccumulation to occur may be a source of risk to higher trophic organisms because some of the metals detected could be accumulated through the terrestrial foodchain. However, given the nature of habit in the immediate vicinity of the site, significant exposure pathways are not likely to be complete.

Inorganic and organic chemicals were detected in soil, sediment, and surface-water samples at Site 6 (SWDIV 1995b). Toxicological comparisons were made for each of the media sampled. Risks of adverse effects to potential receptors were characterized by comparing maximum observed concentrations to the toxic effect levels judged most appropriate. The comparison of observed inorganic chemical concentrations to background levels indicated that most of the detected elements were present above the background levels. The assessment of potential soil toxicity to plants revealed that PAHs, 4,4'-DDD, 4,4'-DDE, 4,4'-DDT, diesel, and metals (including Cd, Cr, Cu, Pb, Hg, Ni, and Zn) may pose a risk to plants. Assessment of potential soil toxicity to terrestrial invertebrates showed similar results; PAHs, 4,4'-DDT and its degradation products, diesel, and metals (Cd, Cu, Pb, and Zn) may contribute most of the risk to invertebrates based on available literature toxic-effect levels and earthworm bioassay results. The assessment of potential soil toxicity to terrestrial vertebrates revealed that 4,4'-DDT and its degradation products, as well as heavy metals, posed the greatest risk. Seven chemicals (Cd, Pb, Hg, Zn, 4,4'-DDD, 4,4'-DDE, 4,4'-DDT) exceeded safe soil concentrations based on accumulation in earthworms and subsequent ingestion and accumulation in birds. All chemicals except 4,4'-DDD had been retained during screening against literature toxic effect levels for terrestrial vertebrates. Chemicals that exceeded any of the criteria used for plants, invertebrates, or vertebrates were retained as final soil chemicals of ecological concern. Safe soil concentrations were calculated based on bioaccumulation of toxicants by earthworms and subsequent ingestion and bioaccumulation by birds.

Toxicity of Site 9 surface soils was assessed for soils collected from 2 sampling locations using the earthworm survival test and lettuce germination and growth tests. The sampling locations (9BAS11 and 9BAS16) were selected because of the high metal and diesel contamination detected in the initial surface soil samples, but the measured contaminant concentrations in soil collected for the bioassays were in the low range of bioassay test soil metal and diesel concentrations. Toxicity to lettuce growth and earthworm survival was observed at 1 location, representing some risk of exposure by plants and terrestrial animals to Site 9 soil. However, metals and diesel did not appear to be contributing factors to toxicity at that location, and the minimal toxicity observed at the site could not be ascribed to any particular contaminant on the basis of the test results.

Many of the metals detected in Site 24 soils were below background levels and, therefore, were not assessed for potential toxicity. Semivolatile and volatile chemicals, as well as several chlorinated compounds, were detected in site soils. Although the bioaccumulative potential for the semivolatile and volatile chemicals may be low, they could cause some risk to higher trophic organisms if they were considered ecologically significant. However, such exposure was not expected to occur.

Conclusions and limitations
Although special-status species received particular attention in the characterization of ecological receptors in the vicinity of Group A sites, other species that are representative of the foodchains or that may contribute to ecosystem structure near the sites were also considered. Little or no published toxicological information was identified relating directly to the special-status species at or near the Group A sites.

The conclusions of the ERA for Group A sites were based on an assessment of field surveys of receptor populations and habitats; chemical concentrations in media and biota; potential toxicity to primary receptors as determined via comparisons with reported toxic effect levels and calculated criteria; potential bioaccumulation of contaminants in secondary receptors, as determined via comparisons with calculated soil criteria based on food-chain bioaccumulation; and potential toxicity and bioaccumulation of contaminants to primary receptors as determined via bioassays.

Potential bioaccumulation of contaminants in secondary receptors was evaluated via comparison with recommended and calculated soil criteria based on food-chain bioaccumulation. Results of these comparisons indicated that As, Cd, Pb, Hg, Zn, *alpha*-chlordane, *gamma*-chlordane, 4,4'-DDD, 4,4'-DDE, 4,4'-DDT, and dieldrin were present at concentrations that may bioaccumulate within the foodchain at 1 or more sites.

The use of calculated soil criteria for the evaluation of bioaccumulation results in some uncertainty (the effects of which were discussed in the risk assessment). Studies were used that reported no-effect levels, accumulation in the liver, or accumulation in eggs. However, uncertainty factors of 1,000 were applied to the calculations for 4,4'-DDD and 4,4'-DDE because the receptors were wild species and the reported endpoint was mortality in either the receptor or the embryo.

The laboratory toxicity and bioaccumulation tests using plants and soil invertebrates yielded information on the relative toxicity of sampling locations in relation to extent of contamination. The results confirmed the extent of toxicity suggested by the literature assessment. Toxicity at the reference location occurred in earthworms but not in lettuce and can probably be explained by soil texture instead of toxic contaminants.

Chemical contaminant levels were analyzed in biota, including earthworms at 3SD43 and filamentous algae at 6BAS1 and 6BAS2. Location 3SD43 is down-drainage of the pesticide wash rack and immediately above the Santa Margarita River. Soil from this location was also relatively nontoxic to animals and plants in the bioassays, as was the sediment from the Site 6 vicinity (6BAS) and the river channel (6BADSM1 and 6BADSM2). The general characterization of bioaccumulation potential for organochlorine pesticides and heavy metals was limited to laboratory investigations using site soils. Chemical analyses of field-collected earthworms and algae and laboratory bioassay earthworms, lettuce, and nutsedge were conducted at the conclusion of the bioaccumulation studies.

Laboratory bioaccumulation results and measurements of field earthworm contaminant concentrations indicate that metals and organochlorines were bioaccumulated. Earthworms collected from the field contained higher levels of some inorganics than the concentrations accumulated by earthworms during the 28-d bioassay. Reasons for these differences are not clear. The field-collected earthworms had low concentrations of 4,4'-DDE (<1 mg/kg) but no other organochlorines. In the bioassays, lettuce and earthworms accumulated several organic and inorganic chemicals to levels that could cause adverse effects in consumer organisms.

Inherent limitations are associated with interpreting the toxicity testing and soil chemistry results for MCB Camp Pendleton soils. The most toxic locations of the Group A sites contain relatively high and toxic levels of a number of contaminants, many of which could individually cause toxicity in laboratory tests. For example, location 3B18 displayed a high level of toxicity in laboratory tests and contained high soil concentrations of As, herbicides, and diesel. Synergistic or additive effects of these chemicals are unknown, and the toxicity effect levels derived from tests on dilution series cannot be attributed to any single chemical.

Several data objectives were only partially met during the ERA sampling and analysis. In most cases, the lack of data did not impede the risk-assessment process. The lack of field biota samples for assessment of contamination was unexpected, but the 3 field samples and the laboratory bioaccumulation results are considered to support the risk-assessment conclusions adequately for Sites 3 and 4.

The goal of the ERA was to evaluate the ecological risks associated with known or suspected contamination at the MCB Camp Pendleton Group A sites. The ultimate objectives of this effort are to protect soil, sediment, and water quality; to maintain ecosystem structure and function; and to reduce ecological risks to an acceptable level. Within the context of the uncertainties discussed in this section, the overall goals and objectives were met. The general conclusion of the risk assessment is that there is evidence of ecological impairment associated with soil contamination at some Group A sites.

The exposure routes are likely to be primarily through soil ingestion and dermal contact of invertebrates and plant absorption through roots and secondarily through consumption of contaminated plants and soil invertebrates. Vertebrates at greatest risk of exposure include ground-feeding birds, small mammals, reptiles, and amphibians.

Kesterson Reservoir

An ERA was conducted in 1992 (Ohlendorf and Santolo 1994) and revised in 1993 (CH2M Hill 1993) to evaluate potential effects of wildlife exposure to Se in the Kesterson Reservoir under future conditions. The methods and results of this risk assessment are summarized here. However, readers are referred to the description by Ohlendorf and Santolo (1994) for further details.

Background

Kesterson Reservoir and the San Luis Drain were constructed by the U.S. Bureau of Reclamation (USBR) between 1968 and 1975 (USBR 1986; Ohlendorf 1989). The reservoir is located in Merced County within the San Joaquin Valley of California (Figure 5-3). Before 1988, Kesterson Reservoir consisted of 12 shallow (average 1 to 1.5 m deep) ponds, totaling about 520 ha, that were designed to serve as evaporation and holding basins for subsurface drainage waters from the western San Joaquin Valley (USBR 1984, 1986). Shallow saline groundwater collected by subsurface field drains was transported to Kesterson Reservoir by the San Luis Drain.

Following the discovery of high Se concentrations in Kesterson Reservoir and adverse effects to aquatic birds, the U.S. Bureau of Reclamation (USBR) halted the inflow of drainage to the reservoir, dewatered the reservoir, and filled lower-elevation portions to prevent groundwater from rising to the surface (USBR 1986; USDI 1989). The drying and filling of Kesterson Reservoir converted the site to upland habitat consisting of grassland habitat that includes the higher elevation; upland habitat that existed at the reservoir before it was dried and filled; filled habitat that includes formerly low-lying areas that were filled with soil to prevent the occurrence of seasonal wetlands; and open habitat that includes former cattail areas that were not filled but were disced to eliminate habitat potentially attractive to wildlife, particularly tricolored blackbirds. Grassland habitat covers about 30% of the site, filled habitat about 60%, and open habitat 10%.

Monitoring has been conducted since 1987 to measure Se concentrations among plants and animals at the site, to document habitat and faunal changes, and to determine whether adverse effects are occurring in the ecosystem (USBR 1992). The findings of that monitoring program, in conjunction with monitoring of soils and groundwater (LBL 1990; Benson et al. 1990, 1992, 1993) served as the primary data for this risk assessment.

Existing flora and fauna of the reservoir are described in more detail in the various monitoring reports, but especially in USBR (1991). Based on the existing habitats found at the site, changes in flora and fauna are expected to occur within the next 20 years. These changes are described in CH2M Hill (1993) and summarized by Ohlendorf and Santolo (1994) on the basis of the various analyses and professional judgments of the site's monitoring program personnel.

Studies conducted at Kesterson Reservoir during 1983–1985 showed that high levels of Se were bioaccumulated by aquatic plants, invertebrates, fish, and birds (USBR 1986; Hothem and Ohlendorf 1989; Ohlendorf 1989; Ohlendorf et al. 1990). The most pronounced effects in wildlife species were found in birds that fed regularly in the Reservoir ponds. Grebes, shorebirds, coots, and waterfowl had high rates of embryo mortality or developmental abnormalities, and adult birds also died as a result of Se toxicosis. Through a series of field and laboratory studies, these effects were attributed to high concentrations of Se in the birds' tissues resulting from ingestion of high-Se diets. This bioaccumulation of Se occurred because of their exposure to the Se-rich foodchain in the reservoir. The Se in the reservoir's foodchain was traced to the water received by the reservoir and to the groundwater collected by the field drains that contributed to the reservoir's inflow.

Ephemeral pools that form under current conditions (i.e., post-filling)—and those expected to occur in the future—will result from the accumulation of rainfall, rather than rising groundwater (Benson et al. 1990; LBL 1990). The filling of topographically lower portions of Kesterson Reservoir effectively eliminated the probability of groundwater rising above the soil surface. Nevertheless, surface-water Se concentrations in some pools exceed the recommended safe levels of 2 to 5 mg/L. The potential occurrence and effects to aquatic birds were evaluated, along with potential effects to terrestrial wildlife.

General approach and objectives
The ERA (CH2M Hill 1993; Ohlendorf and Santolo 1994) was conducted by analyzing data available from the Kesterson Reservoir Biological Monitoring Program through February 1993 in relation to other published and unpublished reports.

The objectives of the biological monitoring program were to assess the impact of the site on local and migratory wildlife, to provide a basis for adjusting the site management, to verify the effectiveness of cleanup actions at the site, and to provide a basis for modifying future biological monitoring.

A substantial amount of information is available concerning the hazards of dietary waterborne Se to wildlife, particularly aquatic birds (Eisler 1985b; Ohlendorf 1989; Skorupa and Ohlendorf 1991). Criteria available from those sources were used to evaluate risks at the site in the event that portions of the site become flooded during wet years.

The objectives of this risk assessment (CH2M Hill 1993; Ohlendorf and Santolo 1994) were to:

1) review available pertinent information about Se from Kesterson and in other terrestrial ecosystems,

2) estimate the most likely future levels of Se in various biota (plants and animals) at the site, based on current levels in biota, knowledge of the Se inventory at the site, and projections of future biologically available Se levels for soils and water provided by Lawrence Berkeley Laboratory (LBL),

3) assess the risks of adverse effects to animals that could be caused by the site's Se inventory (based on observed current and estimated future levels of biologically available Se in various media),

4) assess the significance of the site's Se toxicosis risks,

5) identify contingency plans for reducing any potentially significant risks of Se toxicosis, and

6) identify information needed to improve management efficiency for the site or other projects.

Exposure assessment
Earlier studies had shown that Se is the primary contaminant of concern at the site; other inorganics and organochlorine compounds were not accumulated to significant concentrations by food-chain organisms living in the Kesterson Reservoir ponds or in the San Luis Drain (Saiki 1986; Hothem and Ohlendorf 1989; Schuler et al. 1990). Although boron (B) accumulated in some of the aquatic plants to levels that were potentially harmful to waterfowl reproduction (Smith and Anders 1989), available evidence suggests that the transfer of B to avian eggs is not sufficient to cause embryotoxicity (Ohlendorf et al. 1993).

Generalized exposure pathways for the site's biota are illustrated in Figure 5-8. These pathways are described in more detail elsewhere (CH2M Hill 1993; Ohlendorf and Santolo 1994). All exposed plants and animals typically would be terrestrial species, but aquatic species would occur in ephemeral pools formed by rainwater during extended periods of heavy rainfall.

For modeling purposes, common plant species were grouped into 4 categories based on ecological considerations and Se concentrations. These 4 plant groups will be components of the various plant communities that occur at the site over time at varying degrees of dominance. Grasses and perennials are generally lower in Se than transitional and persistent annual plant species. Both grasses and persistent annuals are currently wide-

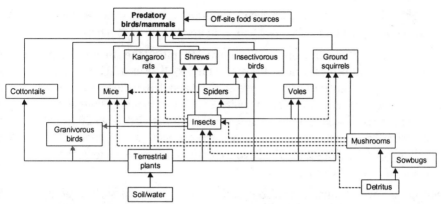

Figure 5-8   Pathways for exposure of terrestrial wildlife to Se at the former Kesterson Reservoir site

spread at the site and are expected to persist over time. Perennials are currently limited in their abundance and distribution, but they are expected to become more widespread with increasing dominance over time. Transitional annuals have higher Se levels than the other plants sampled, but these are mostly invader species that are expected to be replaced by slower growing annuals and perennials at the site.

Wildlife exposure was characterized on a sitewide basis because most of the wildlife species of interest can move readily from one habitat type to another and also from one area to another (Ohlendorf and Santolo 1994). Available information was used to construct a model that relates Se concentrations in various components of the ecosystem under current conditions and predicts concentrations that can be expected to occur in the next 20 years. The model takes into account 3 different projections for water-extractable Se in soils at a depth of 15 cm to 1 m. Water-extractable Se and the 15 cm to 1 m soil depth are considered the best indicators of bioavailable Se for plant uptake, based on other studies. The 3 runs of the model show the expected Se concentrations for biota when Se bioavailability in soils is moderate, low, or high.

Most of the animals that were included in the biological monitoring program are resident on the site. In addition, 4 representative predatory birds and mammals were included in the assessment; their potential exposure was modeled to reflect the portion of their home range that might occur on the site.

Insects and other herbivores were assumed to feed on various kinds of plants in proportion to their expected frequency of occurrence in the site. For insects and other consumers, a fractional weighting factor (SI) was assigned to each component of their diet and the transfer factor (as concentration in consumer divided by concentration in food item) was determined. The weighting factor assigned to each plant group that was represented in the diet of the consumers was adjusted in accordance with expected frequency of the plant group in the future (because dietary shifts are expected). However, the transfer factors remained constant because no changes in uptake rate were expected.

The Se concentrations in plants and animals inhabiting the site are not expected to change markedly during the next 20 years (Table 5-2). If Se bioavailability remains moderate, average concentrations are expected to be about 10 to 20% greater than current levels in most biota. With low bioavailability, Se concentrations in plants and animals are expected to be somewhat lower than the current levels (5 to 10%) after 20 years. The highest or "worst case" expected concentrations in most plants and animals are about 20 to 35% above those in 1989–1992. The Se concentrations are expected to be higher in mushrooms than in all other organisms.

During years with annual rainfall about 50% more than normal, surface rainwater pools are expected to occur over large areas within the site (Benson et al. 1990). In the event of a 100-y annual rainfall year, pools may occur over most of the site, especially from early February to mid-March. Se and salts present at the soil surface dissolve in these pools, potentially creating Se concentrations ranging from less than detection to several hundred micrograms per liter.

Table 5-2   Mean Se concentrations expected to occur in plants and animals at the former Kesterson Reservoir Site in 2012 under varying levels of bioavailability compared to 1989-1992 means (μg/g, dry weight)

Samples	1989-1992 Mean	Expected concentrations		
		Moderate bioavailability	Low bioavailability	High bioavailability
Soil[a]	0.07	0.22	0.05	0.39
Grasses	2.5	3.2	2.3	3.6
Transitional annuals	4.3	5.1	4.1	5.6
Persistent annuals	3.9	4.5	3.7	4.9
Perennials	2.5	2.6	2.4	2.7
Mushrooms	209.0	290.0	188.0	343.0
Insects	8.3	9.7	7.7	10.5
Spiders	10.9	12.7	10.1	13.8
Cottontails	8.3	9.8	7.6	10.8
Mice	6.9	8.3	6.4	9.1
Kangaroo rat	4.3	5.6	4.3	6.2
Shrew	20.7	23.7	18.9	25.9
Insectivorous birds	7.8	9.0	7.2	9.9
California vole	11.2	13.1	10.3	14.3
Ground squirrel	10.6	12.3	8.6	14.1
Kit fox[b]	1.7	1.9	1.5	2.1
Coyote[b]	4.4	4.9	4.1	5.3
Red-tailed hawk[b]	5.3	6.2	4.9	6.9
Northern harrier[b]	6.6	7.8	6.1	8.6

[a]Water-extractable 15 cm-1 m depth
[b]Liver values; others are whole-body values

The rainwater pools that were observed during 1989 to 1991 disappeared too quickly to develop significant populations of aquatic plants or invertebrates and they received no significant wildlife use. In contrast, aquatic invertebrates were present in some pools during 1992 and 1993 in sufficient numbers for aquatic birds to feed there.

Aquatic invertebrates collected from 6 of the pools during March 1992 contained highly variable Se concentrations (6.0 to 48 µg/g dry weight; geometric mean 12.4 µg/g) that were about 6 to 10 x normal background. Waterborne total recoverable Se concentrations in these pools ranged from 3.0 to 13 µg/L (geometric mean 8.07 µg/L).

Observations during March, April, and May 1992, and February and March 1993 indicate that migrant shorebirds and waterfowl used rainwater pools at the site. Counts of birds using these pools showed that bird numbers declined as the pools disappeared. It is also expected that aquatic birds will use surface-water pools that form in future years and persist long enough to develop populations of aquatic plants or invertebrates. The nesting season (March to June) is the most critical exposure period for potential adverse effects.

Effects assessment

The Se concentrations in small mammals are expected to remain below those measured during a study in 1984 when the reservoir was partially flooded with agricultural drainwater. In that study (Clark 1987), there was no clear effect of Se on small mammal reproduction, although whole-body analyses by species for all ponds in the reservoir averaged about 11 µg/g. That level of Se in prey species was sufficient to suggest concern for possible effects on predators, such as raptorial birds, raccoons, coyotes, and the endangered San Joaquin kit fox. Follow-up studies of screech owls, raccoons, coyotes, and kit foxes suggest that adverse effects of Se should not be expected in those or similarly exposed predators at the site (Wiemeyer and Hoffman, Clark et al. 1989, Paveglio and Clifton 1988).

The Se concentrations in insectivorous birds (e.g., meadowlarks and barn swallows) are not expected to increase to biologically significant levels. No effects have been observed in meadowlarks or swallows that nest at the site, and Se concentrations in these species have declined since 1988.

Available data indicate that consumption of mushrooms by wildlife at the site is very limited. The species most likely to be affected would be those that have small home ranges and feed on very localized food resources, such as some of the small mammal species. More mobile animals, e.g., birds, are less likely to feed consistently in small areas or on a narrow range of foods that could be affected by the seleniferous mushrooms.

The Se concentrations found in aquatic invertebrates from the pools provide the best measurement for characterizing potential risks to aquatic birds at the site. Although Se concentrations in bird eggs provide a more direct and easily interpreted measurement, no eggs were available from birds known to be using the pools during 1992. Se concentrations in eggs of birds feeding extensively in rainwater pools can be expected to be in the range where reproduction would be adversely affected.

Attractiveness of the pools to aquatic birds would increase in proportion to their size and persistence (Ohlendorf and Santolo 1994). Avian food would probably not be abundant in the pools unless they persisted for several weeks. If they did, there probably would be large areas of wetland habitat on nearby state and federal refuges, duck clubs, farm lands, or other areas. This regional flooding would diminish the attractiveness of the site's pools, and the numbers of birds they would attract may be small. Thus, the exposed birds would represent a small fraction of the regional waterfowl and shorebird populations.

During March 1992, the surface water pools at the site were used by aquatic birds, most of which were migrant shorebirds that would not nest in the region. Bird use decreased during April, and essentially all of the aquatic birds had left the site by May. Bird use of wetland areas nearby on Kesterson NWR appeared to be greater than within the site, although a comparative census was not conducted. Observations during February and March 1993 indicated that migrant shorebirds and waterfowl again used pools at the site, and similar use can be expected in future years.

Ecological risks and site management
Terrestrial habitats - The model used in the risk assessment (CH2M Hill 1993; Ohlendorf and Santolo 1994) produced estimates of the Se concentrations that could be expected to occur in plants and animals living at the site. Because of the large variability in the soil-plant Se relationships, Monte Carlo simulation (Press et al. 1986) for year 10 (2002) was used to describe the uncertainties associated with the estimated Se concentrations in terrestrial plants and in the overall diets of several bird and mammal species.

Each Monte Carlo simulation included 100 runs using randomly selected values for water-extractable soil Se. These values were taken from the range between low and high projected water-extractable soil-Se concentrations, assuming a uniform distribution within that range. Data from the monitoring program show that the plant-soil Se relationship is log-normal. Therefore, for each randomly selected soil-Se concentration a corresponding plant-Se concentration was randomly selected from within the log-normal distribution of expected values. The range of those expected values for plants was based on the regression relationship for soil Se to plant Se and the variability in that relationship. The results of these simulations for plants and selected animals are illustrated in Ohlendorf and Santolo (1994).

Mean Se concentrations in the diets of small mammals are expected to be lower than 10 µg/g. Laboratory studies with rats fed diets containing wheat with biologically incorporated Se (6.4 µg/g diet) showed depressed weight gain and changes in organ weights of the rats (Halverson et al. 1966). However, no effects of Se on body condition or liver weights of small mammals were observed at Kesterson Reservoir during 1984 when mean Se concentrations were higher than those expected in the next 20 years (Clark 1987).

The Se concentrations in small mammals (Ohlendorf and Santolo 1994) are expected to remain below those measured in 1984 at Kesterson Reservoir by Clark (1987). In that study, there was no clear effect of Se on small mammal reproduction, although whole-body analyses by species for all ponds at Kesterson Reservoir averaged about 11 µg/g. Similarly, the risk assessment indicated that adverse effects should not be expected in predatory birds or mammals, in part because the reservoir represents only a portion of the home range for most predators.

The greatest risks of Se exposure to terrestrial wildlife are those associated with consumption of mushrooms. Wildlife receptors could be exposed by eating the mushrooms directly or by eating other consumers of mushrooms. However, no effects have been observed in wildlife as a result of the seleniferous mushrooms, and wildlife consumption of mushrooms has been very limited (usually only in trace quantities). Until a more immediate threat related to mushrooms is identified, no mitigation/remediation/management actions should be required.

Aquatic habitats - Potential exposure of aquatic birds (such as waterfowl and shorebirds) to seleniferous rainwater pools may become significant if rainfall is adequate to form extensive persistent pools. This could occur if rainfall is greater than normal or if much of the rainfall occurs during a short period in late winter or early spring. If this occurred and the pools persisted for several weeks, they probably would become attractive to waterfowl and shorebirds. This would be of greatest concern during late winter and spring when birds are preparing to nest.

Waterborne Se concentrations of 10 µg/L have been associated with impaired hatchability in shorebirds and concentrations of 10 to 20 µg/L have been associated with teratogenic effects (Skorupa and Ohlendorf 1991). Uptake and loss of Se occurs rapidly in mallards when their dietary exposure changes (Heinz et al. 1990; Heinz 1993; Heinz and Fitzgerald 1993). These studies indicate that birds could accumulate enough Se within 1 or 2 weeks of feeding on high-Se invertebrates in pools containing 10 to 30 µg/L of Se that reproductive success could be affected. (Similarly, when exposure to elevated dietary Se ends, the risk of adverse effects drops quickly.)

The species of birds (waterfowl and shorebirds) that are most likely to be affected by seleniferous rainwater pools are protected by the Migratory Bird Treaty Act 1972. Attractiveness of the pools to aquatic birds would increase in proportion to their size and persistence. Avian food would probably not be abundant in the pools unless they persisted for several weeks. If they did, there probably would be large areas of wetland habitat on nearby portions of wildlife refuges, duck clubs, or other nearby areas. This regional flooding would diminish the attractiveness of the site's pools, and the numbers of birds they would attract may be small. Thus, the exposed birds would represent a small fraction of the regional waterfowl and shorebird populations. Thus, waterborne Se concentrations in the ranges that have been found or predicted for rainfall ponding within the site are of concern for aquatic birds that may nest there. This potential for migratory birds to be affected suggests a need for a management plan that could be implemented in the event of significant rainwater ponding in the site.

Conclusions and limitations

The 2 greatest potential sources for significant ecological effects resulting from the site's Se inventory appear to be those related to mushrooms (because of Se exposure to their consumers) in the terrestrial habitats and persistent rainwater pools that may occur over large areas if annual rainfall is more than 50% greater than normal. If these rainwater pools are present for several weeks in late winter or early spring, they could develop significant populations of aquatic plants and invertebrates that would be consumed by aquatic birds. Those species appear to be more sensitive to the adverse effects of Se than terrestrial birds or mammals. Although surface-water pools in the site disappeared before the nesting season for most aquatic birds during spring 1992, management plans for controlling exposure of aquatic birds appear to be the greatest current need for site management.

Limitations and uncertainties associated with the model used in this assessment were described and information needs were identified to help focus the research and monitoring so that it provides the most useful information for site management (Ohlendorf and Santolo 1994).

Acknowledgments - Each of the 3 case studies was conducted as a team effort involving a large number of technical and supporting staff from CH2M Hill. Earl Byron, Kathy Freas, Gary Santolo, Marjorie Castleberry, and Trudy Pulley each made major contributions to one or more of the studies. CH2M Hill document production staff in Sacramento performed heroic feats in completing our reports and this manuscript.

The case studies were performed with funding provided by the Southwest Division Naval Facilities Engineering Command (for NWS Seal Beach and MCB Camp Pendleton) or the USBR (for Kesterson Reservoir). I acknowledge the excellent working relationships developed with SWDIV (especially Ed Dias, Jeff Kidwell, and Ellen Casados, as well as other SWDIV staff and the two installations) and USBR (Mike Delamore and Art Tuma). The work at MCB Camp Pendleton was conducted in close cooperation with International Technology Corporation in Irvine, California; Dave Mark, Mary Parker, and others at IT were especially helpful throughout the project.

I appreciate the approval of the U.S. Navy Southwest Division Naval Facilities Engineering Command for use of the information from our work on Seal Beach Naval Weapons Station and Marine Corps Base Camp Pendleton. Marcel Dekker, Inc., is acknowledged for granting permission to use previously published material concerning the ERA for Kesterson Reservoir. Anonymous reviewers provided useful comments concerning the draft manuscript, and their contributions are appreciated.

References

Benson SM, Tokunaga TK, Zawislanski P. 1992. Anticipated soil selenium concentrations at Kesterson Reservoir. Berkeley CA: University of California, Lawrence Berkeley Laboratory, Earth Sciences Division. LBL-33080.

Benson SM, Tokunaga T, Zawislanski P, Wahl C, Johannis P, Zavarin M, Yee A, Tsao L, Phillips D, Ita S. 1993. 1991–1992 Investigation of the geochemical and hydrological behavior of selenium at Kesterson Reservoir. Berkeley CA: University of California, Lawrence Berkeley Laboratory, Earth Sciences Division. LBL-33532.

Benson SM, Tokunaga TK, Zawislanski P, Yee AW, Daggett JS, Oldfather JM, Tsao L, Johannis PW. 1990. Hydrological and geochemical investigations of selenium behavior at Kesterson Reservoir. Berkeley CA: University of California, Lawrence Berkeley Laboratory, Earth Sciences Division. LBL-29689.

Beyer WN. 1990. Evaluating soil contamination. Biological Report 90(2). Washington DC: U.S. Department of the Interior, Fish and Wildlife Service.

[CCME] Canadian Council of Ministers of the Environment. 1991. Interim Canadian environmental quality criteria for contaminated sites. Prepared by the CCME Subcommittee on Environmental Quality Criteria for Contaminated Sites, Environmental Quality Guidelines Division, Water Quality Branch, Environment Canada, Ottawa ON. CCME EPC-CS34.

CH2M Hill. 1993. Ecological risk assessment for Kesterson Reservoir. Prepared for U.S. Bureau of Reclamation, Mid-Pacific Region, Sacramento CA.

Clark Jr DR. 1987. Selenium accumulation in mammals exposed to contaminated California irrigation drainwater. *Sci Total Environ* 66:17–168.

Clark Jr DR, Ogasawara PA, Smith GJ, Ohlendorf HM. 1989. Selenium accumulation by raccoons exposed to irrigation drainwater at Kesterson National Wildlife Refuge, California, 1986. *Arch Environ Contam Toxicol* 18(787–794.

[CSWRCB] California State Water Resources Control Board. 1992. Amendments of the water quality control plan for inland surface waters in California, Water Quality Control Plan for Inland Surface Waters of California, Resolution No. 91-33, adopted and effective 11 Apr 1991. Amendments November 1992.

Eisler R. 1985a. Cadmium hazards to fish, wildlife, and invertebrates: A synoptic review. Washington DC: U.S. Fish and Wildlife Service. Biological Report 85(1.2).

Eisler R. 1985b. Selenium hazards to fish, wildlife, and invertebrates: A synoptic review. Washington DC: U.S. Fish and Wildlife Service. Biological Report 85(1.5).

Eisler R. 1986a. Chromium hazards to fish, wildlife, and invertebrates: A synoptic review. Washington DC: U.S. Fish and Wildlife Service. Biological Report 85(1.6).

Eisler R. 1986b. Polychlorinated biphenyl hazards to fish, wildlife, and invertebrates: A synoptic review. Washington DC: U.S. Fish and Wildlife Service. Biological Report 85(1.7).

Eisler R. 1987a. Mercury hazards to fish, wildlife, and invertebrates: A synoptic review. Washington DC: U.S. Fish and Wildlife Service. Biological Report 85(1.10).

Eisler R. 1987b. Polycyclic aromatic hydrocarbon hazards to fish, wildlife, and invertebrates: A synoptic review. Washington DC: U.S. Fish and Wildlife Service. Biological Report 85(1.11).

Eisler R. 1988a. Arsenic hazards to fish, wildlife, and invertebrates: A synoptic review. Washington DC: U.S. Fish and Wildlife Service. Biological Report 85(1.12).

Eisler R. 1988b. Lead hazards to fish, wildlife, and invertebrates: A synoptic review. Washington DC: U.S. Fish and Wildlife Service. Biological Report 85(1.14).

Eisler R. 1989. Molybdenum hazards to fish, wildlife, and invertebrates: A synoptic review. Washington DC: U.S. Fish and Wildlife Service. Biological Report 85(1.19).

Eisler R. 1990a. Boron hazards to fish, wildlife, and invertebrates: A synoptic review. Washington DC: U.S. Fish and Wildlife Service. Biological Report 85(1.20).

Eisler R. 1990b. Chlordane hazards to fish, wildlife, and invertebrates: A synoptic review. Washington DC: U.S. Fish and Wildlife Service. Biological Report 85(1.21).

Eisler R. 1993. Zinc hazards to fish, wildlife, and invertebrates: A synoptic review. Washington DC: U.S. Fish and Wildlife Service. Biological Report 10.

Halverson AW, Palmer IS, Guss PL. 1966. Toxicity of selenium to post-weanling rats. *Toxicol Appl Pharmacol* 9:477–484.

Heinz GH. 1993. Selenium accumulation and loss in mallard eggs. *Environ Toxicol Chem* 12:775–778.

Heinz GH, Fitzgerald MA. 1993. Reproduction of mallards following overwinter exposure to selenium. *Environ Pollut* 81:117–122.

Heinz GH, Pendleton GW, Krynitsky AJ, Gold LG. 1990. Selenium accumulation and elimination in mallards. *Arch Environ Contam Toxicol* 19:374–379.

Hothem RL, Ohlendorf HM. 1989. Contaminants in foods of aquatic birds at Kesterson Reservoir, California, 1985. *Arch Environ Contam Toxicol* 18:773–786.

[LBL] Lawrence Berkeley Laboratory. 1990. Hydrological, geochemical, and ecological characterization of Kesterson Reservoir: Annual Report, 1 Oct 1988–30 Sep 1989. LBL-27993. University of California, Berkeley, Earth Sciences Division, Berkeley, CA.

Linder G, Ingham E, Brandt CJ, Henderson G, Corvallis Environmental Research Laboratory. 1992. Evaluation of terrestrial indicators for use in ecological assessments at hazardous waste sites. Corvallis OR: USEPA. EPA/600/R-92/183.

Maughan JT. 1993. Ecological assessment of hazardous waste sites. New York: Van Nostrand Reinhold.

[NAS/NAE] National Academy of Sciences/National Academy of Engineering 1973. Water quality criteria 1972 (Blue Book). USEPA Ecological Research Series. Washington DC: USEPA. EPA-R3-73-033.

[NAS] National Academy of Sciences. 1980. Mineral tolerance of domestic animals. Washington DC: National Academy.

Ohlendorf HM. 1989. Bioaccumulation and effects of selenium in wildlife. In: Jacobs LW, editor. Selenium in agriculture and the environment. SSSA Special Publication No. 23. Madison WI: American Society of Agronomy and Soil Science Society of America. p 133–177.

Ohlendorf HM. 1993. Marine birds and trace elements in the temperate North Pacific. In: Vermeer K, Morgan KH, Siegel-Causey D, editors. The status, ecology, and conservation of marine birds of the North Pacific. Canadian Wildlife Service Special Publication, Ottawa. p 232–240.

Ohlendorf HM, Hothem RL. 1995. Agricultural drainwater effects on wildlife in central California. In: Hoffman DJ, Rattner BA, Burton Jr GA, Cairns Jr J, editors. Handbook of ecotoxicology. Chelsea MI: Lewis Publishers. p 577–595.

Ohlendorf HM, Hothem RL, Bunck CM, Marois KC. 1990. Bioaccumulation of selenium in birds at Kesterson Reservoir, California. *Arch Environ Contam Toxicol* 19:495–507.

Ohlendorf HM, Hothem RL, Welsh D. 1989. Nest success, cause-specific nest failure, and hatchability of aquatic birds at selenium-contaminated Kesterson Reservoir and a reference site. *Condor* 91:787–796.

Ohlendorf HM, Risebrough RW, Vermeer K. 1978. Exposure of marine birds to environmental pollutants. Washington DC: U.S. Fish and Wildlife Service. Wildlife Research Report 9.

Ohlendorf HM, Santolo GM. 1994. Kesterson Reservoir—past, present, and future: An ecological risk assessment. In: Frankenberger Jr WT, Benson S, editors. Selenium in the environment. New York: Marcel Dekker. p 69-117.

Ohlendorf HM, Skorupa JP, Saiki MK, Barnum DA. 1993. Food-chain transfer of trace elements to wildlife. In: Allen RG, Neale CMU, editors. Management of irrigation and drainage systems: integrated perspectives. Proceedings of the 1993 National Conference on Irrigation and Drainage Engineering. Park City, UT; 21–23 Jul 1993. New York: American Society of Civil Engineers. p 596–603.

Opresko DM, Sample BE, Suter GW. 1994. Toxicological benchmarks for wildlife: 1994 revision. Oak Ridge TN: Health Science Research Division and Environmental Sciences Division, Oak Ridge National Laboratory. ES/ER/TM-86/R1.

Paveglio FL, Clifton SD. 1988. Selenium accumulation and ecology of the San Joaquin kit fox in the Kesterson National Wildlife Refuge Area. U.S. Fish and Wildlife Service: Los Banos CA.

Phillips PT. 1988. California state mussel watch ten year data summary 1977–1987. Water Quality Monitoring Report No. 87-3. Sacramento CA: State Water Resources Control Board, Sacramento, Division of Water Quality.

Press WH, Flannery BP, Teukolsky SA, Vetterling WT. 1986. Numerical recipes—the art of scientific computing. New York: Cambridge University.

Puls R. 1988. Mineral levels in animal health, diagnostic data. Clearbook, BC, Canada: Sherpa International.

Rasmussen D. 1992. Toxic substances monitoring program, 1990 data report. Water Quality Monitoring Report 92-1WQ. Sacramento CA: State Water Resources Control Board, Division of Water Quality.

Saiki MK. 1986. Concentrations of selenium in aquatic food-chain organisms and fish exposed to agricultural tile drainage water. In Howard AQ, editor. Selenium and agricultural drainage: implications for San Francisco Bay and the California Environment. Proceedings Second Selenium Symposium. Tiburon CA: Bay Institute of San Francisco. p 25–33.

Schmitt CJ, Brumbaugh WG. 1990. National contaminant biomonitoring program: concentrations of arsenic, cadmium, copper, lead, mercury, selenium, and zinc in U.S. freshwater fish, 1976–1984. *Arch Environ Contam Toxicol* 19:731–747.

Schmitt CJ, Zajicek JL, Peterman PH. 1990. National contaminant biomonitoring program: residues of organochlorine chemicals in U.S. freshwater fish, 1976–1984. *Arch Environ Contam Toxicol* 19:748–781.

Schuler CA, Anthony RG, Ohlendorf HM. 1990. Selenium in wetlands and waterfowl foods at Kesterson Reservoir, California, 1984. *Arch Environ Contam Toxicol 19:845–853.*

Shacklette HT, Boerngen JG. 1984. Element concentrations in soils and other surficial materials of the conterminous United States. Professional Paper 1270. Washington DC: U.S. Geological Survey.

Skorupa JP, Ohlendorf HM. 1991. Contaminants in drainage water and avian risk thresholds. In: Dinar A, Zilberman D, editors. The economics and management of water and drainage in agriculture. Boston MA: Kluwer Academic. p 345–368.

Smith GJ, Anders VP. 1989. Toxic effects of boron on mallard reproduction. *Environ Toxicol Chem* 8:943–950.

State of California. 1993. Status of the Bay Protection and Toxic Cleanup Program. Staff Report. Bay Protection and Toxic Cleanup Program, State Water Resources Control Board, Sacramento CA.

Stickel LF. 1973. Pesticide residues in birds and mammals. In: Edwards CA, editor. Environmental pollution by pesticides. New York: Plenum. p 254–312.

Suter II GW. 1993. Ecological risk assessment. Boca Raton FL: Lewis.

[SWDIV] Southwest Division Naval Facilities Engineering Command. 1991a. Draft Final Work Plan, Marine Corps Base Camp Pendleton. Prepared by Jacobs Engineering Group, Inc.

[SWDIV] Southwest Division Naval Facilities Engineering Command. 1991b. Draft Final RI/FS Sampling and Analysis Plan, Marine Corps Base Camp Pendleton. Prepared by Jacobs Engineering Group, Inc.

[SWDIV] Southwest Division Naval Facilities Engineering Command. 1992. Naval Weapons Station Seal Beach, California. Installation Restoration Program, Final Wildlife Refuge Study Work Plan.

[SWDIV] Southwest Division Naval Facilities Engineering Command. 1993a. Draft Final Ecological Risk Assessment Work Plan, Marine Corps Base Camp Pendleton. Prepared by Jacobs Engineering Group, Inc.

[SWDIV] Southwest Division Naval Facilities Engineering Command. 1993b. Remedial Investigation/ Feasibility Study, Group A Sites. Sampling and Analysis Plan. Marine Corps Base Camp Pendleton. Ecological Risk Assessment, Draft Final 26 Feb 1993.

[SWDIV] Southwest Division Naval Facilities Engineering Command. 1993c. Remedial Investigation/ Feasibility Study, RI Report for Group A Sites. Draft Final 15 Oct 1993.

[SWDIV] Southwest Division Naval Facilities Engineering Command. 1995a. Naval Weapons Station Seal Beach, Installation Restoration Program, Final National Wildlife Refuge Study Report.

[SWDIV] Southwest Division Naval Facilities Engineering Command. 1995b. Engineering Evaluation/ Cost Analysis (EE/CA) for Group A Site 3, Pest Control Wash Rack, and Site 6, DPDO (DRMO) Scrap Yard. Draft Final 21 Jun 1995.

[USBR] U.S. Bureau of Reclamation. 1984. San Luis Unit, Central Valley Project California. Inf. Bull. 1, 2, 3, and 4. Mid-Pacific Region, Sacramento CA.

[USBR] U.S. Bureau of Reclamation. 1986. Final environmental impact statement, Kesterson Reservoir. Mid-Pacific Region, in Cooperation with U.S. Fish and Wildlife Service and U.S. Army Corps of Engineers.

[USBR] U.S. Bureau of Reclamation. 1991. Kesterson Reservoir biological monitoring report and 1992 biological monitoring plan. Mid-Pacific Region, Sacramento CA.

[USBR] U.S. Bureau of Reclamation. 1992. Kesterson Reservoir biological monitoring report and 1993 biological monitoring plan. Mid-Pacific Region, Sacramento CA.

[USDI] U.S. Department of the Interior. 1989. Submission to California State Water Resources Control Board in Response to Order No. WQ-88-7. Effectiveness of Filling Ephemeral Pools at Kesterson Reservoir, Kesterson Program Upland Habitat Assessment, and Kesterson Reservoir Final Cleanup Plan. Sacramento CA.

[USEPA] U.S. Environmental Protection Agency. 1990. USEPA Region IX/State of California/Marine Corps Federal Facility Agreement, Marine Corps Base Camp Pendleton.

[USEPA] U.S. Environmental Protection Agency. 1991a. Ecological assessment of superfund sites: An overview. ECO-Update 1(2):1–8, Office of Solid Waste and Emergency Response Publication No. 9345.0-05I. Washington DC.

[USEPA] U.S. Environmental Protection Agency. 1991b. Technical support document for water quality-based toxics control. Office of Water, Washington, DC. EPA/505/2-90-001.

[USEPA] U.S. Environmental Protection Agency. 1992a. Framework for Ecological Risk Assessment. EPA/630-R-92/001. Risk Assessment Forum, U.S. Environmental Protection Agency, Washington DC.

[USEPA] U.S. Environmental Protection Agency. 1992b. Developing a work scope for ecological assessments. ECO-Update 1(4):1–15, Office of Solid Waste and Emergency Response Publication No. 9345.0–05I. Washington DC.

[USEPA] U.S. Environmental Protection Agency. 1992c. Informal Resolution of Dispute for MCB Camp Pendleton/Revised Appendix A of Federal Facility Agreement.

[USEPA] U.S. Environmental Protection Agency. 1992d. Quality Criteria for Water 1992 (poster), Office of Water Regulations and Standards, Washington DC.

[USEPA] U.S. Environmental Protection Agency. 1993. Wildlife exposure factors handbook. EPA/600/R-93/187. Washington DC.

[USFWS and USN] U.S. Fish and Wildlife Service and the U.S. Navy. 1990. Final environmental impact statement. Endangered species management and protection plan. Naval Weapons Station Seal Beach, Seal Beach National Wildlife Refuge.

[USN] U.S. Navy. 1985. Initial assessment study of Naval Weapons Station, Seal Beach, California. Naval Energy and Environmental Support Activity (NEESA) 13–062, Port Hueneme CA.

[USN] U.S. Navy. 1989. Remedial Investigation verification step for Naval Weapons Station Seal Beach, California. Naval Energy and Environmental Support Activity (NEESA) 21–0038, Port Hueneme CA.

Chapter 6

Sediment quality assessments: selected issues and results from the National Oceanic and Atmospheric Administration's National Status and Trends Program

Edward R. Long

In recent years, measures of sediment quality have been used increasingly as components of comprehensive ecological assessments. Despite the availability of standardized protocols, a number of controversial issues exist regarding sediment quality assessments. Four issues are discussed in this chapter: 1) the spatial extent of sediment toxicity relative to industrial harbors, 2) the accuracy of numerical sediment quality guidelines in predicting toxicity, 3) the significance of ammonia in causing sediment toxicity, and 4) the sensitivity of amphipods compared to other taxa used in toxicity tests. Data from regional surveys of sediment quality performed by the National Oceanic and Atmospheric Administration in the Hudson-Raritan estuary (New York, New Jersey), Tampa Bay (Florida), Pensacola Bay (Florida), and San Pedro Bay (California) were used to address each issue. Based upon those data, it appears that the toxicity of sediments to sensitive taxa was most severe in the industrial harbors and waterways of each region surveyed, but it was not restricted to only those areas. Also, about 90% of the samples in which toxicant concentrations equaled or exceeded numerical guidelines were significantly toxic to 1 or more taxa in laboratory toxicity tests. Ammonia, a potentially highly toxic chemical commonly found in sediments, appeared to contribute substantially to toxicity in a very small proportion of samples tested (about 3%). Finally, solid-phase toxicity tests performed with amphipods were more sensitive than those performed with other adult taxa, but they were considerably less sensitive than invertebrate gametes and embryos exposed to the pore waters of sediments.

Toxicants such as trace metals, pesticides, and petroleum constituents have an affinity for fine-grained particles and organic matter in the water column, and these contaminated particulates tend to settle to the bottom of bays and estuaries (Tessier and Campbell 1987). Toxicants associated with fine-grained particles can accumulate in low-energy depositional areas, and, therefore, often provide a relatively stable record of historical and recent accumulations. Contaminated sediments may pose risks to resident biota, seafood, and human consumers of seafood (NRC 1989).

Comprehensive ecological risk assessments (ERAs) of areas with potential toxicant problems often include analyses of bed sediments. Ideally, the most comprehensive assessments include assays of chemical concentrations, sediment toxicity, and the composition of resident benthic populations (Long 1989).

Assessments of sediment quality that include toxicity tests have been performed as a part of predredging surveys, hazardous waste site assessments, ambient monitoring of discharges, regional bioeffects surveys, and surveys of potential "hotspots." A variety of protocols and standardized methods have been developed for testing sediment toxicity (ASTM 1990; USEPA/USA 1991; USEPA 1991; Hill et al. 1993). These protocols and methods have been subjected to considerable review, scrutiny, and refinement. Also, many different approaches to the classification of contaminated sediments have been developed and compared (USEPA 1992; Adams et al. 1992). They have also received considerable review and discussion. Nevertheless, the methods used in sediment quality assessments are not without controversy.

In this review 4 specific issues will be discussed, including the following:

1) the spatial extent of sediment toxicity in industrialized/urbanized bays,
2) the accuracy of numerical sediment quality guidelines in predicting toxicity,
3) the significance of ammonia in causing sediment toxicity, and
4) the sensitivity of amphipods relative to other taxa used in toxicity tests.

The nature of each issue and its implications will be described. These issues often have arisen as a result of differences in the interpretation of data, differences in the expectations and objectives of studies, and differences in programmatic agendas and mandates. This chapter will focus mainly upon the technical aspects of each issue.

In the discussion of each topic, relevant data from surveys funded by National Oceanic and Atmospheric Administration's (NOAA) Coastal Ocean Program and performed by NOAA's National Status and Trends (NS&T) Program will be described to provide perspective on each topic. As a part of these NOAA programs, regional surveys of selected bays and estuaries are being performed nationwide to assess the spatial extent and magnitude of sediment toxicity and contamination (Long et al. 1992; Wolfe et al. 1993). These surveys were designed to provide information on the size and severity of sediment contamination and toxicity problems in the nation's major embayments. They were accompanied by assays of toxicant-related biological effects in resident bivalves and demersal fish. Matching chemical and toxicity data were generated from samples collected throughout each study area. A battery of toxicity tests was performed on each sample using relatively sensitive organisms. Chemical analyses were performed for trace metals, ammonia, chlorinated hydrocarbons, and petroleum constituents. These data were used in this chapter to address each topical issue.

Methods

In the NS&T Program, surveys are performed in major embayments that were selected based upon their potential for causing adverse biological effects among the living resources. Chemical data from the monitoring component of the NS&T Program were examined nationwide. Embayments with sampling sites that showed relatively high chemical concentrations were identified and selected for the intensive surveys. Thus far, the major areas that have been selected include Boston Harbor, Long Island Sound, the Hudson-Raritan estuary, Newark Bay, Charleston Harbor, Savannah River, Biscayne Bay, Tampa Bay, Pensacola Bay, San Pedro Bay, San Diego Bay, and San Francisco Bay. Several smaller bays were included also.

Stratified-random survey designs were used and sampling stations were selected to represent conditions throughout each survey area (Wolfe et al. 1993). Samples were collected in industrialized channels and maritime harbors suspected of being highly contaminated, in mid-bay and rural regions suspected of being contaminant dilution zones, and in the least contaminated regions near the entrance to the bays. Sampling effort was invariably greatest in the areas suspected of being most contaminated and in the adjacent transition or dilution zones where changes in conditions were most probable.

Only surficial sediments (upper 2 cm) were collected to represent relatively recent contamination. Non-contaminating methods and instruments were used to collect each sample. Portions of each sample were tested for toxicity and other portions were analyzed for chemical concentrations. A number of federal, academic, and commercial laboratories performed the tests and analyses for NOAA (see Acknowledgments).

In most of the surveys, 3 types of toxicity tests were performed. First, 10-d amphipod survival tests were performed with whole (solid-phase) sediments, using the standardized protocols of ASTM (1990), with *Rhepoxynius abronius* on the Pacific coast and *Ampelisca abdita* on the Atlantic and Gulf coasts. Second, pore water was extracted with gentle pressure, frozen, thawed, and tested in a dilution series (100%, 50%, and 25% salinity-adjusted pore water), following the methods of Carr and Chapman (1992). Pore waters from the Pacific coast were tested either with abalone embryos (*Haliotis rufescens*) or urchin gametes (*Strongylocentrotus purpuratus*). Pore waters from the Atlantic and Gulf coasts were tested with the gametes or embryos of the urchin *Arbacia punctulata*. Finally, the microbial bioluminescence (Microtox) test was performed with dichloro-methane (DCM) extracts of the sediments, following protocols used in Puget Sound (USEPA 1991) and San Francisco Bay (Long and Markel 1992). The results of the toxicity tests for each sample were compared to those from a nontoxic control sample to determine statistically significant differences (e.g., with analysis of variance [ANOVA] and Dunnett's t-test, $P < 0.05$).

Chemical analyses were conducted with the performance-based methods of the NS&T Program (Lauenstein and Cantillo 1993). These methods differed somewhat among the laboratories and survey areas but invariably complied with the quality assurance requirements of the NS&T Program. Details of specific methods were described in contractor reports, published technical reports, and articles prepared for each study area (e.g., Long et al. 1994).

Results and discussion

Spatial extent of sediment toxicity in industrialized/urbanized bays

A significant issue is whether toxicity of sediments is restricted only to industrialized/ urbanized harbors and hazardous waste sites or extends more widely throughout the major bays. The spatial scales of biological effects attributable to contamination or hypoxia may range from less than 10 km^2 to over 100,000 km^2, depending upon the type of contamination, within bays and along major coastlines (O'Connor et al. 1987). The spatial extent of contaminated sediments may differ among bays, ranging from small localized hotspots in some bays to more widespread contamination in other areas (NRC 1989). However, the distribution and spatial patterns of contamination are poorly documented in most areas (NRC 1989; Power and Chapman 1992).

Chemical concentrations in most bays are highest nearest the contaminant sources, i.e., in or near the harbors and ports. Frequently, the contaminants enter the systems from storm drains, other nonpoint sources, cargo docks, ship repair yards, spills, leaks, and illegal discharges. Consequently, sediments from the inner harbors nearest these sources often are the most contaminated. If elevated concentrations of toxic chemicals alone determine toxicity, then toxicity would be expected only in those inner harbor areas.

Before sediment toxicity tests were used as survey tools in baywide assessments, they were used primarily in predredging studies (Power and Chapman 1992). Consequently, the use of these tests was restricted to primarily the industrial harbors and channels that were in need of dredging and, often, were the most likely to be toxic. Very little or no information was gathered from areas further removed from the inner harbors. Also, test organisms, e.g., adult clams and polychaetes, used in the predredging studies to facilitate analyses of contaminant bioaccumulation often were relatively resistant to toxicants. Consequently, these species rarely showed toxicity. More sensitive species may detect toxicity over much broader areas in which toxicants have accumulated in only moderate concentrations. Furthermore, if contaminants in sediments are readily bioavailable, then even relatively low concentrations may be sufficient to trigger significant toxicity in tests performed with highly sensitive taxa.

Sediment samples from San Pedro Bay, California and vicinity that were significantly toxic to amphipods (*R. abronius*) were distributed widely throughout the survey area (Figure 6-1). Three samples were collected at each of 33 sites and 6 samples were collected at 2 sites to provide information on within-site variability (Sapudar et al. 1994). A total of 61 of 105 samples (58%) were significantly toxic ($P < 0.05$) relative to controls in this study area. Most of the samples (29 of 45, or 64.4%) from the inner channels and harbors of Los Angeles and Long Beach were significantly toxic to the amphipods. Also, most of the samples (20 of 24, or 83.3%) from Alamitos Bay (near Seal Beach) and Anaheim Bay/Huntington Harbor were toxic. These areas are highly industrialized and/or surrounded by densely urbanized regions. In addition, some samples (9 of 27, or 33.3%) from the outer regions of the San Pedro Bay system were toxic seaward to the perimeter breakwater, suggesting that toxicity was not restricted to the inner harbor areas. None of the 6 samples collected beyond the breakwater were toxic in this test. These data suggest that the incidence of toxicity was highest in the inner reaches of the study area and that it decreased incrementally in the outer bay and seaward of the bay entrance.

Results of amphipod toxicity tests performed with 90 samples collected during 1991 from Tampa Bay, Florida are illustrated in Figure 6-2. Significantly toxic samples were restricted mainly to the northern portion of Hillsborough Bay, the most highly industrialized lobe of the Tampa Bay estuary. Of 21 samples tested, 10 (47.6%) were significantly different from controls. However, a few samples (i.e., 7 of 66, or 10.6%) from other regions of the estuary, including Bayboro Harbor and lower Boca Ciega Bay near St. Petersburg, were significantly toxic to the amphipods. Overall, the incidence of samples that were toxic to the amphipods was relatively low in the Tampa Bay estuary (10 of 90 samples, or 11%). In additional testing during 1992, none of the 75 samples collected in Tampa Bay was toxic to the amphipods (Long et al. 1994).

In contrast to the amphipod test, the sea urchin fertilization tests performed

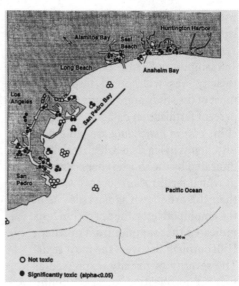

Figure 6-1   *Distribution of sampling stations in San Pedro Bay, California that were either significantly toxic or nontoxic to amphipod survival* (Rhepoxynius abronius).

Figure 6-2   *Distribution of sampling stations in Tampa Bay, Florida that were either significantly toxic or nontoxic to amphipod survival* (Ampelisca abdita)

with 100% sediment pore water collected during 1991 and 1992 indicated a very high incidence of toxicity (130 of 165 samples, or 79%) in Tampa Bay, and toxicity was widespread throughout most of the study area (Figure 6-3). The percent fertilization data for the sea urchin *Arbacia punctulata* are plotted as histograms in Figure 6-3; high toxicity is indicated by the shortest bars. Stations in which fertilization success was less than 10% are shown as asterisks. As in the amphipod tests, the sea urchin tests indicated that samples from northern Hillsborough Bay were the most toxic. The severity of toxicity (expressed as percent fertilization success) diminished down the bay toward its confluence with middle Tampa Bay. In addition, this test indicated that samples from many other areas were highly toxic, including those from the western lobe of Old Tampa Bay, from Bayboro Harbor and Boca Ciega Bay

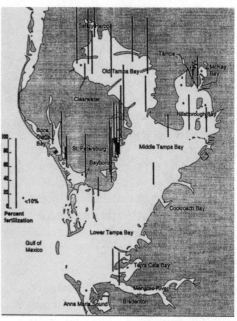

Figure 6-3   *Average percent fertilization success of sea urchin eggs* (Arbacia punctulata) *exposed to 100% sediment pore water from 55 sampling sites in Tampa Bay, Florida*

(near St. Petersburg), and from Anna Maria Sound, the lower Manatee River, and Cockroach Bay. Samples collected from one site each in middle Tampa Bay and lower Tampa Bay were significantly toxic. The nontoxic samples were collected in much of Old Tampa Bay and several bayous adjoining middle Tampa Bay.

In Pensacola Bay, Florida none of the 40 samples collected was toxic to amphipods (*A. abdita*). However, in the sea urchin tests (*A. punctulata*) the pore waters were toxic to egg fertilization in 3 samples and to normal morphological development in 11 samples. All of the samples that were toxic to morphological development were collected in peripheral bayous or in the Pensacola harbor adjoining the Pensacola Bay (Figure 6-4). Samples from the highly industrialized Bayou Chico were particularly toxic based upon the morphological development test. The three samples that were toxic in the tests of fertilization success were collected in Bayou Grande adjoining a military base, in western Pensacola Bay between the mouths of Bayou Grande and Bayou Chico, and at the head of East Bay in an area that receives little industrial pollution. The data from this survey suggest that toxicity was restricted to a very small portion of the area.

In the Hudson-Raritan estuary, 46% of the samples (54 of 117) were significantly toxic in the amphipod tests (*A. abdita*). Toxicity was most prevalent in samples from the East

River (17 of 18 samples, or 94.4%) and Newark Bay/ Arthur Kill (12 of 12 samples) (Figure 6-5). Relatively high toxicity in the East River decreased into Long Island Sound and into the upper New York Harbor. Also, relatively high toxicity in Newark Bay and Arthur Kill diminished into Raritan Bay. However, some samples from the lower Hudson River, upper harbor, lower harbor, western Raritan Bay, lower Raritan River, and Sandy Hook Bay were significantly toxic. Collectively, 10 of 44 samples (22.7%) from Raritan Bay and western Long Island Sound were toxic. In addition, some samples (4 of 9, or 44.4%) collected beyond the mouth of the estuary were significantly toxic in this test.

Estimates of the spatial patterns and extent of toxicity are, in part, functions of the relative sensitivities of the assays that are used in forming the estimates. The spatial patterns of toxicity in Tampa Bay estimated with the amphipod survival tests and the sea urchin fertilization tests differed remarkably. Similarly, none of the samples from Pensacola Bay was toxic to amphipods, whereas some were toxic to sea urchin fertilization and embryological development. Despite the remarkable differ-

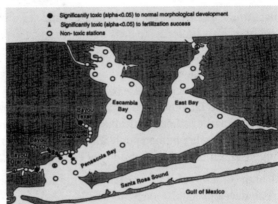

Figure 6-4   *Distribution of sampling stations in Pensacola Bay, Florida that were either toxic to fertilization success of eggs and/or toxic to normal morphological*

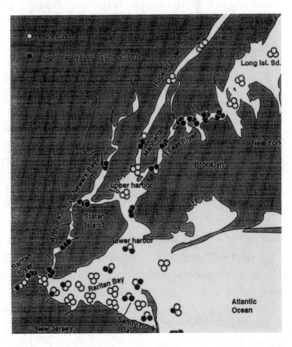

Figure 6-5   *Distribution of sampling stations in the Hudson-Raritan estuary of New York and New Jersey that were either significantly toxic or not toxic to amphipod survival (Ampelisca abdita)*

ences in the sensitivities of the amphipod and sea urchin gamete tests, the amphipods very frequently indicated toxicity in samples that were highly toxic to the sea urchins.

The data from the surveys of San Pedro Bay, Pensacola Bay, Tampa Bay, and the Hudson-Raritan estuary suggest that the incidence and severity of toxicity is highest in the inner harbors and channels of these bays. In Pensacola Bay very few samples were toxic and toxicity was relatively narrowly restricted to the most industrialized bayous and the municipal harbor adjoining the bay. Compared to the other 3 study areas, Pensacola Bay has a much smaller human population, and most of the industrial and municipal development is centered around the city of Pensacola.

All of the other 3 areas are much more industrialized and urbanized, and the industrial/urban development is much more widespread. Accordingly, although the incidence of toxicity was highest in the inner harbors, it was not restricted exclusively to those areas. In all 3 estuaries, there was a clear pattern of high toxicity in the inner harbor areas diminishing seaward. For example, high toxicity to amphipods in the East River diminished rapidly into western Long Island Sound. Also, high toxicity in Arthur Kill and the lower Raritan River diminished seaward into outer Raritan Bay. High toxicity in the ports of Los Angeles and Long Beach diminished into the outer regions of San Pedro Bay and diminished again into the Pacific Ocean. High toxicity in northern Hillsborough Bay diminished down the estuary and into Old Tampa Bay.

Nevertheless, in each case some samples collected beyond the inner harbors were significantly toxic. Some samples from outer San Pedro Bay were toxic. Some samples from middle Tampa Bay, lower Tampa Bay, western Old Tampa Bay, and the relatively rural Cockroach Bay were toxic. Samples from western Pensacola Bay and the upper East Bay, both removed from highly industrialized harbors, were toxic. Some samples from outer Raritan Bay, lower New York harbor, and offshore beyond the mouth of the Hudson-Raritan estuary were toxic. Therefore, based upon the data gathered thus far, it appears that toxicity to relatively sensitive taxa extends beyond the inner reaches of the industrialized bays.

Accuracy of numerical sediment quality guidelines in predicting toxicity

Numerical sediment quality guidelines or criteria have been proposed or developed by several investigators, using a variety of different methods (NRC 1989; USEPA 1992; Adams et al. 1992). Three basic approaches to the development of numerical standards have been pursued: the equilibrium-partitioning approach based upon physical chemistry models, the laboratory approach based upon spiked sediment bioassays, and the field approach based upon various analyses of matching chemical and biological information. In addition, the weight-of-evidence approach used by NOAA's NS&T Program has been used to develop informal, numerical guidelines (Long and MacDonald 1992). The latter approach is based upon a compilation and evaluation of the cumulative experience gained from the 3 preceding approaches. All 4 approaches represent attempts to protect living marine resources that are exposed to chemical contamination of sediments. All 4 approaches are based upon some measure of adverse biological effects, such as toxicity, associated with or caused by chemical toxicants in the sediments.

Numerical guidelines must meet some minimum requirements if they are to be used with confidence by environmental scientists and regulators. First, they must be based upon measures of adverse effects that are biologically or ecologically significant. Second, they must be based upon good research and must be protective of multiple, relatively sensitive species. Third, they must be accompanied by estimates or quantification of their reliability. Finally, and, most importantly, they must be field-validated with independent datasets not used in their derivation and demonstrated to correctly predict toxicity. Ideally, the field validation should be performed in environments with complex mixtures of toxicants to simulate situations in which they most often would be applied.

The technical basis and predictability of effects-based, numerical sediment guidelines or criteria have been questioned (NRC 1989; Spies 1989; Giesy and Hoke 1990). Each of the approaches to the development of sediment quality guidelines has certain strengths and weaknesses in the concepts or theory underlying the approach (Adams et al. 1992; Sapudar et al. 1994). In the final analysis, to be useful, guidelines must be demonstrated to work. That is, they must predict some adverse biological effect, such as acute toxicity, when exceeded.

The weight-of-evidence approach first published by Long and Morgan (1990) was further described by Long and MacDonald (1992). It is based upon the calculations of the 10th and 50th percentile of the chemical concentrations associated with adverse effects in a database assembled from as many available studies as possible. The 10th percentile of the effects data was referred to as the effects range-low (ERL) and the 50th percentile (the median) was referred to as the effects range-median (ERM). Effects range-low and ERM values were offered by Long and Morgan (1990) for numerous trace metals and organic toxicants. Using similar methods, MacDonald (1993) and MacDonald et al. (1992) have applied the weight-of-evidence approach to the development of numerical guidelines for Florida and Canada, respectively. The database used to derive these guidelines included information on the chemical concentrations associated with acute mortality and other endpoints among a variety of taxa, mainly crustaceans.

The database used by Long and Morgan (1990) to derive guidelines for the NS&T Program was refined by excluding datasets from freshwater studies and expanded with additional data from recent saltwater studies. Based upon the new database, revised guideline values were prepared (Long, MacDonald et al. 1995). Accompanying the revised guidelines were estimates of their reliability in identifying chemical concentrations associated with adverse effects. The reliability of each guideline was estimated by calculating the incidence of study endpoints in which adverse effects were reported over the concentration ranges established by the 2 guideline values. For example, Long, MacDonald et al. (1995) determined that 6 of 64 studies (9.4%) reported adverse effects at Cu concentrations below the ERL value of 34 ppm. In contrast, 36 of 43 studies (83.7%)

reported adverse effects at concentrations that equaled or exceeded the ERM value of 270 ppm for Cu. At Cu concentrations ≥ the ERL, but lower than the ERM, 32 of 110 datapoints (29.1%) showed adverse effects. Long, MacDonald et al. (1995) concluded that there was a relatively high degree of confidence in the guidelines for Cu. For most chemicals the incidence of toxic effects was 10 to 25% at concentrations below the ERL values and 75% or greater at concentrations above the ERMs.

Since the ERM values represent the median (midpoint) of the effects datasets, they should be predictive of effects in roughly 50% of the cases when equaled or exceeded. In the following discussion, it was hypothesized that an exceedance of the ERM value for any single chemical should trigger toxicity. That hypothesis was tested by analyzing the matching chemical and toxicity data from the NOAA surveys of Tampa Bay, San Pedro Bay, and the Hudson-Raritan estuary. The predictability of the guidelines was determined in each area by comparing the number of samples in which at least 1 ERM value was exceeded by any amount to the number of those samples that were actually toxic (i.e., significantly different from controls) in any of the tests.

The ERL values were not intended to predict toxicity; rather, they were intended to represent the concentration below which effects would rarely occur and above which effects could possibly occur. Therefore, the number of samples in which none of the ERL values was equaled was compared to the number of those samples that were nontoxic in all tests.

Matching chemistry and toxicity data were generated for 44 samples in the San Pedro Bay, California survey (Table 6-1). One-half of those samples was significantly toxic in amphipod survival tests and 40 were toxic in the abalone embryo development tests of 100% pore waters. There were no samples in which all chemical concentrations were below the ERL values. Among the 44 samples, there were 6 in which at least 1 ERL value (but none of the ERMs) was exceeded. Among these 6 samples, 3 were toxic in the amphipod tests, and all 6 were toxic in the abalone tests. There were 38 samples in which at

Table 6-1   Incidence of toxicity in amphipod survival tests (with Rhepoxynius abronius) *and abalone embryo development tests (n=44)*

Chemical concentrations	Number of samples	Number (and percent) of samples that were significantly toxic		
		Amphipods	Abalone embryos	Either test
Overall toxicity	44	22 (50%)	40 (91%)	42 (95%)
All chemicals < all ERLs	0	—	—	—
1 ≥ ERL, all < all ERMs	6	6 (100%)	3 (50%)	6 (100%)
1 or more chemicals ≥ ERM	38	19 (50%)	34 (89%)	37 (97%)

Table 6-2   Incidence of toxicity to amphipod survival (with Ampelisca abdita) or either of
four test endpoints in Hudson-Raritan estuary samples (n=38)

| Chemical concentrations | Number of samples | Number (and percent) of samples that were significantly toxic | |
		Amphipods	Any of 4 tests
Overall toxicity	38	21 (55%)	28 (74%)
All chemicals < all ERLs	2	0	0
1 ≥ ERL, all < all ERMs	4	2 (50%)	3 (75%)
1 or more chemicals ≥ ERM	32	19 (59%)	24 (75%)

least 1 chemical equaled or exceeded its respective ERM value. A total of 19 of the 38 samples (50%) actually were significantly toxic to amphipod survival and 34 of the 38 (89%) were toxic to abalone embryo development. Of the 38 samples expected to be toxic, 37 actually were toxic in either of the 2 tests, for an overall agreement of 97%. Most of the agreement between predicted and actual toxicity was acquired with the abalone embryo tests of the pore waters.

In the Hudson-Raritan estuary, both chemical analyses and toxicity tests were performed on 38 samples (Table 6-2). Four tests were performed: amphipod survival with *A. abdita*, bivalve embryo survival and embryological development with *Mulinia lateralis* in exposures to aqueous phase elutriates, and microbial bioluminescence in Microtox tests of organic solvent extracts. Of these 38 samples 2 were expected to be nontoxic (all chemical concentrations were less than the ERLs) and both were not toxic in all of the 4 tests. There were 4 samples in which at least 1 ERL was exceeded, but no ERMs were exceeded. Two of those 4 samples were toxic to amphipod survival and 3 of 4 were toxic in any of the tests. Of the 32 samples in which 1 or more concentrations exceeded an ERM, 19 (59%) were toxic to the amphipods, and 24 (75%) were toxic in at least 1 of the 4 tests.

In Phase 1 (performed during 1991) of the Tampa Bay survey, both complete chemistry and toxicity data were generated for 16 samples. Sediments were tested with amphipods (*A. abdita*), sea urchin (*A. punctulata*) fertilization in 100% pore water, and microbial bioluminescence. In Phase 2 of the Tampa Bay survey, chemical and toxicity data were generated for 45 samples. Only the *A. abdita* survival tests and *A. punctulata* fertilization tests were performed in Phase 2. The data (*n* = 61) from both phases of the survey were merged (Table 6-3). Neither of the 2 samples with all chemical concentrations below the ERL values was toxic. Among the 33 samples in which at least 1 ERL, but no ERMs, was exceeded, 1 was toxic in the amphipod tests and 25 were toxic in any of the 2 (Phase 2) or

Table 6-3   Incidence of toxicity in amphipod survival tests (with Ampelisca abdita*) or any of 3 tests in Tampa Bay (n=61)*

Chemical concentrations	Number of samples	Number (and percent) of samples that were significantly toxic	
		Amphipods	Any of 2 or 3 tests
Overall toxicity	61	8 (13.1%)	50 (82.0%)
All chemicals < all ERLs	2	0	0
1 ERL, all < all ERMs	33	1 (3.0%)	25 (75.8%)
1 or more chemicals ERM	26	7 (26.9%)	25 (96.1%)

Table 6-4   Summary of the incidence of toxicity in samples from San Pedro Bay, Hudson-Raritan estuary, and Tampa Bay in which 1 or more chemicals equalled or exceeded an ERM value

Survey area	Amphipod survival	Any of the tests performed
San Pedro Bay	19/38 (50.0%)	37/38 (97.4%)
Hudson-Raritan Estuary	19/32 (59.4%)	24/32 (75.0%)
Tampa Bay	7/26 (26.9%)	25/26 (96.1%)
Combined totals	45/96 (46.9%)	86/96 (89.6%)

3 (Phase 1) tests. A total of 26 samples had at least 1 concentration greater than an ERM, 7 of which were toxic to the amphipods, while 25 were toxic to the sea urchin gametes exposed to the 100% pore waters. Most of the agreement between predicted and actual toxicity was attained with the sea urchin tests.

The results from San Pedro Bay, Hudson-Raritan estuary, and Tampa Bay (summarized in Table 6-4) provide an overall estimate of predictability. These data indicated that 46.9% and 90% of the samples in which at least 1 ERM value was exceeded were toxic in the amphipod tests and any 1 of the tests, respectively. The agreement between predicted and actual toxicity was poorest (75%) in the Hudson-Raritan estuary in which no porewater test was performed. If the Hudson-Raritan estuary data were excluded, the agreement between predicted and actual toxicity would be 97% (62 of 64 samples). The predictability of the guidelines clearly increased with the inclusion of the highly sensitive porewater tests performed with early life stages.

Additional field validations should be performed with data from other geographic areas, sedimentological types, test types, and chemical mixtures. The incidence of Type I errors (no toxicity observed when expected) and Type II errors (toxicity observed when not expected) should be determined. Predictability should be quantified in areas with high ammonia concentrations that may confound toxicity/chemistry relationships.

Significance of ammonia in causing sediment toxicity

The taxa used most frequently in ERAs are those that are ecologically important and relatively sensitive to contaminated sediments. These species may differ in their sensitivities to different types of toxicants, but, none are sensitive to only 1 or a few related chemicals. Generally, they are sensitive to a broad range of substances. One of the strengths of using toxicity tests in sediment quality assessments is the expectation that the tests may detect the presence of chemicals not suspected or measured in chemical analyses (Power and Chapman 1992). However, all test species are sensitive to varying degrees to some naturally occurring factors in sediments, e.g., high concentrations of fine-grained particles and ammonia. A mathematical model was developed (DeWitt et al. 1988) to account for the effects of fine-grained particles on the survival of the marine amphipod *Rhepoxynius abronius*. Also, changes in the concentrations of organic carbon in contaminant-spiked sediments altered considerably the toxicity of the test materials (Swartz et al. 1990).

In some surveys of sediment quality, the apparent effects of ammonia in freshwater and saltwater toxicity tests were observed (Ankley et al. 1990 and Jones and Lee 1988, respectively). In laboratory tests, Kohn et al. (1994) determined the lethal concentrations of ammonia and the un-ionized form of ammonia to amphipods. The issue is whether ammonia plays a relatively major or minor role in the toxicity of sediments to test organisms. The conditions in which ammonia is produced may be exacerbated by anthropogenic inputs. However, since ammonia per se is a naturally occurring toxin and is derived, in part, from natural microbial processes, there are limited regulatory tools to reduce or eliminate toxicity problems caused by ammonia. Furthermore, if toxicity in sediments were caused largely by ammonia, the results of toxicity tests would not be particularly useful in regulating anthropogenic toxicants.

The relationship between fertilization success of sea urchin gametes (*A. punctulata*) exposed to sediment pore waters from Tampa Bay and the concentration of un-ionized ammonia in the pore waters is illustrated in Figure 6-6. The EC50 is 600 μg NH₃/L for un-ionized ammonia in this particular toxicity test (Carr et al. 1996). The Spearman-rank correlation was highly

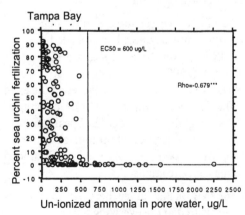

Figure 6-6   *Percent sea urchin fertilization success of Arbacia* punctulata *eggs in toxicity tests of Tampa Bay, Florida sediment pore waters plotted against the concentrations of un-ionized ammonia in the pore water (μg/l). n = 165.*

significant (Rho = –0.679, *P* < 0.001, *n* = 165), indicating a strong relationship between fertilization success and the concentration of un-ionized ammonia. Fertilization success diminished rapidly (usually to 0% fertilization) at un-ionized ammonia, concentrations above the EC50 value. Of the 165 samples tested, only 14 exceeded the un-ionized ammonia EC50 value in the test chambers (all 14 samples were toxic). Also, numerous samples caused low or no fertilization success at very low concentrations of un-ionized ammonia and toxicity in these samples was attributable to other factors.

The concentrations of un-ionized ammonia also were measured in the overlying water in the amphipod test chambers during the second phase of the Tampa Bay survey. Ammonia concentrations in the sediment pore water may have been higher but were not measured. As in the sea urchin tests, amphipod survival was significantly correlated (Rho = –0.337, *P* < 0.001) with the concentrations of un-ionized ammonia (Figure 6-7). However, none of the 75 samples equaled or exceeded the calculated LC50 concentration (830 µg/L) or the no-observed-effect concentration (NOEC) (estimated as 236 µg/L, associated with 86.0% survival) reported for *A. abdita* (Kohn et al. 1994) and none of the samples was significantly toxic to the amphipods.

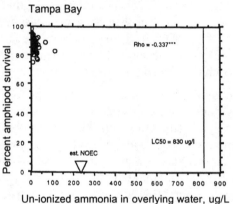

Figure 6-7   *Percent survival of* Ampelisca abdita *in toxicity tests of Tampa Bay, Florida sediments plotted against the concentrations of un-ionized ammonia in the overlying water in the test chambers (µg/l) (n = 75)*

In San Pedro Bay (Figure 6-8) none of the 105 samples equaled or exceeded the LC50 value determined for *R. abronius* (1590 µg/L) (Kohn et al. 1994). None of the samples exceeded the estimated NOEC (677 µg/L, associated with 96.0% survival) (Kohn et al. 1994). One sample had nearly 600 g/L un-ionized ammonia and was significantly toxic. The Spearman-rank correlation between amphipod survival and the concentration of un-ionized ammonia was not significant (Rho = –0.032, *P* > 0.05). Amphipod survival varied widely among the samples over a narrow range in ammonia concentrations.

In the Newark Bay survey there was no apparent relationship between un-ionized ammonia measured in the overlying water of the test chambers during 57 amphipod survival tests with *A. abdita* (Figure 6-9). The correlation between the concentration of un-ionized ammonia and amphipod survival was not significant (Rho = –0.105, *P* > 0.05). In the majority of the samples, the un-ionized ammonia concentrations were below the detection limits of 3.5 µg/L. Only 6 samples exceeded the estimated NOEC (236 µg/L), and none equaled or exceeded the LC50 concentration of 830 µg/L (Kohn et al. 1994). In the sample with the highest concentration of un-ionized ammonia (620 µg/L), amphipod survival was 111% relative to the controls.

Collectively, among the surficial samples tested from all 3 study areas, only 3% (14 of 402) of the samples had un-ionized ammonia concentrations that equaled or exceeded the respective EC50 or LC50 value. In the amphipod tests, un-ionized ammonia concentrations equaled or exceeded the NOEC, and, therefore, may have contributed to significant toxicity in 1 sample from San Pedro Bay, 5 samples from Newark Bay, and none from Tampa Bay (for an overall incidence of 6 in 237 samples, or 2.5%). In the pore waters, the un-ionized ammonia concentrations were sufficiently high to cause or contribute to toxicity in a number of samples only from Tampa Bay. These data suggest that ammonia did not contribute substantially to toxicity measured with these protocols in surficial saltwater sediments.

Relative sensitivity of solid-phase amphipod tests compared to other toxicity tests

The use of amphipods as test organisms in sediment toxicity tests has increased over recent years as the protocols for these tests have developed. Amphipods were determined in laboratory tests to be sensitive to toxicants in sediments (Swartz et al. 1985). They are more sensitive than many other taxa used in sediment toxicity tests (Swartz et al. 1979; ASTM 1990). Several species were

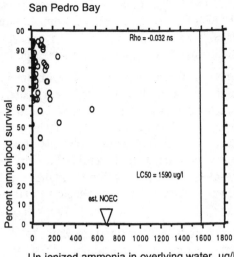

Figure 6-8   *Percent survival of* Rhepoxynius abronius *in toxicity tests of San Pedro Bay, California sediments plotted against the concentrations of un-ionized ammonia in the overlying water in the test chambers (µg/l) (n = 105)*

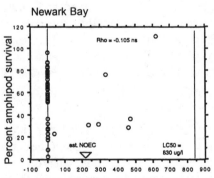

Figure 6-9   *Percent survival of* Ampelisca abdita *in toxicity tests of Newark Bay, New Jersey sediments plotted against the concentrations of un-ionized ammonia in the overlying water in the test chambers (µg/l) (n = 57)*

added to the list of taxa eligible for use in assessments of prospective dredging material (USEPA/USA 1991). Therefore, sediment samples from waterways previously identified as nontoxic with relatively resistant taxa could be identified in subsequent surveys as highly toxic based upon results of tests performed with amphipods.

There are many regulatory and environmental implications that could occur as a result of the use of amphipods in sediment toxicity tests. For example, upland, confined disposal of dredge materials, additional treatment of effluents, or cleanup and remediation of hazardous waste sites—all of which are costly—could be required when samples fail the amphipod tests. If the amphipod tests are unreasonably sensitive, numerous regulatory actions triggered by results of toxicity tests performed with these taxa may lead to needless expenditures of funds. On the other hand, if the amphipod tests are reasonably sensitive and predictive of ecological effects and damage, their use in ERAs may facilitate improvements in environmental quality.

Amphipods are used in tests of whole (solid-phase) sediments. Comparisons were made between the solid-phase amphipod tests and a variety of other types of tests, including porewater tests performed with gametes and embryos of invertebrates, elutriate tests performed with bivalve embryos, microbial bioluminescence tests performed with organic solvent extracts, and solid-phase tests performed with other adult taxa.

The numbers of samples identified as significantly toxic ($P < 0.05$) in 6 different tests are compared with data from the Hudson-Raritan estuary (Table 6-5). Data issued in numerous public notices by the U. S. Army Corps of Engineers (New York District) from 1985 through 1993 were assembled, and the incidence of toxic samples was calculated (Long, Wolfe et al. 1995). Solid-phase tests were performed with grass shrimp (*Paleomonetes pugio*), sandworms (*Nereis virens*), and hardshell clams (*Mercenaria mercenaria*). Samples were collected throughout the entire area, but most of them came from the highly industrialized waterways, shipyards, harbors, construction sites, piers, and inner-harbor channels. Samples usually were collected with corers and composited among several depths and several stations within the prospective dredging area. Of the 92 samples tested, 12.0% were significantly toxic to *P. pugio*, 7.6% were toxic to *N. virens*, and none were toxic to *M. mercenaria*.

In the 1991 and 1992 surveys of the Hudson-Raritan estuary performed by NOAA, samples were collected throughout the entire area, including much of the area tested in the predredging studies (Long, Wolfe et al. 1995). However, many samples were collected beyond the inner harbor areas tested in the predredging studies (Figure 6-5) and only the upper 2 cm were retained for testing. With portions of each sample, solid-phase tests were performed with *Ampelisca abdita*, liquid-phase tests of elutriates were performed with the embryos of the clam *Mulinia lateralis*, and microbial bioluminescence tests were performed with organic solvent extracts of the sediments. In these surveys, the incidence of toxicity was 58.6% in the amphipod tests, 26.6% in the clam larvae tests, and 40.5% in the bioluminescence tests (Table 6-5). The incidence of toxicity should have been lower in the NOAA survey because, unlike the predredging studies, samples were collected throughout the estuary, not only in the inner harbor areas. The incidence of toxicity was considerably higher in these tests than in the tests performed in the pre-dredging surveys. Among the 3 tests, the solid-phase amphipod tests were the most sensitive to the samples as indicated by the highest incidence of toxic samples.

Because of significant differences in the sampling design, methods, and time frame the data from the predredging and NOAA studies may not be highly comparable. Therefore, the relative sensitivity of some of the taxa was further

Table 6-5   Incidence of significantly toxic samples in the Hudson-Raritan estuary in sediment toxicity tests in predredging studies or in tests performed with amphipods, clam larvae, or microbial bioluminescence in a survey conducted by NOAA

	Toxic samples/ total samples	Percent toxic
Pre-dredging surveys (1985–1993)		
Grass shrimp survival	11/92	12.0%
Sandworm survival	7/92	7.6%
Clam suvival	0/92	0.0%
NOAA 1991 and 1992 surveys:		
Amphipod survival	102/174	58.6%
Clam larvae survival/ development	29/109	26.6%
Microbial bioluminescence	47/116	40.5%

evaluated by comparing dose-response data from bioassays of the same substance. In 4-d tests performed with cadmium chloride (CdCl) in sea water, the LC50s calculated for *A. abdita* ranged from 200 to 580 µg/L (Redmond et al. 1994). In contrast a 4-d CdCl LC50 of 1700 µg/L was calculated for *Macoma balthica*, a bivalve mollusk (McLeese and Ray 1986). The 4-d CdCl LC50 for *N. virens* was 9300 µg/L (Eisler and Hennekey 1977). These data confirm that the amphipods were more sensitive than polychaetes and mollusks to Cd.

In both Tampa Bay and Pensacola Bay, amphipod survival tests of solid-phase sediments, sea urchin fertilization tests of 100% pore water, and microbial bioluminescence tests of organic solvent extracts were performed on portions of the same samples. In both bays the incidence of significantly toxic samples was much higher in the sea urchin and Microtox tests than in the amphipod tests (Table 6-6). In Pensacola Bay none of the samples was toxic to the amphipods, whereas 80% were toxic to microbial bioluminescence.

In San Francisco Bay, data from numerous different studies performed from 1985 through 1990 were compiled and the incidence of toxicity to amphipods (*R. abronius*) in solid-phase tests was compared to that of bivalve larvae (*M. edulis* or *C. virginica*) exposed to elutriates of the same samples (Long and Markel 1992). The incidence of toxicity was very similar (50.4% versus 57.4%) in the 2 tests (Table 6-7).

In San Pedro Bay, 105 samples were tested in a survey performed jointly by the California State Water Resources Control Board and NOAA in 1992 (Sapudar et al. 1994). The incidence of toxicity identified by the solid-phase amphipod tests (*R. abronius*) and the 100% porewater tests performed with abalone larvae (*H. rufescens*) were very different (Table 6-7). Of the 105 samples, 88.5% were toxic to the abalone larvae and 58.1% were toxic to the amphipods.

Based upon the data from these surveys, the solid-phase amphipod test was more sensitive than other tests performed with adult taxa, but it was not the most sensitive among the 3 types of tests commonly used by NOAA. It appears to be intermediate in sensitivity relative to the somewhat resistant adult clams, shrimp, and sandworms used in dredge material assessments and the highly sensitive invertebrate embryos and gametes used in the assays of pore waters. These observations confirm the results of previous comparisons in sensitivity of the solid-phase tests performed with amphipods and the porewater tests performed with sea urchin gametes (Carr and Chapman 1992).

Table 6-6　Incidence of significantly toxic samples in Tampa Bay and Pensacola Bay, Florida based upon sediment toxicity tests performed with amphipods, sea urchin gametes, or microbial bioluminescence in surveys conducted by NOAA

	Toxic samples/ total samples	Percent toxic
Tampa Bay:		
Amphipod survival	10/165	6.1%
Sea urchin fertilization	130/165	78.8%
Microtox bioluminescence	24/90	27.0%
Pensacola Bay:		
Amphipod survival	0/40	0.0%
Sea urchin embryo development	11/40	27.5%
Microtox bioluminescence	32/40	80.0%

Table 6-7　Incidence of significantly toxic sediment samples in San Francisco Bay and San Pedro Bay, California in toxicity tests performed with amphipods, bivalve larvae, or abalone embryos

	Toxic samples/ total samples	Percent toxic
San Francisco Bay:		
Amphipod survival	56/111	50.4%
Bivalve embryo development	112/198	57.4%
San Pedro Bay:		
Amphipod survival	61/105	58.1%
Abalone embryo development	93/105	88.5%

Conclusions

Sediments are highly complex and variable media in which to quantify chemical contamination and biological effects. The 4 topics discussed in this chapter represent only a portion of the technical issues concerning the field of sediment quality assessments. Other equally important issues include the methods for estimating the bioavailability of toxicants, the most effective means of measuring effects to resident benthic communities, and the ecological significance of toxicity measured in laboratory tests. Also, little is known of the effects of sediment disturbance caused during sample collection upon the results of chemical analyses and toxicity tests.

The data from the NOAA surveys performed in the Hudson-Raritan estuary, Newark Bay, Tampa Bay, Pensacola Bay, and San Pedro Bay lead to a number of conclusions. The observations and conclusions regarding the 4 selected issues based upon the data from the NOAA surveys certainly should not be viewed as definitive. Other data from other regions or from the use of different protocols could provide different results.

Toxicity of sediments clearly is most frequent and severe in the industrialized harbors and channels of these bays, but it is not restricted to only those areas. Some samples collected in dilution zones, located seaward or down-bay from the harbors, also were toxic in some tests, especially those with the highest sensitivity. The spatial extent and patterns in toxicity are specific to each bay and dependent upon the sensitivity of each test.

About 90% of the samples from the NOAA regional surveys in which 1 or more chemicals equaled or exceeded an ERM value of 25 were significantly toxic in at least 1 of 2 to 4 laboratory tests that were performed. Approximately 50% of the samples were toxic in the less sensitive amphipod survival tests. These data suggest that the guidelines may be highly predictive of toxicity to relatively sensitive taxa and early life stages. A majority of the concordance between predicted and actual toxicity was observed in the highly sensitive tests of pore waters.

The results of the toxicity tests were highly correlated with ammonia concentrations in Tampa Bay, but not in Newark Bay or San Pedro Bay. Except in Tampa Bay, none of the samples equaled or exceeded the respective LC50 or EC50 concentration for ammonia. Also, very few samples equaled or exceeded the estimated no-observed-effect concentrations. In the tests of pore waters from Tampa Bay sediments, 14 of 165 porewater samples exceeded the EC50 concentration and all 14 samples were highly toxic to sea urchin gametes. In these surveys of surficial saltwater sediments, ammonia did not appear to contribute substantially to toxicity in most laboratory tests. However, the contribution of ammonia to toxicity in tests of deeper sediment strata or in freshwater sediments may be much greater.

In recent years amphipods have been used more frequently in sediment quality assessments largely because of their relative sensitivity to sediment-sorbed toxicants. Data from the Hudson-Raritan estuary suggest that they were more sensitive than adult taxa commonly used in predredging studies. However, in other survey areas they were either roughly equivalent in sensitivity or the least sensitive in batteries of different tests. Tests of pore waters performed with invertebrate gametes or embryos were most sensitive in these surveys. Comprehensive assessments should include a battery of complementary toxicity tests with a range in sensitivities and response endpoints.

Acknowledgment - Funding for the regional surveys was provided by NOAA's Coastal Ocean Program. Advice, review, and assistance in preparation of this manuscript were provided by Douglas Wolfe, Andrew Robertson, Michael Salazar, and Jo Linse (NOAA/Office of Ocean Resources Conservation and Assessment). USEPA Region 2, Battelle Ocean Sciences, and Science Applications International Corporation performed sample collecting, chemical analyses, and toxicity tests in the Hudson-Raritan estuary, including Newark Bay. Science Applications International Corporation, the Florida Department of Environmental Protection, the National Biological Service (NBS), and the Skidaway Institute of Oceanography performed sample collecting, toxicity tests, and chemical analyses in Tampa Bay. The Florida Department of Environmental Protection and NBS performed sample collecting and toxicity tests in Pensacola Bay. The California State Water Resources Control Board provided matching funds, and California Department of Fish and Game and the University of California-Santa Cruz performed sample collecting, chemical analyses, and toxicity tests in San Pedro Bay.

References

Adams WJ, Kimerle RA, Barnett Jr JW. 1992. Sediment quality and aquatic life assessment. *Environ Sci Technol* 26(10):1863–1876.

Ankley GT, Katko A, Arthur JW. 1990. Identification of ammonia as an important sediment-associated toxicant in the Fox River and Green Bay, Wisconsin. *Environ Toxicol Chem* 9:313–322.

[ASTM] American Society for Testing Materials. 1990. Standard guide for conducting 10-day static sediment toxicity tests with marine and estuarine amphipods. Philadelphia PA: ASTM. 24 p. E 1367 - 90.

Carr RS, Chapman DC. 1992. Comparison of solid-phase and pore water approaches for assessing the quality of marine and estuarine sediments. *Chem Ecol* 7:19–30.

Carr RS, Long ER, Windom HL, Chapman DC, Thursby G, Sloane GM, Wolfe DA. 1996. Sediment quality assessment studies of Tampa Bay, Florida. *Environ Tox Chem* 15:1218–1231.

DeWitt TH, Ditsworth GR, Swartz RC. 1988. Effects of natural sediment features on survival of the phoxocephalid amphipod *Rhepoxynius abronius*. *Mar Environ Res* 25:99–124.

Eisler R, Hennekey RJ. 1977. Acute toxicities of Cd^{2+}, Cr^{+6}, Hg^{2+}, Ni^{2+}, and Zn^{2+} to estuarine macrofauna. *Arch Environ Contam Toxicol* 6(2/3):315–323.

Giesy JP, Hoke RA. 1990. Freshwater sediment quality criteria: Toxicity bioassessment. In: Baudo R, Giesy J, Muntau H, editors. Sediments: chemistry and toxicity of in-place pollutants. Boca Raton FL: Lewis. p 265–348.

Hill IR, Matthiessen P, Heimbach F. 1993. Guidance document on sediment toxicity tests and bioassays for freshwater and marine environments. From workshop on sediment toxicity assessment held at Slot Moermond Congrescentrum, Renesse, The Netherlands. Society of Environmental Toxicology and Chemistry - Europe. 105 p.

Jones RA, Lee GF. 1988. Toxicity of U.S. waterway sediments with particular reference to the New York Harbor area. In: Chemical and biological characterization of sludges, sediments, dredge spoils and drilling muds. Philadelphia PA: ASTM. p 403–417. ASTM STP 976.

Kohn NP, Word JQ, Niyogi DK, Ross LT, Dillon T, Moore DW. 1994. Acute toxicity of ammonia to four species of marine amphipod. *Mar Envir Res* 38:1–15.

Lauenstein GG, Cantillo AY. 1993. Sampling and analytical methods of the National Status and Trends Program, National Benthic Surveillance and Mussel Watch Projects. 1984–1992. Volume 1 Overview and summary of methods. NOAA Tech. Memo. NOS ORCA 71. Silver Spring MD: NOAA. 117 p.

Long ER. 1989. The use of the sediment quality triad in classification of sediment contamination. In: Contaminated marine sediments—assessment and remediation. Washington DC: National Academy. p 78–99.

Long ER, MacDonald DD. 1992. National status and trends program approach. Chapter 14. In: Sediment classification methods compendium. Washington DC: USEPA. EPA 823-R-92-006.

Long ER, MacDonald DD, Smith SL, Calder FD. 1995. Incidence of adverse biological effects within ranges of chemical concentrations in marine and estuarine sediments. *Environ Manag* 19(1):81–97.

Long ER, Markel R. 1992. An evaluation of the extent and magnitude of biological effects associated with chemical contaminants in San Francisco Bay, California. NOAA Tech. Memo. NOS ORCA 64. Seattle WA: NOAA. 86 p.

Long ER, Morgan LG. 1990. The potential for biological effects of sediment-sorbed contaminants tested in the National Status and Trends Program. NOAA Tech. Memo NOS OMA 52. Seattle WA: NOAA. 175 p.Long ER, Wolfe DA, Robertson A, Bricker SB. 1992. Sediment toxicity surveys as pollution assessment tools. MTS 1992 Proceedings 1:240–249. Washington DC: Marine Technology Society.

Long ER, Wolfe DA, Carr RS, Scott KJ, Windom HL, Lee R, Calder FD, Sloane GM, Seal T. 1994. Magnitude and extent of sediment toxicity in Tampa Bay, Florida. NOAA Tech. Memo. NOS ORCA 78. Silver Spring MD: NOAA.

Long ER, Wolfe DA, Scott KJ, Thursby GB, Stern EA, Peven C, Schwartz T. 1995. Magnitude and extent of sediment toxicity in the Hudson-Raritan estuary. NOAA Tech. Memo. NOS ORCA 88. Silver Spring MD: NOAA. 230 p.

MacDonald DD. 1993. Development of an approach to the assessment of sediment quality in Florida coastal waters. Prepared by MacDonald Environmental Sciences, Ltd., Ladysmith, British Columbia. Prepared for Florida Department of Environmental Regulation. Tallahassee, FL. Vol. 1. 128 p. Vol. 2. 117 p.

MacDonald DD, Smith SL, Wong MP, Mudroch P. 1992. The development of Canadian marine environmental quality guidelines. Ecosystem sciences and evaluation directorate, conservation and protection. Ottawa, Ontario: Environment Canada. 32 p.

McLeese DW, Ray S. 1986. Toxicity of $CdCl_2$, CdEDTA, $CuCl_2$, and CuEDTA to marine invertebrates. *Bull Envir Contam Toxicol* 36(5):749–755.

[NRC] National Research Council. 1989. Contaminated marine sediments—assessment and remediation. Washington DC: National Academy. 493 p.

O'Connor TP, Norton MG, Mearns AJ, Wolfe DA, Duedall IW. 1987. Scale of biological effects. In: O'Connor TP, Burt WV, Duedall IW, editors. Oceanic processes in marine pollution. Volume 2. Physicochemical processes and wastes in the ocean. Malabar FL: Robert E. Krieger Publishing Company. p 1–7.

Power EA. Chapman PM. 1992. Assessing sediment quality. In: Burton Jr GA, editor. Sediment toxicity assessment. Boca Raton FL: Lewis. p 1–18.

Redmond MS, Scott KJ, Swartz RC, Jones JKP. 1994. Preliminary culture and life-cycle experiments with the benthic amphipod Ampelisca abdita. *Environ Toxicol Chem* 13(8):1355–1365.

Sapudar RA, Wilson CJ, Reid ML, Long ER, Stephenson M, Puckett M, Fairey R, Hunt J, Anderson B, Holstad D, Newman J, Borosik S. 1994. Sediment chemistry and toxicity in the vicinity of the Los Angeles and Long Beach Harbors. Project Report. Prepared by California State Water Resources Control Board and National Oceanic and Atmospheric Administration. CSWRCB, Sacramento, CA. 77 p.

Spies RB. 1989. Sediment bioassays, chemical contaminants and benthic ecology: New insights or just muddy water? *Mar Environ Res* 27:73–75.

Swartz RC, DeBen WA, Cole FA. 1979. A bioassay for the toxicity of sediment to marine macrobenthos. *J Water Pollu Cont Fed* 51: 944–950.

Swartz RC, DeBen WA, Jones JKP, Lamberson JO, Cole FA. 1985. Phoxocephalid amphipod bioassay for marine sediment toxicity. In: Cardwell RD, Purdy R, Bahner RC, editors. Aquatic toxicology and hazard assessment: seventh symposium. Philadelphia PA: ASTM. p 284–307. ASTM STP 854.

Swartz RC, Schults DW, DeWitt TH, Ditsworth GR, Lamberson JO. 1990. Toxicity of fluoranthene in sediment to marine amphipods: A test of the equilibrium partitioning approach to sediment quality criteria. *Envir Toxicol Chem* 9:1071–1080.

Tessier AP, Campbell GC. 1987. Partitioning of trace metals in sediments: Relationships with bioavailability. In: Thomas R, Evans R, Hamilton A, Munawar M, Reynoldson T, Sadar H, editors. Ecological effects of in situ sediment contaminants. Dr. W. Junk. *Developments in Hydrobiology* 39. p 43–52.

[USEPA] U.S. Environmental Protection Agency. Region 10. 1991. Recommended guidelines for conducting laboratory bioassays on Puget Sound sediments. Seattle WA: USEPA, Puget Sound Estuary Program. 82 p.

[USEPA] U.S. Environmental Protection Agency. 1992. Sediment Classification Methods Compendium. Washington DC: USEPA. EPA 823-R-92-006.

[USEPA/USA] U.S. Environmental Protection Agency and U. S. Army. 1991. Evaluation of dredged material proposed for ocean disposal. Testing Manual. Washington DC: USEPA. EPA-503/8/91/001.

Wiemeyer SN, Hoffman DJ. 1986. Reproduction in eastern screech-owls fed Selenium. *J Wildl Manage* 60(2):332–341.

Wolfe DA, Long ER, Robertson A. 1993. The NS&T bioeffects surveys: design strategies and preliminary results. In: Magoon OT, Wilson WS, Converse H, Tobin LT, editors. Coastal zone 1993. Proceedings of the 8th Symposium on Coastal and Ocean Management. Volume 1. New York NY: American Society of Civil Engineers.

Chapter 7

Use of tributyltin by commercial sources and the U.S. Navy: fate-and-effects assessment and management of impacts on the marine environment

Aldis O. Valkirs, Brad Davidson, Lora Lee Kear, Roy L. Fransham,
Peter F. Seligman, and Joseph G. Grovhoug

Note: The contents of this chapter are presented in an attempt to link environmental tributyl-tin (TBT) concentrations and the consequences of legislative action to restrict TBT antifouling paint usage with biological effects on organisms. Environmental TBT measurements and toxicity studies are common in the literature, but studies addressing both are far fewer in number. While elements of this chapter may be useful in a structured risk assessment, this chapter was not intended to serve as a risk assessment. Its focus on fate and effects of TBT usage in antifouling paints, environmental concentrations, legislative actions, and toxicity to marine species is discussed in a broader sense.

Legislative action restricting the use of TBT antifouling paints has resulted in a thorough assessment of major input sources and a reduction of environmental TBT concentrations to levels below those considered adequate for the protection of most marine species in most regions monitored for several years. This chapter reviews this process and focuses on TBT monitoring activities in San Diego Bay, California and Pearl Harbor, Hawaii. The decrease in surface-water TBT concentrations has been approximately an order of magnitude in yacht harbors and nearby open water regions. Tissue TBT concentrations also have indicated decreasing levels following the trend observed in surface waters. Sediment concentrations have decreased in some areas, while no decreases over several years have been observed in others. In situ and laboratory bio-assay testing have indicated that the existing surface-water and tissue TBT concentrations measured are generally below levels found to have no effect on several sensitive marine species. Some large yacht harbors still exhibit surface-water TBT values near the lowest concentrations found to adversely affect some marine species.

The presence of naval vessels painted with TBT antifouling paints in a semi-enclosed berthing area in Pearl Harbor was well correlated with surface-water TBT concentrations. Decreasing surface-water TBT concentrations were measured during periods when ships painted with TBT were absent. In situ bioassay data from Pearl Harbor indicated that the highest TBT concentrations measured (14 to 21 ng/L) during the presence of several naval ships did not approach the no-effect level (40 ng/L) determined with fouling communities and several single species exposed to TBT under flow-through testing conditions.

Tributyltin is not highly persistent in the water column indicating a half-life on the order of 1 to 2 weeks. The persistence of TBT in marine sediments indicates a much longer residency. In some ambient marine sediments little or no decrease in sediment TBT concentrations was measured during a period of several years. It is likely that the continued, although decreased, input of TBT from legal use of TBT antifouling paints will result in continuous low nanogram per liter TBT water concentrations. Some release of TBT from sediments may also act as a relatively long-term input. Long-term monitoring of several regions has shown, however, that existing surface-water TBT concentrations should remain low and below water-quality criteria limits, or possibly decrease further with time.

The use of TBT in antifouling paints has resulted in worldwide environmental concern from the early 1980s to the present. Multinational legislation has been enacted to control the use of TBT and its presence in freshwater and marine environments. Numerous studies have been published documenting the environmental presence, toxicity, persistence, and fate of TBT. In this chapter we will discuss the results of some legislative actions and long-term monitoring of TBT in the marine environment. Degradation and distribution of TBT, as well as toxicity at environmental concentrations in both high-input sites and relatively clean sites will be considered. As the body of literature concerning the above topics has grown enormously in the 1980s and 1990s, this review of the literature will be limited to specific studies that permit a discussion of risk from the current level of TBT in the marine environment.

Tributyltin in the marine environment has received worldwide attention. Generally, legislation restricting the use of TBT in antifouling paints has closely followed legislation enacted in France in 1982. Antifouling paints containing TBT were banned on pleasure craft less than 25 m in length, except on aluminum hulled vessels. The release rates of TBT antifouling paints and percent content allowed vary somewhat with respect to restrictions on use. The overall aim of the restrictions on use has been to lessen the substantial input of TBT leaching from antifouling paints applied to pleasure craft. With the input from pleasure craft limited by restricted use of TBT antifouling paints, remaining inputs may largely be attributed to large commercial and military vessels. Huggett et al. (1992) cite data presented to the Virginia Department of Agriculture and Consumer Services in 1986 estimating TBT input from pleasure craft at 70%, while 28% and 2% was estimated from commercial and military sources, respectively. In addition to restricting use of TBT antifouling paints, several countries have set limits on environmental TBT concentrations. The marine TBT concentrations allowed typically range from 2 to 10 ng/L in seawater (USEPA 1988; Dowson et al. 1994; Ritsema 1994).

The U.S. Navy (USN) was actively investigating the fleetwide implementation of TBT antifouling paints in the mid 1980s. In 1985, the USN released a document entitled "Environmental Assessment (EA), Fleetwide Use of Organotin Antifouling Paint" (USN 1984). A monitored antifouling paint implementation plan was proposed using low-release-rate paints. The USN's risk-assessment plan from 1980 to 1989 included: 1) monitoring water, sediments, and tissues in a number of harbors and estuaries; 2) measuring the release of TBT from test-ship hulls, dry docks, and other sources; 3) conducting acute and chronic toxicity studies using measured concentrations, including microcosm studies to evaluate long-term exposure and species diversity; and 4) measuring TBT degradation, persistence, and partitioning and developing numerical models for predicting TBT concentrations (Huggett et al. 1992). In 1989, the USN decided not to use TBT antifouling paints. The results of several studies referred to above will be considered herein to determine the environmental risk posed by TBT in the marine environment prior to and after completion of long-term monitoring in San Diego Bay and Pearl Harbor, Hawaii.

Methods

Approach and sampling methods

Monitoring strategy

A great deal of data has been collected in the course of the USN's monitoring of TBT in marine waters. Accordingly, this section provides a detailed summary description of the monitoring program (previously reported in Valkirs et al. 1991) in San Diego Bay and Pearl Harbor. As part of the risk-assessment process, ambient TBT water concentration measurements were begun in 1982, and a formal monitoring program was initiated after the U.S. Congress passed the Organotin Antifouling Paint Control Act (OAPCA) in 1988, which required the USN to monitor harbors in which steel-hulled vessels painted with TBT coatings were home-ported.

The approach to designing a meaningful harbor monitoring program was guided by previous experience in measuring low parts-per-trillion butyltin levels during baseline studies (Grovhoug et al. 1987). Detection of changes in butyltin concentrations in water, sediment, and tissue samples over time within specific locations was a principal goal. Station selection and coverage was designed to provide sufficient sampling sites to typify various regions within each harbor. Quarterly water-column sampling was initiated to possibly detect seasonal changes in butyltin concentrations. Because of their integrative nature, and at times limited availability, tissue samples were collected from selected stations on a semiannual basis. Likewise, sediments were collected semiannually from the same locations as water samples. In San Diego Bay, an abundance of mussels permitted quarterly collection of tissue samples. Sediments were collected quarterly in San Diego Bay as well. Due to the absence of naval vessels painted with TBT antifouling paint in San Diego Bay, quarterly water, sediment, and tissue sampling were discontinued after April 1991. We have added some surface-water data collected in April 1992 and in July 1994 in order to test our previous predictions of trends in decreasing TBT concentrations. Additional sediment and tissue samples were collected in April 1992 as well. Data collected were evaluated to discern any changes in TBT concentrations and to determine if legislative restrictions on TBT paint use had resulted in lower environmental concentrations. In Pearl Harbor, data analysis focused on determining if TBT loading from naval vessels was directly correlated with harbor TBT concentrations in the main harbor regions.

Originally, individual stations within San Diego Bay and Pearl Harbor were compared to characterize TBT concentrations in each harbor and event-specific effects (Grovhoug et al. 1987). The data from these stations were subsequently grouped into several harbor regions for analysis. The regional mean TBT concentrations were then examined rather than emphasizing a single station where the TBT concentration may vary widely due to water movement. Large TBT concentration variability has been reported previously (Huggett et al. 1986; Clavell et al. 1986; Stang et al. 1989), particularly at entrances to yacht harbors or berthing areas.

Each harbor was divided into study regions that were defined by 1 or more of the following factors: physiographic features, dredged-channel limits, water motion characteristics, and vessel use pattern. Four regions were defined in San Diego Bay (Figure 7-1) primarily based on current velocity patterns and use characteristics (Seligman, Grovhoug, and Richter 1986; Seligman et al. 1989). Each region contained at least 3 key stations which provided a minimum of 3 surface samples during each sampling period. The northern region (I) is characterized by high current velocities and rapid flushing rates and includes most of the shipping channels and dredged areas of the bay. The southern region (II) is largely shallow with low-velocity currents and longer water residence times. The south bay area is also important as a nursery ground for numerous fish and invertebrate species. U.S. Navy-use areas (III), including several USN berthing areas, are moderately well-flushed. Marinas and commercial boat basins (IV) are generally characterized by moderate to dense aggregations of vessels in enclosed embayments with reduced flushing characteristics (Seligman et al. 1989). A total of 816 surface-water samples were analyzed for TBT from the 4 regions studied.

Pearl Harbor was subdivided into 8 regions (Figure 7-2) by geographic and use-pattern factors: Main Channels (a composite region comprising the Entrance Channel, South Channel and North Channel regions), Southeast Loch, Rainbow Marina (a small pleasure boat facility with a capacity of about 70 vessels located in the Aiea Bay area in the northeastern corner of Pearl Harbor), East Loch, Middle Loch, West Loch, Dry Dock #2, and Dry Dock #4.

Significant interactions were found in San Diego Bay between station location and depth and between station location and tide (Seligman et al. 1986). Combining stations into regions and sampling at specific tidal stages and water depths enabled direct hypothesis testing using a simplified 1-way analysis of variance (ANOVA). The stations within a region were considered as replicates and all individual samples collected at a particular station and time were pooled. Although resulting in reduced degrees of freedom, this strategy was necessary because between-station variability in a region often proved greater than within-station variability. All references to significance levels reported were at the $P = 0.05$ level.

Prior to analysis, data were examined for conformance to the ANOVA assumption of homogeneity of variance by use of the Levene's test. The data showed significant

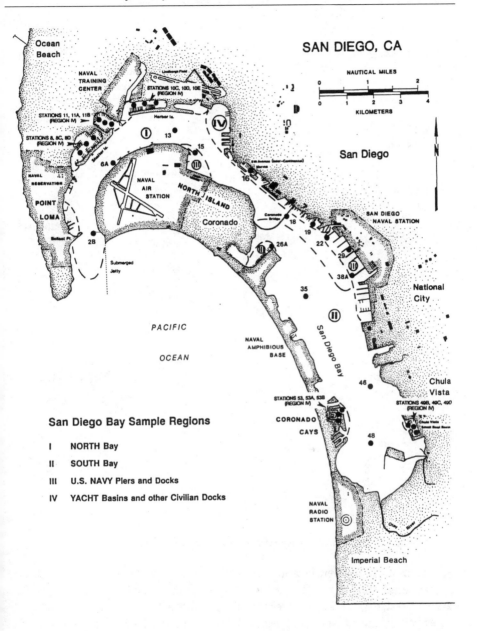

Figure 7-1   *San Diego Bay sample stations and regions (Valkirs et al. 1991)*

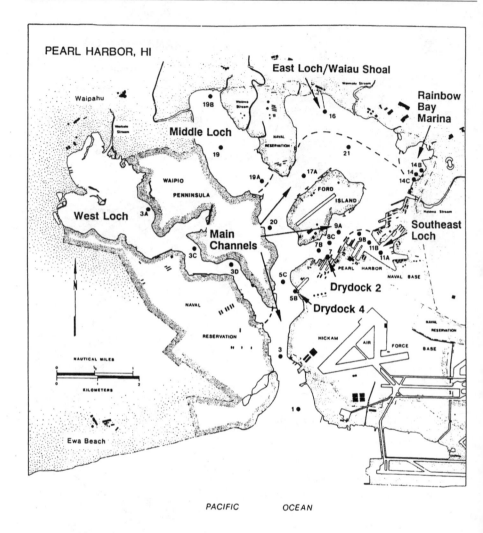

Figure 7-2   Pearl Harbor sample stations and regions (Grovhoug et al. 1989)

heteroscedasticity and were logarithmically transformed (Log + 0.5) and rechecked prior to hypothesis testing by the use of 2 1-way ANOVA models. San Diego and Pearl Harbor data were tested for between-survey period variability within harbor regions. Multiple range testing (Student-Newman Kuels test) determined which survey periods or regions had statistically comparable ($P = 0.05$) means. Values presented in figures are untransformed means that reflect the actual TBT concentrations.

The regional approach used for water-TBT-concentration data analysis was not considered entirely practical for the analysis of sediment-TBT-concentration data. While water bodies may be typified by circulation and use patterns, marine sediments may be less homogenous due to origins and activities such as dredging. Kram et al. (1989a) identified differences in sediment grain size, clay mineralogy, and percent organic carbon in sediments from San Diego Bay, Pearl Harbor, Honolulu Harbor, and Norfolk, Virginia. These factors were shown to influence highly the degree of TBT adsorption by sediments (Kram et al. 1989a). A study in Puget Sound, Washington has documented significantly heterogenous sediment-TBT distributions from site to site as well as within a single site (Krone et al. 1989). Differences in sediment TBT concentrations were, therefore, examined on a station-by-station basis using a 1-way ANOVA where statistical comparisons were made over time. The data were not transformed because sample sizes were constant within and between sampling intervals. Sediment values reported in this study are not corrected for percent organic carbon or grain size. Tissue TBT data were also examined on a station-specific basis since local differences in water movement and distance from point sources could significantly affect TBT concentrations.

Field procedures

All seawater samples collected during the monitoring surveys were obtained at 0.5 m below the surface. Caution was exercised to avoid contamination of the water samples from the surface microlayer, which can exhibit high concentrations of butyltins (Maguire and Tkacz 1987). In Hawaii, water samples were not collected at predetermined tidal conditions, since tidal effects have been shown to be insignificant (Grovhoug et al. 1989). However, in San Diego Bay water samples were collected during low slack tide because tidal effects have been shown to influence butyltin measurements in that embayment (Seligman, Grovhoug, and Richter 1986). Samples were collected in 1-L polycarbonate bottles and placed in ice within insulated storage chests until moved (within 8 h) into a laboratory freezer for storage until analyzed.

Initially, sediment samples were obtained with a stainless steel Van Veen grab sampler that collected approximately 3 to 4 L of sediment. About 150 ml of sediment from the uppermost 2 cm layer of each grab was carefully removed and placed into 250 ml high-density polyethylene bottles. One to three (typically 3) samples were obtained at each station sampled, and the samples were then treated in the same manner as the water samples until analysis. Since early 1989, sediment samples were collected with a smaller, spherical steel grab sampler.

Tissue samples were collected from local, naturally occurring bivalve populations rather than from transplanted specimens. This approach was taken, with its limitations in availability, because we believe that TBT tissue burdens in natural populations provide the most accurate environmental TBT data reflecting increases or decreases in water TBT values. In San Diego Bay, tissue samples were taken from an indigenous mussel species, *Mytilus edulis*. All mussels were collected from approximately the same tidal level, near mean lower low water. Lengths of the individual mussels were recorded prior to removing the soft tissue. Mussel specimens collected in San Diego Bay were frozen whole and were dissected prior to analysis. Individuals were pooled within replicate samples to provide adequate tissues for analysis.

Laboratory procedures

Water samples were collected in polycarbonate plastic 1-L bottles, which have previously been shown to be nonadsorptive to butyltins and have been recommended as a suitable container for water samples containing butyltins in a NOAA report addressing aquatic butyltin sampling and analysis (Dooley and Homer 1983; Valkirs et al. 1986; Young et al. 1986; Carter et al. 1989). Frozen storage of environmental water samples in polycarbonate bottles for 4.3 months in our laboratory has shown no more than a 15% loss of the initial TBT concentration (Valkirs et al. 1990). This loss is consistent with the relative standard deviations of methods employing hydride derivatization for analysis of TBT in seawater (Valkirs, Seligman et al. 1987).

When water samples were collected prior to 1987, detection limits were approximately 5 ng/L. Recent improvements in the quartz furnace design and silanization of the cryotrap used to collect butyltin hydrides have resulted in detection limits as low as 0.2 ng/L for the hydride derivatization atomic absorption (HDAA) method used in this study. The data reported in this study have therefore been qualified on the basis of similar detection limits. Data reported prior to 1987 were reviewed and presented if detection limitations were not approached. Values below detection limits where no signal was apparent were estimated by a distributional approach similar to that recently reported by Helsel (1990). Relatively few values below detection limits were estimated. In San Diego Bay only 1% of the surface-water TBT measurements used in this analysis report were estimated. In Pearl Harbor 14% of the surface-water values used were estimated from regions other than Southeast Loch where all measurements were above levels requiring estimation.

Several TBT measurements recorded were at or below 1 ng/L. These data were used in subsequent statistical analysis procedures since censoring the dataset at very low concentrations would have removed available data. Others have commented that data should be used for analysis procedures even if values are below detection limits (Porter et al. 1988). We calculated our TBT limit of detection (LOD) and limit of quantification (LOQ) using procedures reported by the American Chemical Society (ACS) Committee on Environmental Improvement (ACS 1980; ACS 1983). Typically, LOD levels in our laboratory have ranged from 0.2 to 0.7 ng/L as tributyltin chloride, while LOQ levels have varied from 0.6 to 2.4 ng/L (Valkirs et al. 1991). The standard deviation of replicate analysis was approximately 20% of the mean in each session, which was consistent with replicate measurements at higher TBT concentrations.

Analysis of tissue and sediment sample extracts was performed by Grignard derivatization with hexylmagnesium bromide. Butyltin derivatives were separated and detected by gas chromatography and flame photometric detection. Samples were quantified by comparison of analyte signal with the internal standard (tripentylhexyltin) response factors. Detection limits were in the range of 10 to 20 ng/g wet weight. Complete details of the analytical system and procedure used for water, tissue, and sediment analysis are reported in Stallard et al. (1989). All seawater, tissue, and sediment values reported in this study were as the respective butyltin chloride species. Measurements reported in this study were not corrected for recovery. In 66 of 76 samples collected from Pearl Harbor, San Diego Bay, and Chesapeake Bay, percent recovery of TBT added to samples (1 to 6 ng) exceeded 75%.

Whole unfiltered seawater was measured directly by hydride derivatization followed by purging and trapping the evolved hydrides. Tin hydrides were then volatilized and detected by hydrogen flame atomic absorption spectroscopy in a quartz burner. Studies by Valkirs et al. (1986), Valkirs, Stallard et al. (1987), and Johnson et al. (1987) have shown that unfiltered seawater samples with low particulate concentrations generally have very little TBT associated with the particulate fraction (< 5%). Thus, measurement of TBT in the dissolved phase and that available to hydride derivatization on particulates essentially accounted for very nearly all TBT present in an unfiltered seawater sample.

In a recent analytical intercomparison, TBT in ambient seawater samples was analyzed by several different methods by several laboratories, including the Naval Research and Development Center (Readman and Mee 1991). Results from 7 laboratories were in good agreement for a spiked water sample giving a mean TBT concentration of 178 ± 26 ng/L. Results from a yacht marina sample showed a greater variation with a mean concentration of 366 ± 93 ng/L. Atomic absorption and gas chromatographic-flame photometric methods produced results of similar accuracy and precision in this study. When our results were compared to those of other laboratories, agreement was seen with laboratories using extraction-derivatization-gas chromatographic-flame photometric detection (GC-FPD) methods. The results of the analysis of an ambient offshore seawater sample were similar to those seen in an earlier methods intercomparison we conducted with the National Bureau of Standards (Valkirs, Seligman et al. 1987). A mean value of 8.7 ± 7 ng/L was reported by 5 laboratories (Readman and Mee 1991). Our value of 5.5 ng/L compares well with this mean and suggests that our data concerning low TBT concentrations in ambient seawater samples are likely comparable with measurements made by other methods.

An additional intercomparison was conducted (unpublished data) with Battelle Ocean Sciences (Duxbury, Massachusetts), using a surface-water sample from Shelter Island yacht harbor in San Diego Bay. A surface-water sample was collected in a single polycarbonate bottle and divided into 2 sets of 7 replicate 1-L samples. Each set of samples was frozen and later analyzed by a single method at each laboratory. In our laboratory, the samples were analyzed by the HDAA method described above. The Battelle Laboratory used a hexyl-magnesium bromide derivatization method followed by gas chromatography separation and GC-FPD. The results compared well and were not significantly different giving a t-test P value of 0.10. The mean TBT concentration determined by our laboratory was 71 ng/L with a standard deviation of 15 and a coefficient of variation of 21%. The mean TBT concentration measured by the Battelle Laboratory was 54 ng/L with a standard deviation of 19 and a coefficient of variation of 35%. Although only a single sample was comparatively analyzed, the replicated analysis gave further indication that the HDAA and Grignard derivatization GC-FPD methods gave comparable TBT values.

Tributyltin degradation

In addition to monitoring TBT in marine waters, we have also studied degradation rates in several harbors, as well as in marine sediments (Seligman, Valkirs et al. 1986; Seligman et al. 1988, 1989; Lee et al. 1989). The degradation studies of TBT in seawater generally have been performed in situ using 0.5 to 8.0-dm^{-3} polycarbonate plastic or Pyrex glass bottles. Ambient unfiltered seawater was spiked with either un-radiolabeled tributyltin chloride (TBTCL), or with radiolabeled bis(tri-n-butyltin) oxide. Bottles were incubated at the test sites for several days in light and dark conditions under natural temperature conditions. The bottles were incubated at a depth just below the surface. Sediment degradation experiments were also conducted under incubated conditions either in aquaria or in the laboratory (Stang and Seligman 1986; Stang et al. 1992).

Toxicity studies

Five toxicity studies relevant to San Diego Bay and Pearl Harbor and performed by naval researchers during the mid to late 1980s and early 1990s are discussed here. Experimental details are reported in the cited references. Two of these studies were conducted in San Diego Bay, either using caged mussels in situ to determine the effect of water and tissue TBT concentrations on growth (Salazar and Salazar 1991), or using large portable microcosms in situ (Salazar et al. 1987). Both studies gathered information over several months under environmental or near environmental conditions. The mussel growth study (Salazar and Salazar 1991) focused on the effects of environmental TBT exposure in situ, while also considering other environmental factors such as temperature and chlorophyll variations. Both tissue and seawater TBT concentrations were measured and linked with growth effects providing valuable information for exposure assessments. A range of TBT tissue and water concentrations was identified where probable detrimental effects would occur. No-effect levels were also determined. The microcosm study assessed TBT effects on several species in an attempt to approximate natural conditions. Although several experimental factors complicated interpretation of the results, some useful long-term exposure data on growth rates were collected at TBT concentrations approaching the level measured in yacht basins at that time.

The third study involved a laboratory life-cycle exposure test with the near-shore mysid shrimp *Acanthomysis sculpta* (Davidson et al. 1986). Mysids are considered appropriate species for long-term toxicity testing and have proven to be sensitive and reliable test species in dredge bioassays (Salazar and Salazar 1985). No-observed-effect limits for long-term mortality, growth, and reproductive processes were determined in this study with carefully controlled and measured TBT concentrations. This study provided valuable information, which was generally lacking at the time, for toxicity evaluations conducted by the U.S. Environmental Protection Agency (USEPA).

The fourth study was also conducted in the laboratory with *Mytilus edulis* larvae for a period of 25 d (Lapota et al. 1993). These experiments provided valuable information on the effects of dibutyltin (DBT) and TBT on mussel larvae growth and mortality. This study is important in part because TBT effects were reported at very low exposure levels, thus permitting evaluation of environmental risk where very little data are available.

The fifth study was performed in situ in Pearl Harbor, Hawaii from a dock-side facility built on Ford Island (Henderson 1985). Fouling communities and native species, as well as *Crassostrea virginica*, were tested under flow-through conditions with ambient seawater containing 5 measured TBT treatment levels ranging from 0.04 to 2.5 μg/L. This study is cited because of its site-specific relevance. Results from this study will be compared to monitoring data from Pearl Harbor to evaluate risk from existing TBT concentrations.

Results and discussion

Case studies—monitoring results

San Diego Bay

Tributyltin monitoring studies conducted in 1986 indicated that TBT concentrations were increasing with time in yacht harbors and other regions (Valkirs et al. 1991). This was likely due to the growing use of TBT antifouling paints in the private sector, since only 2 naval ships painted with TBT paint were stationed in San Diego Bay, and the input from large commercial vessels has likely been relatively constant. San Diego Bay is not a highly active commercial port, and commercial use of TBT antifouling paints was already established. Quarterly monitoring of 4 regions in San Diego Bay was initiated in October 1988. Less frequent monitoring was conducted from 1986 to 1988. The results of these monitoring surveys are presented in Figures 7-3 and 7-4. Clearly, surface-water TBT concentrations have decreased considerably in the most recent monitoring data following restrictions on use of TBT antifouling paint enacted in California in January 1988. The February 1988 monitoring data are effectively pre-legislative from a temporal perspective. Significant (ANOVA) decreases were determined in the yacht, naval, and south bay regions since February 1988 (Valkirs et al. 1991). Analysis of the surface-water monitoring data presented in Figures 7-3 and 7-4 indicates that the monitoring data tend to be represented by high, intermediate, and lower values. Highest values are characteristic of pre-legislative monitoring data; however, multiple-range-test analysis following ANOVA testing indicated that statistically significant distinctions between high, intermediate, and lowest values were seldom present. Intermediate value multiple-range-test groupings tended to overlap with both higher and lower groups. In the north bay region, signifi-

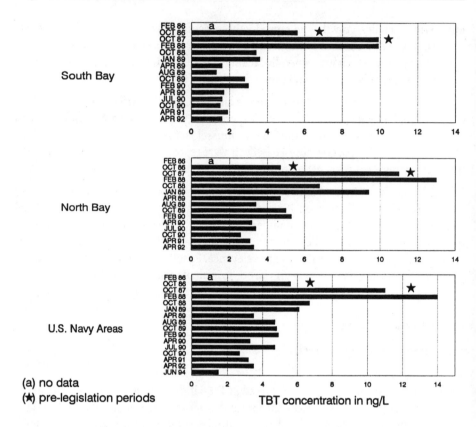

(a) no data
(★) pre-legislation periods

TBT concentration in ng/L

Figure 7-3   San Diego Bay surface-water TBT from the North (N = 74), South (N = 138), and Naval (N = 185) regions in ng/L

cantly lower TBT surface-water concentrations were measured in samples collected during the August 1989 and April 1990 to April 1992 monitoring periods compared to TBT values from the pre-legislative October 1987 and February 1988 periods (Figure 7-3). South bay monitoring data indicated that mean TBT concentrations were significantly lower in samples collected during the August 1989 and October 1990 monitoring periods than those collected in February 1988. The south bay data provide a good example of widely overlapping multiple-range-test groups focused within a relatively narrow concentration range. In the navy region, mean TBT surface-water values were significantly lower during the October 1990 to June 1994 monitoring periods compared to the pre-legislative monitoring periods in October 1987 and February 1988. Significantly lower values were also measured in the April 1989, February 1990 and April 1990 monitoring periods. Analysis of the yacht harbor monitoring data indicates the same trend seen in the other 3 regions studied where some of the most recent monitoring periods exhibited significantly lower mean TBT values than those seen in some of the pre-legislative monitoring

periods (Figures 7-3 and 7-4). In
the yacht harbor region, significantly lower mean surface-water
TBT values were recorded during the April 1992 and June
1994 monitoring periods than
during the February 1986 and
1988 periods.

Quarterly monitoring ceased in
San Diego Bay after July 1990
when naval vessels painted with
TBT paint were no longer stationed there. Some additional
data were collected and are presented in order to support
trends previously reported
(Valkirs et al. 1991). These data
showed that TBT surface-water
concentrations have decreased

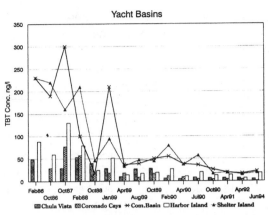

Figure 7-4   *San Diego Bay surface-water TBT from the 5 yacht harbors sampled in ug/L (N = 319). Commercial Basin and Shelter Island Yacht harbor values are represented graphically as connected lines to enhance clarity. These 2 yacht harbors have typically had the highest TBT concentration measured among yacht harbors in San Diego Bay*

exponentially to levels currently under 4 ng/L in all regions of the bay, with the exception
of most of the yacht harbors (Figures 7-4 and 7-5). Individual TBT surface-water data
from 5 yacht harbors (previously averaged together) have been provided to demonstrate

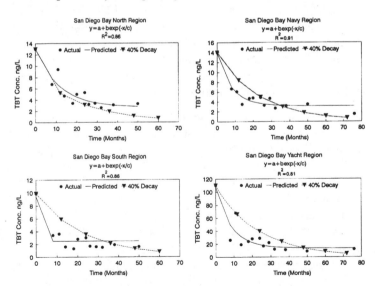

Figure 7-5   *Exponential decreases in San Diego Bay surface-water TBT from the North, South, Navy, and Yacht regions. A theoretical 40% decrease is presented along with predicted trends from measured values.*

the pattern of decreasing concentrations common to all 5 yacht harbors (Figure 7-4). We feel the observed decreases are due to restricted input of TBT from antifouling paints, and that this lessened input is largely from the high numbers of pleasure craft, which numbered 7600 in April 1993 (San Diego Harbor Police). In conversations with yacht repair facilities, the individuals contacted were well informed about TBT restrictions on use. Since most yacht repair facilities in San Diego Bay are found in the Commercial Basin and are under strict monitoring by the Regional Water Quality Control Board, it is unlikely that significant illegal application of TBT antifouling paints is occurring.

Other studies in the U.S. and abroad have reported decreasing trends in TBT water concentrations after legislative restrictions on use, while some have not found evidence of decreasing concentrations. Huggett et al. (1992) reported large decreases in surface-water TBT concentrations from yacht harbors in Chesapeake Bay and San Diego Bay over a period of several years. Hall et al. (1992) have compared TBT surface-water concentrations in marinas and river systems of Chesapeake Bay to evaluate potential effects of restricted use enacted by the State of Maryland in 1987. No significant reductions in TBT concentrations were found between 1986 and 1989. Some individual stations followed over time did show significant reductions, however. The authors commented that their experimental design would not likely detect small gradual decreasing TBT concentrations due to limited sampling frequency. Monitoring programs conducted in England have shown reductions in both freshwater and seawater TBT concentrations as well as in microlayer samples after use restrictions (Adelman et al. 1990; Cleary 1991; Dowson et al. 1993). In some freshwater marinas, TBT was not detectable or was an order of magnitude less than previously reported (Dowson et al. 1994). Ten- and 20-fold decreases have been reported in subsurface and microlayer samples, respectively (Cleary 1991). No clear decreasing trends in seawater TBT concentrations were seen in 6 Dutch marinas after a ban on TBT use on craft smaller than 25 m in 1990 (Ritsema 1994). It was felt that sediment desorption of TBT was a major factor and continuing input source. Illegal usage was also cited as a potential continuing input.

Figure 7-5 presents decreasing TBT concentrations along with a theoretical 40% exponential decrease. An estimated 4 of 10 pleasure vessels might be removed from their moorings on a yearly basis for antifouling paint renewal. Thus, it appears that the actual decreasing TBT concentrations measured approximate the calculated 40% yearly decrease. The high rate of initial decline in TBT concentration also may be explained by the fact that fewer vessels were being painted with TBT paints. Thus, the higher initial release rates characteristic of newly applied TBT paints were less an input source than during pre-restrictive periods. Hall et al. (1992) have reported a decrease in TBT antifouling paint usage from 31% to 6% in 1 year from a boat-owner survey conducted in the Chesapeake Bay. Previously we estimated linear loss of TBT based on monitoring data collected from October 1987 to July 1990 (Valkirs et al. 1991). Recent data indicate that TBT concentrations in San Diego Bay will persist at low ng/L levels for several years in all regions of the bay. It appears that a steady-state condition has been approached wherein large vessels allowed to use TBT antifouling paint, large transient commercial vessels, and possible release from underlying marine sediments will continue to provide an input, although much reduced from previous inputs. With the exception of the large yacht harbors, the USEPA TBT water-quality-criteria concentration of 10 ng/L has been achieved in San Diego Bay based on regional mean values. The California State TBT water-quality criteria of 6 ng/L also has been achieved in most of the bay regions. As stated above, it may be several years before all open areas of San Diego Bay exhibit TBT concentrations still lower than those currently measured, and possibly longer in the yacht harbors where current levels will likely persist. Present environmental surface-water TBT concentrations will be compared with toxicological data later in this chapter.

Sediment TBT concentrations in San Diego Bay have not clearly reflected the same magnitude of decreases observed in water column values in many areas since legislative restrictions on use were enacted in January 1988 and were variable among stations over time (Table 7-1). It is likely that these sediments would tend to adsorb TBT strongly and release TBT slowly to overlying water since the silt + clay percentages (36.7 to 92.4%) and the percentages of expandable minerals (32 to 41%) in the clay fraction are relatively high (Kram et al. 1989a). A strong linear increase in sediment TBT adsorption capacity with increasing percent clay and percent clay + silt has been demonstrated with San Diego Bay sediments (Kram et al. 1989a). Sediments from the yacht harbors selected for monitoring were shown to possess low to intermediate ability to desorb TBT in relation to their percent clay silt fractions and expandable clay mineral index in most cases (Kram et al. 1989a). Sediment from stations located in South San Diego Bay have similar physical characteristics to the sediment at yacht harbor stations and were shown to have a high affinity for TBT adsorption (Kram et al. 1989a). Under these circumstances no rapid loss of TBT over time would be expected, particularly with some continued input from the water column.

No significant decreases have been noted in the yacht harbor stations in data collected from February 1988 to July 1990 (Valkirs et al. 1991). Later data reported in Table 7-1 indicated that sediment TBT concentrations have not significantly decreased in the Shelter Island (Station 08), Chula Vista (Station 49), or Coronado Cays (Station 53) yacht harbors since July 1990. A significant decrease in sediment TBT was seen in the Harbor Island yacht harbor (Station 10) where the level measured in April 1992 was significantly lower than earlier values measured in samples collected during February 1988 and January 1989. Sediment-TBT concentrations in samples collected from other sampling periods were not significantly different. Although recent sediment TBT values have continued to indicate decreasing levels in the Commercial Basin (Station 11), significant differences among sampling periods have not been determined. At stations 13 and 18, the sediment TBT concentrations measured in samples collected during the October 1990 monitoring period were significantly lower than the levels measured during the February 1988 monitoring period. These TBT levels were, however, statistically similar to values measured in samples collected during preceding and later monitoring periods;

Table 7-1 San Diego Bay mean TBT sediment concentrations are indicated. Units are ng/g dry weight (concentrations are mean values where N = 2 to 6).

							Survey				
		Feb '88	Oct '88	Jan '89	Apr '89	Aug '89	Oct '89	Feb '90	Apr '90	Jul '90	Oct '90
Station	Region	TBTCL	TBTCL	TBTCL	TBTCL	TBTCL	TBTCL	TBTCL	TBTCL	TBTCL	TBTCL
02	North	1.7	12	70	33	34	14	28	19	6.7	0.0
06	North	37	16	17	37	21	25	50	34	15	16
08	Yacht	96	97	120	90	74	91	110	83	62	72
10	Yacht	160	56	160	84	80	86	93	68	75	44
11	Yacht	690	1100	530	430	220	400	370	300	340	300
13	North	75	43	39	51	29	45	46	44	36	20
18	North	78	53	64	68	28	52	43	47	38	18
22	Navy	56	240	280	160	130	150	180	120	180	120
35	South		0.0	19	25	26	24	34	18	14	9.7
38	Navy	180	37	40	56	43	51	63	45	42	38
46	South		6.7	8.7	24	22	8.7	36	18	20	13
48	South		0.0	7.7	16	20	10	30	14	14	7.3
49	Yacht		29	29	30	25	22	46	35	21	17
53	Yacht		15	19	45	31	28	38	30	21	22

therefore, no indication of a significant continued trend toward decreasing sediment TBT values is apparent as yet. No trends toward significant decreases in sediment TBT concentrations were noted in the other stations sampled. This mixture of apparent decreasing concentrations and no apparent decreases is also supported in recent studies. In a long-term mesocosm study, Adelman et al. (1990) reported that no measurable sediment TBT degradation was apparent. Stang et al. (1992) found initial rapid (several days) abiotic degradation of TBT in fine-grained natural sediments followed by much slower degradation with time. A recent study (Wuertz et al. 1991) reported significant decreases (78 to 99%) in sediment TBT concentrations from Boston harbor over a 2-y period (1988–1990). Dowson et al. (1994) have reported 90% and greater decreases in sediments from river systems over a 3-y period. Dowson et al. (1993) reported generally decreasing sediment TBT concentrations since 1990 from 6 estuarine river systems in the UK. Sarradin et al. (1991) noted that the degradation of TBT in Arcachon Bay is much slower than that in overlying waters. Site variability within and between sites (Krone et al. 1989) and such factors as organic content of sediments complicate sediment TBT measurements and predictive ability. Indeed, regarding sediment organic content, some studies have shown no correlation (Dowson et al. 1992) with organic content, while others (Yonezawa et al. 1993) have shown correlation with organic content and no correlation with particle size.

Concerning present sediment-TBT concentrations in San Diego Bay, some comment is warranted regarding the potential for toxicity. Salazar and Salazar (1985) conducted standard dredged material bioassays with sediment collected from the Commercial Basin in San Diego Bay. The sediment TBT concentration tested was 780 µg/kg. The initial concentration of TBT in the particulate-phase test water was 490 ng/L. In the solid-phase test water the TBT concentration was 200 ng/L. A mysid shrimp (*Acanthomysis sculpta*), a flatfish (*Citharichthys stigmaeus*), and a copepod (*Acartia tonsa*) were tested in the particulate phase. Solid-phase tests were done with *A. sculpta*, *Macoma nasuta* (clam), and *Neanthes arenaceodentata* (polychaete worm). No statistically significant differences between controls and treatments were found. Control sediment was collected from a site removed from shore facilities off the shore line of North Island (Salazar and Salazar 1985). The Commercial Basin sediment tested would have qualified for ocean disposal under guidelines then administered by the USEPA and the Army Corps of Engineers. Sediments may vary greatly in organic content, grain size and clay mineralogy. Clearly these factors may play a significant role in bioavailability of TBT in sediments. It is of importance to note, however, that sediment TBT concentrations have decreased considerably (if not statistically) in the Commercial Basin as well as in other areas of San Diego Bay (Table 7-1). This is likely a positive development concerning the Bay's environmental status.

Tributyltin concentrations in the tissues of *Mytilus edulis* have generally been declining in San Diego Bay since February 1988 (Table 7-2). Total butyltin measurements from *M. edulis* collected in San Diego Bay (Harbor Island) as part of the NOAA National Status

Table 7-2 San Diego Bay mean tissue concentrations are indicated. Units are ng/g wet weight (concentrations are mean values where N = 3 to 6).

Region	Oct '86 TBTCL	Oct '87 TBTCL	Feb '88 TBTCL	Oct '88 TBTCL	Jan '89 TBTCL	Apr '89 TBTCL	Aug '89 TBTCL	Oct '89 TBTCL	Feb '90 TBTCL	Apr '90 TBTCL	Jul '90 TBTCL
North	100	120	140	53	32	57	53	55	300	65	33
North	110	230	220	150	110	110	110	73	260	94	62
Yacht	690	1600	960	1200	890			350	470	460	350
Yacht	670			420	260	290	210	260	290	240	180
Navy	220	220	490	170	240	210	110	180	180	120	120
Yacht					840	820	380	320	250	400	430
North	360	330	380	140	320	220	180	140	200	120	130
Navy		360		200	390	170	1700	250	190	140	180
South	200	190	240	100	160	110	59		140	60	36
South		200	390		95	51	59	38	110	44	30

and Trends Mussel Watch Project indicate that butyltin tissue levels have decreased approximately 50% from 1987 to 1990 (Uhler et al. 1993). Our data from Station 10 near the mouth of Harbor Island showed that tissue TBT concentrations decreased from 670 ng g^{-1} in October 1986 to 290 ng g^{-1} in February 1990 (Table 7-2) in agreement with the mussel watch trend reported. Tissue TBT concentrations continued to decrease at Station 10. Tissue TBT values in samples collected during the last 3 monitoring periods were significantly lower than those measured in previous monitoring periods. This trend toward decreasing tissue TBT levels seems to have occurred at several other stations as well (Table 7-2). At Station 15, tissue TBT values were significantly lower in samples collected during the April 1990 to April 1992 monitoring periods than in samples collected earlier in October 1986 to February 1988 and in January 1989 to April 1989. Samples from Stations 16, 18, and 22 exhibited significantly lower values than those recorded in earlier monitoring periods during the October 1990 and April 1992 monitoring periods. Samples collected from Stations 26, 44, and 53 exhibited significantly lower tissue TBT concentrations during monitoring periods in April 1990 to April 1992 than in monitoring periods prior to and including February 1988. Other studies that have focused on measurements of TBT in tissues over time have reported varying degrees of declining concentrations (Uhler et al. 1993; Garcia-Romero et al. 1993). Two reports (Wade et al. 1991; Batley et al. 1992) have linked decreasing tissue TBT concentrations to legislative restrictions on use of TBT paints.

The decreases in tissue TBT concentrations generally followed those seen in surface-water concentrations (Figures 7-3 and 7-4) and suggested that natural mussel population TBT burdens were reasonable indicators of ambient TBT water concentrations when values were available from organisms of comparable age, size class, and history. Tissue TBT concentrations from transplanted mussels in San Diego Bay during this same period frequently showed tissue burdens twice as high as those in natural specimens for similar areas in San Diego Bay (Salazar and Salazar 1991). This is likely due to the size of mussels measured and their relative growth rates. Previously (Salazar and Salazar 1991), smaller juvenile mussels that grew faster, possibly taking up more TBT, were used. The natural populations sampled here were mature and slower-growing. Size and growth rate of the individual has been shown to affect the concentration of TBT in tissues (Salazar and Salazar, personal communication). Mussels used in the yacht harbors were placed much closer to vessels and may have experienced higher TBT concentrations on a more frequent basis, although mean values were similar (Salazar and Salazar 1991). Mussels collected in the present study were generally of the same size class, although the scarcity of individuals at some yacht basin stations required the collection of any size to collect enough tissue for analysis. Before comparing tissue burdens between time intervals, a 1-way ANOVA model was run testing size as a covariate. No statistical differences were found in the individuals collected from these locations.

The TBT concentrations measured in bay mussel tissues were at or below 1700 ng g^{-1} in natural mussel specimens collected in this study with the exception of 1 sample collected from the Coronado Cays yacht marina (Station 53) (Table 7-2). Data indicated that TBT concentrations in tissue above 1500 ng g^{-1} likely inhibit growth of bay mussels transplanted to natural field locations in San Diego Bay (Salazar and Salazar 1991). Tissue TBT concentrations recently measured in natural bay mussel populations from San Diego Bay were, therefore, generally not indicative of TBT levels that may inhibit growth. Since April 1989 only 2 tissue TBT concentrations were measured above 500 ng g^{-1}, which is the lower limit of TBT concentrations possibly affecting growth in bay mussels (Salazar and Salazar 1991).

A particularly high mussel-tissue TBT concentration (1700 ng g^{-1}) was measured at Station 22 during August 1989 while the Exxon Valdez super tanker was awaiting repairs at a site approximately 100 m from the Station 22 sampling site (Table 7-2). It is not uncommon for large commercial vessels to be coated with TBT antifouling paint. The coincident presence of the Exxon Valdez at this site for approximately 1 month may well have been responsible for the unusually high TBT value measured. During subsequent monitoring periods when the tanker had been placed in the dry dock for repairs, and after leaving San Diego Bay, tissue TBT concentrations continued to decrease (Table 7-2). In the absence of another known explanation, we strongly feel that the presence of the Exxon Valdez super tanker was the causative factor for the high tissue TBT concentration measured at Station 22 in August 1989.

Pearl Harbor

Post baseline data from Pearl Harbor, Hawaii have been summarized previously (Grovhoug et al. 1989; Seligman et al. 1990). These reports have focused on environmental loading of TBT from vessel painting activity, leaching input, and post-painting temporal and spatial environmental TBT concentrations. This chapter examines the temporal loading of TBT in the Southeast Loch region of Pearl Harbor and its correlation with the presence of naval vessels painted with TBT antifouling paint. Some comparison with TBT surface-water concentrations in other regions of Pearl Harbor will be made, and the significance of current concentrations and TBT concentrations tested in situ in Pearl Harbor with fouling communities and other native species (Henderson 1985) will be considered.

Naval ships have not been painted with TBT antifouling paint in Pearl Harbor or elsewhere since 1987, and no additional ships painted with TBT antifouling paint have been stationed in Pearl Harbor since 1987. An analysis of the surface-water TBT concentration in Southeast Loch and the TBT loading factor in gm/d indicated these variables were well correlated with a correlation coefficient of 0.85 (r^2) (Seligman et al. 1990) and demonstrates the association of environmental TBT-water concentrations in Southeast Loch with TBT loading factors. After 1987 TBT surface-water concentrations decreased, as did loading rates (Seligman et al. 1990). The data presented in Figure 7-6 summarize TBT surface-water concentrations and loading rates from April 1986 until June 1994. Four of 6 ships painted with TBT antifouling paint have been decommissioned during the above

period, and TBT paint has been removed from the USS Leftwich.
Leach rate measurements were
made on the USS Leftwich on 2 occasions during a 7-y period to collect
accurate TBT leaching data. The last
measurements were made during
March 1994 prior to dry-docking
and paint removal and indicated a
leaching rate nearly 20 x lower than
that measured in 1990. The loading
rates presented in Figure 7-6 have
been adjusted to best estimate loading from the USS Leftwich and other
vessels. Details of leach-rate measurements and loading calculations
are described in Grovhoug et al.
(1989).

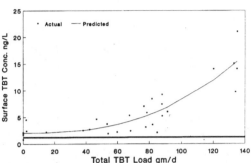

Southeast Loch TBT Loading
y=a+bx^c
R^2=0.80

Figure 7-6   *Pearl Harbor surface-water TBT concentrations in Southeast Loch versus calculated test ship TBT loading. Horizontal line drawn parallel with X axis represents average surface-water TBT concentration measured in 4 monitoring periods when no vessel loading occurred in Southeast Loch due to absence of TBT-painted vessels during those periods.*

The presence of naval vessels
painted with TBT antifouling paint
has continued to correlate with surface-water TBT concentrations in Southeast Loch (Figure 7-6). Our most recent data indicate a correlation coefficient (r^2) of 0.80 for loading
rates versus surface-water TBT values. Our loading estimations are subject to several factors, including the accuracy of leaching rates for TBT. We have measured leaching of TBT
from the USS Omaha once during a 7-y period. The TBT paint applied to the USS Omaha
had the highest leaching rate of the 6 vessels stationed in Southeast Loch (Grovhoug et al.
1989). Since leaching of TBT from antifouling paint applied to the USS Leftwich has
greatly decreased during this period, it is reasonable to assume that the leach rate estimated for the USS Omaha has also greatly decreased. If this is so, our TBT loading estimates for the Omaha may be overestimated. If new (lower) leach rates were available and
the data corrected, this would have the effect of moving some of the concentration of
points in the middle of Figure 7-6 to the left since many represent loading estimates made
several years after the initial leach rate was measured on the USS Omaha. The relationship might then more closely resemble a straight line decrease in TBT surface-water concentration with TBT loading rate. Another point to be considered addresses 4 TBT
surface-water values (at 0 loading) that represent periods when no TBT loading occurred,
since no vessels painted with TBT paint were in port during or preceding those times. We
have drawn a line representing the average TBT concentration of these points across the
lower part of Figure 7-6. This may be considered the background surface-water TBT concentration in Southeast Loch. Its origin may be due to sediment desorption, to
resuspension of sediment due to vessel movements, or possibly to input of TBT from

smaller aluminum hulled vessels that may be painted with TBT paints. We have no information on the latter possibility and cannot estimate any input.

In spite of uncertainties associated with our estimates of TBT loading in Southeast Loch, a relationship between loading and measured surface-water TBT concentrations has been defined. The significance of TBT surface-water concentrations in Southeast Loch may now be evaluated in terms of environmental concentrations, legislative criteria, and toxicity. In July 1989 surface-water TBT was measured at 9.7 ng/L (Seligman et al. 1990). Other regions in Pearl Harbor, with the exception of Rainbow Marina, characteristically exhibited much lower TBT levels. The higher concentrations measured at Rainbow Marina may be attributed to input from pleasure craft as yet unaffected by legislative restrictions on use. The other regions of Pearl Harbor have remained well below the protective limit of 10 ng/L TBT adopted by the State of Hawaii. Surface TBT concentrations in both Southeast Loch and Rainbow Marina have dropped considerably recently and have remained below 10 ng/L since January 1993. These regions both exhibited mean surface-TBT concentrations of 0.8 ng/L during the last monitoring period in June 1994 (unpublished data). With respect to toxicity, surface-water TBT concentrations in Southeast Loch have not approached concentrations shown to be toxic to native species (Henderson 1985). Native fouling species were not affected when exposed to 40 ng/L TBT in in situ flow through testing systems for a period of 2 months. A recent summary of the TBT toxicity literature indicates that among marine faunal species, only neogastropod snails are affected by TBT water concentrations under 10 ng/L (Bryan and Gibbs 1991).

Environmental fate of tributyltin

Our investigations regarding the fate of TBT in the marine environment have focused on degradation rates in seawater, sediments, and adsorption to particulate matter. The half-life of TBT in 46 experiments conducted in a total of 4 diverse harbors has ranged from 4 to 19 d (Seligman et al. 1989). Microbial activity and algal metabolism (Lee et al. 1989) appear to be the principle active factors. This appears so due to longer half-lives in dark treatments and in experimentally poisoned containers. Additionally, in an experiment where the TBT concentration was deliberately set at a high level (744 µg/L) (Seligman, Valkirs et al. 1986), TBT was not degraded in sunlight. Another finding of significance from these studies has indicated that TBT is degraded more rapidly in waters having high TBT concentrations initially, e.g., yacht harbors (Seligman, Valkirs et al. 1986). This suggests that microbes capable of degrading TBT may be present in higher numbers, and may be better adapted to TBT degradation in such areas, compared to areas where TBT water concentrations are lower, e.g., open water bodies. Dibutyltin has been identified as the principal degradation product in our experiments. The close agreement in experiments followed with atomic absorption measurements and those utilizing radioactive tracers has increased our confidence in the accuracy of our results.

It appears that TBT is present mainly in the dissolved phase (typically 90% or more) in seawater from studies previously conducted in our laboratory and elsewhere (Seligman, Valkirs, and Lee 1986; Valkirs et al. 1986; Valkirs, Stallard, and Seligman 1987; Johnson et al. 1987). Settling of particulate matter to sediments provides the pathway for sediment deposition. Sediment TBT concentrations have been found to be approximately 5 x 10^2 to 5 x 10^4 x water-column values (Stang and Seligman 1986; Maguire et al. 1986; Valkirs et al. 1986; Stang and Seligman 1987). Concentration factors in this range are generally consistent with measured partitioning coefficients (Seligman et al. 1989). Such coefficients are themselves dependent on salinity, particle size, organic content, and sediment load (Harris and Cleary 1987).

The behavior of TBT in marine sediments themselves has been shown to be varied. Twenty-four-hour desorption isotherms have shown TBT sediment sorption to be reversible. Sorption coefficients decreased with increasing salinity and varied by a factor of 2 over the salinity range tested under estuarine conditions (Unger et al. 1987). Various sediments from San Diego Bay have shown desorption of TBT under laboratory conditions (Kram et al. 1989b). Using an in situ polycarbonate plastic dome placed in Pearl Harbor sediment, Stang and Seligman (1987) measured an adsorption rate of 0.57 ng $TBT/cm^2/d$. Desorption of TBT was not measurable at these sites. The presence of high amounts of hydrogen sulfide in Pearl Harbor sediments has been cited by Kram et al. (1989b) as a potential interference in the measurement of TBT in Pearl Harbor sediments by HDAA. These authors also draw attention to widely variable effects of physical and chemical sediment characteristics on sorption and desorption of TBT, particularly in Pearl Harbor. Considering such factors, the results reported in the in situ sorption/desorption study conducted in Pearl Harbor (Stang and Seligman 1987) should be considered site-specific and likely influenced by local variables.

Tributyltin degradation has been demonstrated in marine sediments in some laboratory studies (Stang and Seligman 1986; Stang et al. 1992), while other studies have not measured any apparent degradation (Adelman et al. 1990). After incorporation into sediments in a controlled mesocosm study, Adelman et al. (1990) were not able to detect further TBT degradation. The authors cited low temperatures that existed for much of the later part of the 280-d experiment as a possible reason. Stang and Seligman (1986) reported a 162-d half-life for ambient (unspiked) TBT in marine sediments incubated in a laboratory tank experiment. The decrease in TBT was accompanied by an increase in monobutyltin (MBT), while the DBT concentration did not change appreciably. This debutylation process is different from that seen in seawater degradation studies where DBT is the primary degradation product. Analysis of butyltins in sediment cores from San Diego Bay indicated increasing ratios of MBT to total butyltin with core depth, as well as decreasing ratios of tributyltin to total butyltin with core depth (Stang and Seligman 1986). These results support the laboratory incubation study indicating that degradation of TBT to MBT occurs in the sediments analyzed. Further evidence for degradation of TBT was reported by Stang et al. (1992) for sediments from San Diego Bay,

Pearl Harbor, and the Skidaway River near Savannah, Georgia. In the presence of sediments high in silt and clay incubated under ambient field conditions, TBT degradation was rapid and primarily abiotic. The primary degradation product was MBT. Following the rapid initial degradation phase, TBT degraded at a much slower rate. A process in which added TBT sorbed to the incubated sediment, was degraded, and MBT formed and then entered the water phase was described. Stang et al. (1992) cite comparisons of MBT/TBT ratios from surface and bottom water measured in the Shelter Island yacht harbor in San Diego Bay that favored increased MBT in bottom water as supportive environmental evidence for the observed trend in formation of MBT in their degradation studies. A significant distinction was drawn between experiments with added TBT and those where TBT was present in sediment collected near yacht maintenance facilities. The TBT present in the latter sediments is likely present in paint chips of variable size and is not available to the sorption and degradation processes observed with sediments collected from areas where input is from transport to sediments via particulate scavenging.

The data supporting degradation of TBT in sediments may generally be characterized as supportive of significantly longer degradation half-lives than those seen in water. The measurement of degradation products indicates that degradation processes have occurred. The accuracy of these degradation estimates likely varies from study to study and is likely influenced by site-specific and experimental conditions. Our environmental measurements of sediment TBT concentrations in San Diego Bay indicate that sediment degradation processes under environmental conditions may be lengthy, spanning several years where decreases in sediment TBT concentrations have been observed at all (Table 7-1). Decreasing sediment TBT concentrations in some sites and no apparent decreases in others likely reflect the site-specific conditions influencing both input and degradation processes. Where sediment concentrations have not decreased over several years, a situation likely exists where input from the water column and degradation processes are in a steady-state condition.

Toxicity of tributyltin

The subject of TBT toxicity has received wide attention due to the extremely toxic nature of TBT with respect to marine species. The following section will focus on TBT toxicity studies conducted in situ in San Diego Bay and Pearl Harbor, as well as on studies done with indigenous species. Between 1987 and 1990, Salazar and Salazar (1991, 1994) studied mussel growth and tissue TBT accumulation in relation to environmental surface-water TBT concentrations. Eighteen sites were studied in 9 separate mussel transplant experiments of 12 weeks duration per experiment. Surface and bottom water sites separated by 3 m depth were studied in the Shelter Island yacht harbor. The authors draw attention to the utility of serial, sequential studies in their ability to quantify dose-response relationships over a variety of environmentally realistic test conditions and possibilities for first order approximations of environmental risk. The distinction is made between tissue concentrations, which represent actual internal exposure, and contaminant concentration in water or sediment, which represents apparent external exposure.

The results of these experiments provided useful toxicity data for both water- and tissue-level exposure. A zone of possible TBT water concentrations causing negative effects regarding mussel growth was estimated to be between 25 and 100 ng/L. Tributyltin concentrations above 100 ng/L were estimated to lie in a probable effects zone. Concentrations below 25 ng/L were considered to represent a no-effect zone. The corresponding tissue TBT effect zones were estimated to be 0.5 to 1.5 $\mu g\ g^{-1}$ wet weight (possible effects); >1.5 $\mu g\ g^{-1}$ (probable effects); and < 0.5 $\mu g\ g^{-1}$ (no-effect). Severe inhibition of *M. edulis* growth above 4 $\mu g\ g^{-1}$ (dry weight) has been recently reported by Widdows and Page (1993). If it is assumed that mussel tissue is approximately 80% water, then a ratio of 5 may be used to divide dry weight measurements in order to approximate the corresponding wet-weight value. This manipulation predicts that the reported dry-weight value of 4 $\mu g\ g^{-1}$ would be 0.8 $\mu g\ g^{-1}$ wet weight. Thus some agreement is apparent between the no-effect wet-weight TBT tissue concentration estimated by Salazar and Salazar (1991) and the corresponding estimated wet-weight concentration of 0.8 $\mu g\ g^{-1}$ causing negative growth effects reported by Widdows and Page (1993).

Regarding the data reported by Salazar and Salazar (1994), one further important finding must be mentioned. The authors successfully demonstrated the utility of mussel transplant experiments in determining spatial effects regarding TBT exposure. In comparisons between surface-water and bottom-water sites separated by a 3 m depth, significant differences were found in both seawater- and tissue-TBT concentrations. Surface-water TBT was higher and follows the assumption that the primary input into the Shelter Island yacht harbor is leaching of TBT from vessel hulls painted with TBT antifouling paint. After the restrictions on use were enacted, TBT surface-water concentrations dramatically declined (see Figures 7-3 and 7-4), and mussel growth rates significantly increased. Tissue TBT concentrations in mussels located near bottom sediments (1 m) changed little relative to those located near the surface. Considering these data, it would appear that little input of TBT from bottom sediments occurred and that the primary source of TBT exposure originated from surface waters.

The importance of the toxicity data reported above lies in their link to environmental concentrations, both in water and in tissue. In many earlier studies, measurements were often reported for water samples, tissue samples, or, in some cases, for both. However, the link between measurements and effects was not made. It is now possible to estimate risk to species where such a link has been described. Earlier in this chapter it was noted that only 2 tissue-TBT concentration means were measured above 500 ng g^{-1} (the no-effect level estimated by Salazar and Salazar [1991]) since April 1989 (Table 7-2). Only 10 measurements are above 800 ng g^{-1} (the converted threshold level estimated from the data of Widdows and Page [1993]), and none are above this concentration in monitoring periods after August 1989 (Table 7-2). Predictably, the concentrations above 800 ng g^{-1}

are in yacht harbor areas, with the exception of 1 site near the naval region and adjacent to a commercial dry-dock facility. These data indicate that little risk has existed to *M. edulis* from TBT exposure in San Diego Bay and that the existing trend seems to support decreasing TBT concentrations in all areas of the bay.

A second in situ toxicity study conducted in San Diego Bay was performed with a portable environmental test system located at a pier site near the border of the naval and south bay regions. Studies were conducted with flow-through exposure to TBT leached from painted panels for a period of 7 months. Test species were contained in 340-L tanks. Mean TBT concentrations measured were 65, 77, and 193 ng/L (Salazar et al. 1987). Test TBT concentrations were difficult to maintain, resulting in poor dose separation in the lower test concentrations. The results of this study indicated no significant effects on fouling communities (species abundance and biomass), mussel and clam condition indexes, mussel gonad indexes, or oyster growth. The authors commented that variability between replicate test tanks was high, and that tank controls compared to submerged site controls indicated that test specimens were experiencing test-system stress. Both factors in combination with dose-control difficulties may have masked real effects. While experimental difficulties were encountered in this study, the lack of observed effects at the highest concentration tested (193 ng/L) has relevance to the then existing surface-water TBT concentrations measured in the yacht basins. The results suggest that the species tested, not all of which were indigenous to San Diego Bay, may not have been threatened at TBT concentrations near 193 ng/L and less.

Mussel growth rates were examined in a second phase of the in situ study described above. Two tests were performed at TBT water concentrations of 70, 80, and 200 ng/L (Test 1, 196 days), and 40, 50, and 160 ng/L (Test II, 56 days). The results are reported in Salazar and Salazar (1987). After 63 d, all treatments significantly reduced growth in Test I; however, large differences were again noted in the tank controls compared to those submerged in the bay at the site itself (pier controls) suggesting testing stress was a factor in addition to TBT exposure. The authors considered temperature stress and nutritive stress as complicating factors in assessing TBT effects. Testing conditions favored Test II conditions, especially with respect to optimum temperatures. In spite of experimental control difficulties, these studies did provide testing conditions that mimicked environmental conditions (e.g., use of unfiltered seawater, natural phytoplankton exposure, and presence of suspended sediment). Under the testing conditions described, there were no significant mortalities recorded at TBT concentrations up to 200 ng/L. These results suggest that mussel populations may have been able to exist in yacht harbors where TBT concentrations were less than 200 ng/L, provided that other complicating factors were not significant.

Laboratory studies, while perhaps lacking environmental realism, have also provided important TBT toxicity data under controlled conditions with respect to TBT exposure. Here we will consider TBT toxicity data provided from both acute and chronic tests with the mysid shrimp *Acanthomysis sculpta* (Davidson et al. 1986). Although this species does not live in San Diego Bay, it does inhabit the kelp beds directly offshore and outside of the bay and is an accepted test species for dredge spoil bioassays (Salazar and Salazar 1985). The results of the tests with *A. sculpta* gave a 96-h LC50 value of 420 ng/L with closely controlled 24-h static renewal dosing. The long-term life cycle testing results indicated a no-effect concentration (NOEC) of 250 ng/L for mortality at 63 days, growth NOEC values of 310 and 250 ng/L for subadults and adult females, respectively, and an NOEC of 90 ng/L for reproductive effects (egg production). Since this species does not live directly within the confines of San Diego Bay, a direct link may not be made between this species and existing TBT concentrations at that time. However, the toxicity data produced reflects effects to be expected in sensitive species in general, and the toxic and NOECs may be viewed from this perspective. Again, if the TBT concentrations determined in these tests are compared to existing TBT surface-water values measured in San Diego Bay at that time (1986), only surface-water TBT concentrations from the yacht basins are in the range of toxic values determined in the long-term toxicity tests. The 96-h LC50 value of 420 ng/L was not approached in water samples measured in the yacht harbors or elsewhere (Figures 7-3 and 7-4).

Marine algae may be sensitive indicators of marine pollution. In toxicity testing with indigenous algal species from San Diego Bay, Salazar (1985) observed species-specific effects of TBT exposure. The results of 72-h bioassays indicated that a dinoflagellate (*Gymnodinium splendens*) was the most sensitive species tested. Complete mortality was observed at 1500 ng/L. The green flagellate *Dunaliella* sp. exhibited growth inhibition (EC50) at 1500 ng/L TBT. No measurable changes in growth rates were noted with the diatom species *Phaeodactylum tricornutum*. These TBT concentrations are well above those used in the tests with *A. sculpta*, suggesting that the existing TBT concentrations prior to restrictions on use may have been at tolerable levels for some sensitive marine phytoplankton species.

The results of more recent reports will now be considered and compared with those discussed above in order to more completely describe the potential for toxic effects from previous and current environmental TBT concentrations. Long-term toxicity testing was performed under laboratory conditions with larval *Mytilus edulis* (Lapota et al. 1993). A no-effect concentration (growth) of 6 ng/L was determined after a 25-d static renewal exposure period. The lowest concentration producing negative effects was measured at 50 ng/L. The NOEC value is particularly low and approaches values currently and previously present in most areas of San Diego Bay (Figures 7-3 and 7-4). Another recent study (Bushong et al. 1990) has reported NOEC values of 12 to 10 ng/L TBT for copepod (*Acartia tonsa*) larval survival in 6-d chronic flow-through exposure experiments. Lowest measurable effects were noted at 23 to 24 ng/L. Juvenile polychaete worms (*Neanthes arenaceodentata*) exposed to TBT for 10 weeks showed no adverse effects on survival, growth, or reproduction at exposure concentrations of 10 or 50 ng/L (Moore et al. 1991). Dry weight tissue concentrations > 6.3 µg TBT/g dry weight adversely affected growth and reproduction. Tissue concentrations < 3 µg g⁻¹ TBT dry weight showed no detectable effects. If these latter tissue-TBT values are adjusted by a factor of 5 to approximate wet weights, the corresponding TBT concentrations are approximately 1.3 (threshold of effects) and 0.6 µg g⁻¹ (no apparent effects). These values are again similar to those reported by Salazar and Salazar (1991, 1994) and Widdows and Page (1993). In a previous report (Huggett et al. 1992) TBT toxicity data from open harbor regions and yacht harbor regions were compared before and after legislation restricting use of TBT antifouling paints was enacted (Figure 7-7). Clearly, legislation acted to decrease TBT-water concentrations in both San Diego Bay and Norfolk harbor. Surface-water TBT concentrations have further decreased in most regions of San Diego Bay since and have remained similar in Norfolk (unpublished data). Toxicity studies cited above and published since those cited in Figure 7-7 have not reported lower toxicity limits, with the exception of studies addressing imposex in gastropod snails where toxicity regarding sexual development has been exhibited at TBT exposures of 2 to 5 ng/L (Gibbs et al. 1988; Huggett et al. 1992). The general observation that may be drawn from Figure 7-7 remains that TBT concentrations in open-water regions of harbors are not at levels that may be considered harmful to most marine species.

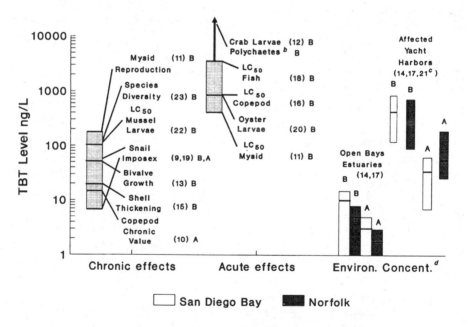

Figure 7-7   Summary of selected tributyltin toxicity data and environmental concentrations (from Huggett et al. 1992). A = After restrictions on TBT antifouling paint were enacted. B = Before restrictions on TBT antifouling paint were enacted. ªOriginal reference numbers in parentheses. ᵇSource: Naval Ocean Systems Center 1991 unpublished data. ᶜSource: Virginia Institute of Marine Science 1991 publication #1726. ᵈLine across each bar indicates mean concentration

Collectively, the data above suggest that the lowest TBT-water concentrations currently present in San Diego Bay are below levels toxic to many sensitive marine species. The larger yacht basins (Harbor Island, Shelter Island, and the Commercial Basin) continue to exhibit surface-water TBT values that border concentrations that have been shown in laboratory studies to demonstrate chronic toxicity to some sensitive marine species. Concerning the NOEC level of 25 ng/L for growth effects on juvenile *M. edulis* (Salazar and Salazar 1991), observations at sites in Shelter Island and Commercial Basin have indicated recruitment of mussel populations in areas where previous populations had disappeared when TBT concentrations were high (150 to 250 ng/L). Surface-water TBT concentrations have remained near 25 ng/L in these yacht harbors for several years (Figure 7-4). While not quantitative evidence, these observations suggest that conditions near those predicted for mussel growth and survival do exist in these heavily populated yacht harbors. The above comments serve to underline the importance of comparison of laboratory data with field data. *Acartia tonsa* is indigenous to San Diego Bay and is a species that may not be able to tolerate existing TBT water concentrations in some yacht harbors. Field data are necessary to test predictive laboratory data. Caution must also be applied to such comparisons, since field observations do not reflect conditions that are as well controlled as laboratory studies with respect to exposure. Field populations of mobile species may in fact migrate to some extent in and out of a yacht harbor e.g., with tidal events. Nonetheless, a correlation of laboratory predictions and field data must be made to estimate the true risk of pollutant exposure to indigenous species. The degree of TBT exposure has decreased greatly in San Diego Bay since restrictions on use were imposed. Both laboratory and field data indicate that most species tested are not endangered by current TBT surface-water concentrations in San Diego Bay, with the possible exception of the Shelter Island, Commercial Basin, and Harbor Island yacht harbors.

Tributyltin concentrations in Pearl Harbor have not been elevated to the extent noted in yacht harbors (Seligman et al. 1990). Only Rainbow Marina, a small pleasure craft marina located within Pearl Harbor, has exhibited TBT surface-water concentrations above 100 ng/L (in July 1987). Accordingly, we will discuss an in situ toxicity study (Henderson 1985) performed in Pearl Harbor with indigenous species wherein TBT was tested at some concentrations approximating those measured in Rainbow Marina. The data from these tests are valuable for comparative purposes since a broad range of species was tested under flow-through exposure conditions with TBT concentrations originating from plastic panels painted with TBT antifouling paint. Thus the leachate produced approximated environmental release. Concentrations were monitored by HDAA analysis of water samples collected from test tanks. No significant effects on settlement or survival of fouling organisms was noted at 40 ng/L TBT. Sabellid feather-duster worms (*Sabellastarte sanctijosephi*), swimming crabs (*Thalamita admete*), glass shrimp (*Palaemon* spp.), and anemones (*Aiptasia pulchella*) also were not affected at 40 ng/L. Anemones and feather-duster worms indicated toxic effects at 500 and 100 ng/L, respectively. The Ford Island testing site was approximately 1 km down-current from the Southeast Loch region where naval vessels painted with TBT antifouling paint were docked. Hence the approximation of actual conditions in Southeast Loch was close to existing conditions. Testing was not conducted in Southeast Loch because of unavailability of space and possible surface-oil contamination. The results of this study indicate that the surface-water TBT concentrations measured in Pearl Harbor, frequently in the range of 1 to 10 ng/L, are not sufficiently high to pose a risk to a wide range of indigenous marine species. The State of Hawaii's limit of 10 ng/L TBT in marine waters would appear to be adequate for the protection of most local species. We are not aware of any studies where TBT toxicity has been demonstrated with indigenous Hawaiian species at TBT concentrations less than 10 ng/L.

Summary and conclusions

The potential deleterious environmental effects posed by elevated TBT concentrations in the marine environments investigated have decreased with time after enactment of legislative restrictions on use. This has been observed on a worldwide basis in several areas. It would appear that the large majority of species will be protected by water-quality criteria ranging from 2 to 10 ng/L TBT, which are concentrations characteristic of both existing open and enclosed water bodies in San Diego Bay and Pearl Harbor. Since some input to the marine environment will continue via input from TBT antifouling paints applied to large private and commercial vessels, and possibly from release from bottom sediments, TBT in marine waters will likely persist at low ng/L concentrations. Accumulation of TBT in open or closed water bodies is not expected because its half-life of 1 to 2 weeks in the waters studied is brief. Legislation has successfully identified and controlled input from private sources that collectively acted to greatly elevate TBT water concentrations in areas such as yacht harbors and influenced outlying waters as well.

Acknowledgment - We would like to thank the following individuals for their assistance in data collection, analysis, and general supportive activities during the course of these studies: G. Vafa, S. Cola, M.O. Stallard, P.M. Stang, J. Vaughn, C. Adema, G. Smith, and B. Thomas. This work was sponsored by the Office of the Chief of Naval Research and David Taylor Research Center under the USN Energy Research and Development Program. Additional support for methods development was provided by the Naval Facilities Engineering Command, Environmental Protection Program.

References

[ACS] American Chemical Society Committee on Environmental Improvement. 1980. Guidelines for data acquisition and data quality evaluation in environmental chemistry. *Anal Chem* 52:2242–2249.

[ACS] American Chemical Society Committee on Environmental Improvement. 1983. Principles of environmental analysis. *Anal Chem* 55:2210–2218.

Adelman D, Hinga KR, Pilson MEQ. 1990. Biogeochemistry of butyltins in an enclosed marine ecosystem. *Environ Sci Technol* 24: 1027–1032.

Batley GE, Scammell MS, Brockbank CI. 1992. The impact of the banning of tributyltin-based antifouling paints on the Sydney rock oyster, *Saccostrea commercialis*. *Sci Total Environ* 122:301–314.

Bryan GW, Gibbs PE. 1991. Impact of low concentrations of tributyltin (TBT) on marine organisms: A review. In: Newman MC, McIntosh AW, editors. Metal ecotoxicology: concepts and applications. Chelsea, MI: Lewis. 399 p.

Bushong SJ, Ziegenfuss MC, Unger MA, Hall Jr LW. 1990. Chronic tributyltin toxicity experiments with the Chesapeake Bay copepod, *Acartia tonsa*. *Environ Toxicol Chem* 9:359–366.

Carter RJ, Turoczy NJ, Bond AM. 1989. Container adsorption of tributyltin (TBT) compounds: Implications for environmental analysis. *Environ Sci Technol* 23:615–617.

Clavell C, Seligman PF, Stang PM. 1986. Automated analysis of organotin compounds: a method for monitoring butyltins in the marine environment. In: Proceedings, Oceans 1986 Conference, Washington DC, 23–25 Sep 1986, Organotin Symposium, Volume 4. p 1152–1154.

Cleary JJ. 1991. Organotin in the marine surface microlayer and subsurface waters of South-West England: relation to toxicity thresholds and the UK environmental quality standard. *Mar Environ Res* 32:213–222.

Davidson BM, Valkirs AO, Seligman PF. 1986. Acute and chronic effects of tributyltin on the mysid *Acanthomysis sculpta*. Proceedings, Oceans 1986 Conference, Volume 4, Organotin Symposium, Washington DC, 23–25 Sep 1986. p 1219–1225.

Dooley CA, Homer V. 1983. Organotin compounds in the marine environment: Uptake and sorption behavior. Technical Report 917. Naval Ocean Systems Center. San Diego, CA.

Dowson PH, Bubb JM, Lester JN. 1994. The effectiveness of the 1987 retail ban on TBT based antifouling paints in reducing butyltin concentrations in East Anglia, UK. *Chemosphere* 28:905–910.

Dowson PH, Preshke D, Bubb JM, Lester JN. 1992. Spatial distribution of organotins in sediments of lowland river catchments. *Environ Pollut* 76:259–266.

Dowson PH, Bubb JM, Lester JN. 1993. Temporal distribution of organotins in the aquatic environment: Five years after the 1987 UK retail ban on TBT based antifouling paints. *Mar Poll Bull* 26:487–494.

Garcia-Romero B, Wade TL, Salata GG, Brooks JM. 1993. Butyltin concentrations in oysters from the Gulf of Mexico from 1989 to 1991. *Environ Pollut* 81:103–111.

Gibbs PE, Pascoe PL, Burt GR. 1988. Sex change in the female dog-whelk, *Nucella lapillus*, induced by tributyltin from antifouling paints. *J Mar Biol Assn* UK 68:715–731.

Grovhoug JG, Fransham RL, Seligman PF. 1987. Butyltin concentrations in selected U.S. harbor systems: A baseline assessment. Technical Report 1155. Naval Oceans System Center. San Diego CA.

Grovhoug JG, Seligman PF, Fransham RL, Cola SY, Stallard MO, Stang PM, Valkirs AO. 1989. Measurement of butyltin concentrations in Pearl Harbor, Hawaii April 1986–January 1988: Pearl Harbor case study. Technical Report 1293. Naval Ocean Systems Center. San Diego CA.

Hall Jr LW, Unger MA, Ziegenfuss MC, Sullivan JA, Bushong SJ. 1992. Butyltin and copper monitoring in a northern Chesapeake Bay marina and river system in 1989: An assessment of tributyltin legislation. *Environ Monit Assess* 22:15–38.

Harris JRW, Cleary JJ. 1987. Particle-water partitioning and organotin dispersal in an estuary. Proceedings, Oceans 1987 Conference, Volume 4, Organotin Symposium, Halifax, Nova Scotia, Canada, 21 Sep–1 Oct 1987. p 1370–1374.

Helsel DR. 1990. Less than obvious. Statistical treatment of data below the detection limit. *Environ Sci Technol* 24:1766–1774.

Henderson RS. 1985. Effects of tributyltin antifouling paint leachates on Pearl Harbor organisms. Site-specific flowthrough bioassay tests. Naval Ocean Systems Center Technical Report No. 1079. San Diego, CA 92152-5000.

Huggett RJ, Unger MA, Seligman PF, Valkirs AO. 1992. The marine biocide tributyltin. Assessing and managing the environmental risks. *Environ Sci Technol* 26:232–237.

Huggett RJ, Unger MA, Westbrook DA. 1986. Organotin concentrations in the southern Chesapeake Bay. In: Proceedings of the Oceans 1986 Conference, Washington DC. 23–25 Sep 1986. Volume 4. p 1262–1265.

Johnson WE, Hall Jr LW, Bushong SJ, Hall WS. 1987. Organotin concentrations in centrifuged versus uncentrifuged water column samples and in sediment pore waters of a northern Chesapeake Bay tributary. In: Proceedings of the Oceans 1987 Conference, Halifax, Nova Scotia, Canada, 28 Sep–1 Oct 1987. Volume 4. p 1364–1369.

Kram ML, Stang PM, Seligman PF. 1989a. Fate and distribution of organotin in sediments of four U.S. harbors. Technical Report 1280. Naval Ocean Systems Center, San Diego, CA.

Kram ML, Stang PM, Seligman PF. 1989b. Adsorption and desorption of tributyltin in sediments of San Diego Bay and Pearl Harbor. *Appl Organometal Chem* 3:523–536.

Krone CA, Brown DW, Burrows DG, Chan SL, Varanasi U. 1989. Butyltins in sediments and waterways in Puget Sound, Washington State, USA. *Mar Poll Bull* 20:528–531.

Lapota D, Rosenberger DE, Platter-Rieger MF, Seligman PF. 1993. Growth and survival of *Mytilus edulis* larvae exposed to low levels of dibutyltin and tributyltin. *Mar Biol* 115:413–419.

Lee RF, Valkirs AO, Seligman PF. 1989. Importance of microalgae in the biodegradation of tributyltin in estuarine waters. *Environ Sci Technol* 23:1515–1518.

Maguire RJ, Tkacz RJ. 1987. Concentration of tributyltin in the surface microlayer of natural waters. *Water Poll Res J Can* 22:227–233.

Maguire RJ, Tkacz RJ, Chau YK, Bengert GA, Wong PTS. 1986. Occurrence of organotin compounds in water and sediment in Canada. *Chemosphere* 15:253–274.

Moore DW, Dillon TM, Suedel BC. 1991. Chronic toxicity of tributyltin to the marine polychaete worm, *Neanthes arenaceodentata*. *Aquat Toxicol* 21:181–198.

Porter PS, Ward RC, Bell HF. 1988. The detection limit. *Environ Sci Technol* 22:856–861.

Readman JW, Mee LD. 1991. The reliability of analytical data for tributyltin (TBT) in sea water and its implications on water quality criteria. *Mar Environ Res* 32:19–28.

Ritsema R. 1994. Dissolved butyltins in marine waters of the Netherlands three years after the ban. *Appl Organomet Chem* 8:5–10.

Salazar SM. 1985. The effects of bis(tri-n-butyltin) oxide on three species of marine phytoplankton. NOSC Technical Report No. 1039. Naval Ocean Systems Center, San Diego, CA 92152-5000.

Salazar SM, Davidson BM, Salazar MH, Stang PM, Meyers-Schulte KJ. 1987. Effects of TBT on marine organisms: Field assessment of a new site-specific bioassay system. Proceedings, Oceans 1987 Conference, Volume 4, Organotin Symposium, Halifax, Nova Scotia, Canada, 21 Sep–1 Oct 1987. p 1461–1470.

Salazar MH, Salazar SM. 1985. Ecological evaluation of organotin-contaminated sediment. NOSC Technical Report No. 1050. Naval Ocean Systems Center, San Diego, CA 92152-5000.

Salazar MH, Salazar SM. 1987. Tributyltin effects on juvenile mussel growth. Proceedings, Oceans 1987 Conference Volume 4, Organotin Symposium, Halifax, Nova Scotia, Canada, 21 Sep–1 Oct 1987. p 1504–1510.

Salazar MH, Salazar SM. 1991. Assessing site-specific effects of TBT contamination with mussel growth rates. *Mar Environ Res* 32: 131–150.

Salazar MH, Salazar SM. 1994. In situ bioassays using transplanted mussels: I. Estimating chemical exposure and bioeffects with bioaccumulation and growth. In: Hughes JS, Biddinger GR, Mones E, editors. Third Symposium on Environmental Toxicology and Risk Assessment, ASTM STP 1218. Philadelphia PA: American Society for Testing and Materials. In press.

Sarradin PM, Astruc A, Desauziers V, Pinel R, Astruc M. 1991. Butyltin pollution in surface sediments of Arcachon Bay after ten years of restricted use of TBT-based paints. *Environ Technol* 12:537–543.

Seligman PF, Grovhoug JG, Fransham RL, Davidson B, Valkirs AO. 1990. U.S. Navy statutory monitoring of tributyltin in selected U.S. harbors. Annual Report: 1989. Naval Ocean Systems Center Technical Report No. 1346, San Diego CA.

Seligman PF, Grovhoug JG, Richter KE. 1986. Measurement of butyltins in San Diego Bay, Ca.: a monitoring strategy. In: Proceedings, Oceans 1986 Conference, Washington DC, 23–25 Sep 1986, Organotin Symposium. Volume 4. p 1289–1296.

Seligman PF, Grovhoug JG, Valkirs AO, Stang PM, Fransham R, Stallard MO, Davidson B, Lee RF. 1989. Distribution and fate of tributyltin in the United States marine environment. *Appl Organomet Chem* 3:31–47.

Seligman PF, Valkirs AO, Lee RF. 1986. Degradation of tributyltin in San Diego Bay, California, waters. *Environ Sci Technol* 20:1229–1235.

Seligman PF, Valkirs AO, Stang PM, Lee RF. 1988. Evidence for rapid degradation of tributyltin in a marina. *Mar Pollut Bull* 19:531–534.

Stallard MO, Cola SY, Dooley CA. 1989. Optimization of butyltin measurements for seawater, tissue, and marine sediment samples. *Appl Organomet Chem* 3:105–114.

Stang PM, Bower DR, Seligman PF. 1989. Stratification and tributyltin variability in San Diego Bay. *Appl Organomet Chem* 3:411–416.

Stang PM, Lee RF, Seligman PF. 1992. Evidence for rapid, nonbiological degradation of tributyltin compounds in autoclaved and heat-treated fine-grained sediments. *Environ Sci Technol* 26:1382–1387.

Stang PM, Seligman PF. 1986. Distribution and fate of butyltin compounds in the sediment of San Diego Bay. Proceedings, Oceans 1986 Conference, Volume 4, Organotin Symposium, Washington DC, 23–25 Sep 1986. p 1256–1261.

Stang PM, Seligman PF. 1987. In situ adsorption and desorption of butyltin compounds from Pearl Harbor, Hawaii sediment. Proceedings, Oceans 1987 Conference, Volume 4, Organotin Symposium, Halifax, Nova Scotia, Canada, 21 Sep–1 Oct 1987. p 1381–1391.

Uhler AD, Durell GS, Steinhauer WG, Spellacy AM. 1993. Tributyltin levels in bivalve mollusks from the east and west coasts of the United States: Results from the 1988–1990 National Status and Trends Mussel watch Project. *Environ Toxicol Chem* 12:139–153.

Unger MA, MacIntyre WG, Huggett RJ. 1987. Equilibrium sorption of tributyltin chloride by Chesapeake Bay sediments. Proceedings, Oceans 1987 Conference, Volume 4, Organotin Symposium, Halifax, Nova Scotia, Canada, 21 Sep–1 Oct 1987. p 1381–1385.

[USEPA] U.S. Environmental Protection Agency. 1988. Ambient water quality criteria for tributyltin. U.S. Environmental Protection Agency, Office of Research and Development, Environmental Research Laboratories, Duluth, Minnesota and Narragansett, Rhode Island.

[USN] U.S. Navy. 1984. Fleetwide Use of Organotin Antifouling Paint: Environmental Assessment; U.S. Navy: Washington, DC. 128 p.

Valkirs AO, Davidson B, Kear LL, Fransham RL, Grovhoug JG, Seligman PF. 1991. Long-term monitoring of tributyltin in San Diego Bay California. *Mar Environ Res* 32:151–167.

Valkirs AO, Seligman PF, Lee RF. 1986. Butyltin partitioning in marine waters and sediments. In: Proceedings, Oceans 1986 Conference, Washington D. C., 23–25 Sep 1986, Organotin Symposium. Volume 4. p 1165–1170.

Valkirs AO, Seligman PF, Olson GJ, Brinckman FE, Matthias CL, Bellama JM. 1987. Di- and tributyltin species in marine and estuarine waters. Inter-laboratory comparison of two ultratrace analytical methods employing hydride generation and atomic absorption or flame photometric detection. *Analyst* 112:17–20.

Valkirs AO, Stallard MO, Seligman PF. 1987. Butyltin partitioning in marine waters In: Proceedings, Oceans 1987 Conference, Halifax, Nova Scotia, Canada, 28 Sep–1 Oct 1987, Organotin Symposium. Volume 4. p 1375–1380.

Valkirs AO, Stallard MO, Stang PM, Frank S, Seligman PF. 1990. Assessment of frozen storage of tributyltin in seawater samples using hydride derivatisation. *Analyst* 115:1327–1328.

Wade TL, Garcia-Romero B, Brooks JM. 1991. Oysters as biomonitors of butyltins in the Gulf of Mexico. *Mar Environ Res* 32:233–241.

Widdows J, Page DS. 1993. Effects of tributyltin and dibutyltin on the physiological energetics of the mussel, *Mytilus edulis*. *Mar Environ Res* 35:233–249.

Wuertz S, Miller ME, DooLittle MM, Brennan JF, Cooney JJ. 1991. Butyltins in estuarine sediments two years after tributyltin use was restricted. *Chemosphere* 22:1113–1120.

Yonezawa Y, Nakata K, Miyakozawa Y, Ochi A, Kowata T, Fukawa H, Sato Y, Masunaga S, Urushigawa Y. 1993. Distributions of butyltins in the surface sediment if Ise Bay, Japan. *Environ Toxicol Chem* 12:1175–1184.

Young DR, Schatzberg P, Brinckman FE, Champ MA, Holm SE, Landy RB. 1986. Summary report— Interagency workshop on aquatic sampling and analysis for organotin compounds. In: Proceedings of the Oceans 1986 Conference, Washington D.C., September 23–25 1986. Volume 4. p 1135–1140.

Chapter 8

Using caged bivalves as part of an exposure-dose-response triad to support an integrated risk-assessment strategy

Michael H. Salazar and Sandra M. Salazar

Results of 9 mussel transplant studies (in situ field bioassays) conducted in San Diego Bay, California are used to demonstrate the utility of caged bivalves in supporting an ecological risk assessment (ERA). The exposure-dose-response (EDR) triad, a framework for collecting exposure and effects data, is presented. Caged bivalves were used as 1 element of the EDR triad. Exposure was estimated by measuring seawater tributyltin (TBT) concentrations, dose by measuring the bioaccumulation of TBT in mussel tissues, and response by measuring growth of caged mussels. Emphasis is placed on using 1) site-specific data for the most TBT-contaminated yacht basin (Shelter Island); 2) end-of-test tissue weights (EOTW) as a growth endpoint, and 3) water and tissue TBT concentrations to characterize exposure and to predict the concentrations where adverse effects will occur. Some of the most useful information and relationships from this assessment would not have been detected using indigenous mussel populations because they were not found at many sites. In previous analyses, multiple measurements of whole-animal wet-weights (WAWW) were used to estimate growth, and these data were used as part of the U.S. Navy's ERA for TBT. Here, growth was estimated using EOTW and provided different perspectives on the potential effects of TBT. Tissue weights indicated that many of the relationships among stations were similar to those obtained based on WAWW. End-of-test tissue weights suggested that existing conditions at the Naval Station were highly stressful to mussels even though TBT was not used on the vessels there. Based on the reevaluation of growth using EOTW for mussels transplanted within San Diego Bay, the predicted tissue concentration for probable effects on mussel growth is lowered from 7.5 to 4 µg TBT/g tissue dry weight. These findings are significant to the TBT risk assessment for Naval Station San Diego because they suggest that the predicted ecological risk associated with TBT was probably underestimated. It is also significant that this tissue concentration is about an order of magnitude lower than that predicted for mortality effects in several different species commonly used in laboratory bioassays. Questions are also raised regarding the environmental significance and regulatory application of laboratory bioassays where chemical equilibrium has not been achieved by using standard protocols.

The purpose of this chapter is to reevaluate the juvenile mussel growth data from San Diego Bay that were used in the Navy's risk assessment for tributyltin (TBT). This characterization of TBT exposure and effects will use end-of-test weights (EOTWs) instead of growth rates based on changes in whole-animal wet-weight (WAWWs). The suggested shift in approach is based on recent results demonstrating that under certain conditions, tissue weights have detected statistically significant differences in growth among sites and identified potentially adverse effects where whole-animal growth rates have not (URS Consultants 1994; Salazar and Salazar 1995; Salazar et al. 1995; Salazar et al. 1996). This chapter will discuss using caged bivalves in a risk-assessment framework, using chemical measurements of bioaccumulation to characterize exposure and biological measurements of growth to characterize effects in caged bivalves, and using the EDR triad as a supplement to the current risk-assessment paradigm. The focus will be on 1) using site-specific data for the most TBT-contaminated yacht basin (Shelter Island); 2) using EOTWs as a growth endpoint, and 3) using water and tissue TBT concentrations to characterize exposure and to predict the concentrations where adverse effects will occur.

Historical perspective

In 1984, the U.S. Navy released an environmental assessment for implementing the use of TBT antifouling coatings on their entire fleet of vessels (USN 1984). The assessment included a TBT monitoring plan through the year 1989. In this plan, San Diego Bay was identified as a particularly important harbor for monitoring because of the large number of naval vessels berthed there and the associated potential for significant ecological effects. It should be emphasized that TBT was not widely used on naval vessels at that time. Pre-implementation monitoring included private yacht basins where TBT concentrations were extremely high because of the large numbers of vessels in a relatively small area and poor flushing in the protected marinas. The pre-implementation monitoring program was based primarily on chemical measurements of TBT in seawater, sediment, and mussel tissues. Sediment and seawater were collected from San Diego Bay and other Navy harbors (Grovhoug et al. 1986; Valkirs et al. 1991). Mussels or oysters were collected from indigenous intertidal populations in the vicinity of the water and sediment samples. Chemical analyses of these tissues provided a characterization of exposure. Potential effects were characterized primarily with traditional laboratory toxicity tests and microcosm studies. A subset of San Diego Bay sites was selected for more intensive exposure and effects monitoring using caged juvenile mussels as an in situ field bioassay.

There is a perception among many that the TBT problem was eliminated with the restrictions imposed by the U.S. Environmental Protection Agency (USEPA) in 1988. It should be made clear that restrictions only applied to vessels < 25 m and that TBT coatings with lower release rates are still used on larger vessels. Additionally, several countries have no restrictions on the use of TBT antifouling coatings. The net result is that there is still a significant input of TBT to the major harbors of the world. Recent surveys in major Canadian harbors have shown elevated concentrations of TBT in mussel tissues and sediments (Maguire et al. 1996). These tissue and sediment concentrations are above those predicted to cause adverse effects in mussels (Page and Widdows 1991) and other benthic organisms (MacDonald, personal communication).

Although the Canadian studies demonstrated that much of the TBT came from continuing sources, other problems remain from TBT input prior to the restrictions. For example, in Puget Sound, a lack of concordance was found between high concentrations of TBT in sediment, apparently altered benthic community assemblages, and little or no apparent toxicity in laboratory bioassays. This indicates a continuing problem for regulators and suggests that traditional approaches are not adequate for reducing uncertainty in ERA. Finally, a recent study using caged mussels secured to offshore light vessels (buoys) in North Sea shipping lanes reported tissue TBT concentrations that were an order of magnitude above the control sites (Widdows et al. 1995). Collectively, the previous studies demonstrate the following: 1) TBT is a continuing problem; 2) caged mussels have provided a cost-effective method for monitoring exposure and effects; and 3) these kinds of measurements can reduce uncertainty in the ERA process.

The in situ field bioassays with caged juvenile mussels in San Diego Bay were conducted as part of a research program for refining the use of bivalves as a bioassessment tool, and the data from this effort were used to support the U.S. Navy's risk assessment for TBT. Bioaccumulation and growth in caged mussels were used to identify site-specific differences, temporal and spatial variability, short- and long-term trends, sources of contamination, and dose-response relationships for TBT in San Diego Bay (Salazar and Chadwick 1991; Salazar and Salazar 1991, 1995). In all previous analyses, these trends and differences were identified using juvenile mussel growth rates estimated from changes in WAWW over time. Recent studies (URS Consultants 1994; Salazar et al. 1995; Salazar et al. 1996; Salazar and Salazar 1996) have shown that changes in soft tissue weights can provide a different perspective on identifying site-specific factors affecting growth. They also support the suggestion that shell growth and tissue growth occur at different rates and can be affected by different chemical and natural stressors (Hilbish 1986).

Characterization of exposure and characterization of effects are 2 major components of the ERA framework described by the USEPA (USEPA 1989). However, there are many different approaches to these characterizations in a risk assessment; e.g., chemical measurements of environmental media, laboratory toxicity tests, evaluation of community structure, comparison to literature values, and modeling. Depending on the level of uncertainty that is acceptable and the questions to be answered, a risk assessment does not necessarily include each of these elements. Some assessments are conducted without collecting site-specific data while others characterize exposure using only chemical measurements of water, sediment, or biological tissues. Risk characterizations commonly rely on bioavailability and toxicity data from the literature, chemical data from the analysis of environmental media, and effects data from community structure analyses. An integrative model is sometimes used to estimate risk from these results. The in situ field bioassays used in the Navy's risk assessment showed bioaccumulation of TBT and associated effects on growth were often different than results from laboratory bioassays, microcosm studies, traditional field monitoring and modeling studies (Salazar 1989; Salazar and Salazar 1996). The juvenile mussel data also suggested that in situ field bioassays can minimize the potential uncertainty associated with the characterization of exposure and effects because these types of manipulative field studies are conducted under the site-specific factors that influence overall risk. Results from these and other studies led to the proposed use of an EDR triad to support the risk-assessment process.

Exposure-dose-response triad

The EDR triad was conceived to support ERAs by including integrated, direct measurements of exposure and effects at several levels of ecological organization (Figure 8-1). It is an integrated approach that is based on weight-of-evidence and is scientifically defensible. An EDR triad is recommended for risk assessments that require site-specific data to more fully characterize exposure and ecological effects and reduce uncertainty.

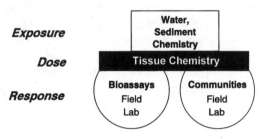

Figure 8-1   Exposure-dose-response triad model

The distinction is made between exposure and dose because of the implications of dose in ERAs. The exposure concentration (i.e., the concentration in environmental media such as water and/or sediment) is often different from the dose (i.e., the concentration of a contaminant at the receptor site) (USEPA 1992). It is important to measure the dose because it has been demonstrated that effects are related to the dose and not necessarily the exposure concentration. Even if both the water and sediment compartments are highly contaminated, this only constitutes the potential for exposure, because bioavailability is controlled by many physical and chemical factors. Exposure is estimated by measuring chemicals in environmental media (water and/or sediment). Dose is estimated by measuring chemicals in tissues. Response is estimated with effects measurements from bioassays and community structure analyses, both of which are conducted in the lab and field.

In Figure 8-1, the top box identifies the exposure element of the triad as chemical analysis of environmental media., and the middle box identifies the dose element of the triad as chemical analysis of animal tissues. The two white circles identify 2 components of the response element of the triad as bioassays and studies of community structure. Each response component consists of field and lab studies. The model also shows how various elements are integrated and how tissue chemistry (bioaccumulation) can create links between 1) exposure and response; 2) lab and field studies, and 3) bioassays and studies of community structure.

One key difference between the EDR triad and other integrated approaches is specifying manipulative field bioassays and community studies as part of the assessment. In the studies described here, bioaccumulation was used as an estimate of the dose, and growth was used to estimate a biological response associated with that dose. In the EDR triad, chemical measurements of environmental media can be considered the external or apparent exposure, and chemical measurements of tissues can be considered the internal exposure or dose. Together, these direct chemical measurements can provide a more complete characterization of exposure than traditional approaches using bioaccumulation measurements from laboratory bioassays or resident field populations. A second key difference is the use of a manipulative community studies in the laboratory and in the field to support the traditional descriptive approach of enumerating species from field-collected samples to analyze community structure. A discussion of community approaches is beyond the scope of this chapter. An overview of the EDR triad will emphasize using caged bivalves as an in situ field bioassay, the in situ field bioassay as a tool for characterizing exposure and effects, and the importance of tissue chemistry and tissue growth as measurement endpoints in the assessment process.

The EDR triad incorporates components of the laboratory and field assessments identified by Long and Chapman (1985) in the original sediment quality triad and extends the exposure-uptake-effects triad suggested by Mearns (1985). Chapman et al. (1992) suggest that integrated assessments should include at least 2 of the following basic elements: sediment toxicity tests, sediment chemical analyses, bioaccumulation, pathology, and community structure. However, the integration of any 2 elements may not ensure direct assessments of exposure and effects. Chemical measurements of environmental media only represent external exposure, and results from laboratory bioassays and analysis of community structure only infer that exposure to internal receptors has occurred. To reduce uncertainty, the most direct method of assessing internal exposure at the receptor is measuring the dose, or tissue burdens. To be consistent with the generic ERA framework, the process should always include a direct characterization of exposure and a direct characterization of effects. Rather than allowing the option of selecting any 2 elements that may not include exposure and response, the EDR triad specifies the use of all 3 elements.

Caged bivalve approach to characterize exposure and effects

The use of in situ field bioassays with caged bivalves is a potentially powerful tool in the risk-assessment process for making these direct measurements. Caging bivalves facilitates the quantification of exposure and response under natural conditions. This reduces the uncertainty associated with extrapolating results from laboratory bioassays conducted under artificial exposure conditions. Using bivalves takes advantage of their ability to concentrate and integrate chemical exposures in their tissues as a dose. Caging facilitates measuring growth to estimate a biological response. Because the bioaccumulation and bioeffects measurements are made synoptically, they provide a direct link between exposure, dose, and response. These manipulative field studies are useful in the risk-assessment process because they bridge the gap between standard laboratory bioassays and traditional monitoring of resident populations for estimating dose and response. In situ field bioassays include advantages of each approach. Laboratory bioassays generally have a high level of experimental control but a very low level of environmental realism (Salazar 1986, 1989). Although test conditions using standardized laboratory protocols are very precise, most results have not been verified under site-specific field conditions. Traditional field monitoring (i.e., estimating effects from benthic community analyses or dose from analysis of resident organisms) generally has a relatively low level of experimental control but a very high level of environmental realism. With in situ field bioassays, test conditions cannot be controlled per se, but different conditions are represented by caging animals at different sites. These results may be more representative than laboratory bioassays because the animals are exposed to all site-specific stressors. Estimating risk from in situ field bioassays minimizes the assumptions that are necessary with standard laboratory and field approaches and provides more useful information for the analysis of risk.

Many species of freshwater and marine bivalves have been used successfully for in situ field bioassays, but the majority of work has focused on mussels because of their availability, distribution, and sensitivity. Resident and transplanted populations of both freshwater and marine bivalves have been used as biomonitors of environmental contamination for almost 30 years, although the use of marine bivalves like *Mytilus* sp. has been more extensive (Godsil and Johnson 1968; Bedford et al. 1968; Young et al. 1976; Eganhouse and Young 1978; Phillips 1980; McMahon 1991). Monitoring resident bivalve populations for the accumulation of contaminants has been the most common form of biomonitoring, but the development of transplant methodologies has increased the use of caged animals and facilitated synoptic measurements of bioaccumulation and bioeffects (Salazar and Salazar 1995). The advantages and disadvantages of using bivalves as in situ test organisms are shown in Table 8-1. A major advantage to using bivalves over other animal groups is that they will accumulate chemicals in their tissues at concentrations that are orders of magnitude above those found in the environment. In some cases, the chemical may not be detectable by chemical analysis of environmental media but is still accumulated by the bivalves and detectable in their tissues. Tissue-chemistry measurements represent the concentrations of chemicals that are biologically available and integrated over time. Therefore, a single tissue measurement can provide more useful information than chemical analyses of thousands of water or sediment samples. Further, bivalves can be easily caged and transplanted to various assessment areas. This approach is particularly helpful in areas where they are not normally found. Some of the most useful relationships between seawater TBT, tissue TBT, and mussel growth that were used in the Navy's risk assessment for TBT would have been undetected by monitoring only resident mussel populations because of their limited distribution in some areas of concern. In addition, the exposure period and the effects of previous variation in natural factors can only be estimated. It is difficult to make repetitive measurements on resident individuals from indigenous populations over time. In situ field bioassays with caged bivalves permit monitoring individual organisms as well as sampling an almost infinite matrix of space and time because the animals can be strategically situated along physical and chemical gradients associated with both the water column

Table 8-1 Advantages and disadvantages of the in situ field bioassay by category: transplants, bivalves, bioaccumulation, and growth

	Transplants	Bivalves	Bioaccumulation	Growth–whole animal tissue
Advantages	Experimental control	Integrate bioavailable contaminants	Concentrations above ambient	Integration of internal biological process
	Environmental realism	Bioconcentrate contaminants	Integration of contaminants, natural factors, manmade non-toxics	Environmentally significant response
	Defined exposure period	Easy to collect, cage, measure	Equivalent to 1000's of water samples	Link to population effects
	Infinite sampling matrix	Large database from field monitoring and lab bioassays	Link between exposure and response	Quantifiable dos-response
	Repetitive, nondestructive sampling	Survive suboptimal conditions	Link between lab and field	Related to environmental exposures
	Monitoring individuals	Any biochemical measurements	Link between bioassays and community structure	Repetitive, nondestructive measurements
	Field validation	Sedentary		Easy for the public to understand
	Exposure system			No special equipment
	Captive biochemical sampling			No specialized training
	Hypothesis testing			More sensitive than survival
Disadvantages	Effects of transplanting	Not found in all areas	Affected by chemical and natural factors	Affected by chemical and natural factors
	Loss of cages from acts of nature, inadvertent capture by moving vessels, vandalism	May not be representative of assessment area	Not all contaminants are accumulated equally	May not be the most sensitive bioeffect
	Cost of collection, sorting deployment	May not be the most sensitive species	Some contaminants may be purged	Tissue and shell growth occur at different factors
		May not directly assess community effects	May not always accurately represent effective dose	Many not directly assess community effects

and sediments. Utilizing animals with a known history facilitates data interpretation and risk estimation.

The primary disadvantages to using caged bivalves as an in situ bioassay are the lack of control in test conditions and the need for uncertain extrapolation to other species and the ecosystem. In general, these disadvantages can be addressed by selecting sites which cover a range of test conditions, using additional species for the in situ bioassays, and assessing community effects with laboratory microcosms (Taub et al. 1987, 1988; Landis et al. 1989) or community transplant studies (Lenihan et al. 1990, 1995).

One of the major criticisms of field monitoring programs that utilize resident animals is that they generally do not include hypothesis testing or measurements of effects. Like most other monitoring programs, the Navy's chemical monitoring program for TBT with resident populations of adult mussels did not include measurements of effects in those mussels. In addition, resident mussels were collected from populations located in the intertidal zone on the shoreline while the water samples for the chemical monitoring were collected from the middle of the yacht basins. These data were not truly synoptic. Our in situ field bioassays with caged bivalves permitted the synoptic collection of growth and water-chemistry data; by segregating the animals, repetitive growth measurements were made over a known period of time and water samples for TBT analysis were taken immediately adjacent to each deployment site. Although the resident mussel populations experienced environmentally realistic conditions during low tide, the caged mussels, which were continuously submerged 1 m below the surface, were constantly exposed to chemicals in the water column.

Characterization of exposure: tissue-residue approach

Bioaccumulation has been identified as a strategic link between the external environment and the organism (Laughlin 1986). The concept of external exposure versus internal exposure is an important one in the risk-assessment process because all contaminants in the surrounding media are not always bioavailable. It has been established that toxicity is caused by the dose of toxic chemicals at the receptor site. Therefore, each measurement of accumulated chemicals could be an integral part of the exposure assessment. Measurements of environmental media (i.e., water or sediment) represent only external chemical exposure. Bioaccumulation, or uptake of chemicals by the organism, is an internal process, and in itself is not an effect. The risk assessor can use bioaccumulation to estimate potential effects at the receptor site. Measurements of bioaccumulation may not be a perfect estimate of the dose because the concentration at the receptor site may be different than the concentration within all tissues. However, measuring accumulated chemicals provides a more reasonable approximation of the actual dose than measuring chemicals outside the organism. Therefore, tissue residues provide another useful tool that can be used to characterize exposure (McCarty and Mackay 1993).

Bioaccumulation can also be used to form other links within the EDR triad. These include linking laboratory and field studies (Mearns 1985), as well as linking single species bioassays and multiple species community studies (Calabrese and Baldwin 1993). The bioaccumulation process is a critical component in toxicokinetic models (Landrum et al. 1992). Several investigators have emphasized the importance of linking bioaccumulation measurements with bioeffects (McCarty 1991; McKim and Schmieder 1991; Cook et al. 1992; Calabrese and Baldwin 1993). Some have even suggested that environmental assessments and regulatory criteria utilize this approach instead of relying only on media concentrations and effects (Friant and Henry 1985). In fact, McCarty (1991) suggests that aquatic bioassay protocols be revised to include bioaccumulation and bioeffects. Calabrese and Baldwin (1993) have provided a format for utilizing maximum acceptable tissue concentrations (MATC) in ERAs. Many of these authors have also stressed the potential utility of in situ measurements and some have advocated the use of caged organisms. These improvements in understanding from in situ bioassays can also reduce the uncertainty in the assessment of risk (McCarty and Mackay 1993).

A review of the current literature indicates that tissue TBT concentrations, or the TBT dose, associated with chronic sublethal effects are similar in a variety of species (Moore et al. 1991; Meador 1997; Meador et al. 1996) and that effects may be more closely associated with the internal dose than the external dose. Meador et al. (1997) compared the lethal dose of TBT associated with 50% mortality in several marine species including 3 species of amphipods, a polychaete worm, and a flatfish. They predicted LR50s (lethal residues for 50% mortality) for TBT that ranged from 41 to 59 µg/g dry weight. In their summary, Moore et al. (1991) point out that the range in TBT tissue burdens associated with adverse biological effects in a number of marine species is between 1 to 15 µg/g dry weight. They concluded that this similarity was surprising given the obvious differences in exposure regimes, test conditions, measurement endpoints, and species differences. It is also interesting to note that the predicted mortality endpoint is about an order of magnitude higher than the sublethal endpoints. The threshold concentration of TBT for adverse effects on growth in *Neanthes* is about 6 µg/g dry weight. (Moore et al. 1991) and for *Mytilus* about 4.0 µg/g dry weight. The mortality endpoint in *Rhepoxynius abronius*, one of the most commonly used laboratory test species, is found at tissue TBT concentrations of 30 and 40 µg/g dry weight (Meador et al. 1996; Meador 1997). Other investigators have also shown that bivalves are more sensitive in side-by-side laboratory bioassays. Burgess and Morrison (1994) compared 10-d amphipod mortality with 7-d mussel growth and found the mussel *Mulinia lateralis* to be more sensitive than amphipods to contaminated sediment. McKinney and Wade (1996) compared survival of the freshwater mussel *Anodonta imbecilis* in 7-d exposures and found it to be more sensitive than survival of a freshwater daphnid in 7-d exposures.

The Meador et al. study (1996) also helps explain the lack of concordance in the Puget Sound sediment quality triad data. Since they demonstrated that it takes amphipods about 45 d to reach chemical equilibrium with TBT in sediment, it is not surprising that the 10-d exposures used in standard protocols would not achieve chemical equilibrium and would not be expected to produce the same results as benthic communities that were in equilibrium. A similar problem has recently been identified by Salazar et al. (1997) when using *Macoma nasuta* in standard bioaccumulation tests with a 28-d exposure period. Mussels (*Mytilus trossulus*) caged in the water column for 60 d accumulated higher concentrations of dioxins and furans in their tissues than did clams. Mussel tissues showed a much better relationship with those chemicals in the sediment than clam tissues exposed directly to the sediment in laboratory bioassays. While it is possible that these chemicals may not have been biologically available to the clams, it seems more likely that the exposure period was not long enough to reach chemical equilibrium or that the animals were stressed during the laboratory experiment and not able to accumulate biologically available chemicals.

Characterization of effects

Growth is often used as a measure of effects because it provides an integration of many biological processes (Bayne et al. 1985; Salazar and Salazar 1995; Salazar and Salazar 1996). The initial effects characterization for the San Diego Bay mussel data was based on growth rates developed from multiple measurements of WAWW over the course of the exposure period. The utility of EOTW as a sensitive effects endpoint was examined in the current analysis because WAWW (i.e., shell + soft tissue + internal water) may not accurately reflect changes in tissue biomass. Since mussel tissues only represent about 30% of WAWW, a loss in tissue weight would be difficult to detect by measuring whole-animal weights alone. Further, mussel tissues are approximately 80% water, and any loss in tissue mass would be replaced by water between the shells. This adds to the difficulty in detecting changes in tissue weight by measuring WAWW. Stressed bivalves can rapidly reabsorb tissue while healthy, and unstressed individuals can rapidly add tissue weight.

Although the multiple measurements of WAWW have been as discriminating as single EOTW in many instances, tissue weights have provided a different perspective on responses associated with exposure to chemical and natural stressors. Tissue weights are more sensitive indicators of stress when growth has been slow (Salazar and Salazar 1995) and when irregular shell shape and weight reduced the accuracy of growth measurements (Salazar et al. 1995). Changes in weights can be most useful when evaluating and interpreting tissue chemistry data. The increase or decrease in chemical concentration (e.g., mg chemical/g mussel tissue) must be considered with respect to changes in tissue mass during the exposure period. An apparent decrease in chemical accumulation could be explained by a concurrent increase in tissue mass rather than contaminant depuration. This growth dilution process has been used to explain the reduction in methyl mercury concentrations in freshwater mussel tissues that were associated with the highest growth rates (Salazar et al. 1996). The methyl mercury content of these animals on a per animal basis (mg chemical/animal) increased at all sites during the exposure period and demonstrated that the methyl mercury was biologically available. On a concentration basis, it appeared that methyl mercury was not biologically available at all sites. Measuring tissue weights not only helps explain the growth endpoint, but the exposure process as well. For example, In a Puget Sound transplant study, mussels at the control site had significantly higher tissue weights but significantly lower increases in WAWWs (USR Consultants 1994). The growth metrics were so different that it may have been inappropriate to compare treatment sites with the control site.

Methods

Nine in situ bivalve bioassays were conducted in San Diego Bay, California, between 1987 and 1990. In each test, juvenile (10 to 12 mm shell length) mussels (*Mytilus galloprovincialis*) were caged for 84 d at selected test sites. The generic measurement endpoints were survival, bioaccumulation, and growth. Growth was estimated from changes in WAWW, shell lengths, and EOTW. Although most sites were located 1 m below the water surface, animals were also transplanted 1 m above the bottom at a few sites to evaluate potential TBT exposure from sediment. A total of 18 sites were evaluated during these studies. For simplicity, only 4 sites will be discussed here in some detail. Three of those sites were located 1 m below the surface (i.e., Shelter Island yacht basin [SI], Naval Station San Diego [NAV], and a control site [CON]), and 1 site was located 1 m above the bottom (Shelter Island Deep [SID]). The Shelter Island sites near the mouth of San Diego Bay were selected because of the high TBT concentrations in water, sediment, and tissues of resident mussels (Valkirs et al. 1991). SI and SID were separated by only 3 m vertical distance. The Naval Station site near the head of San Diego Bay was selected to evaluate conditions before the introduction of TBT antifouling paints. The control site near the mouth of San Diego Bay was selected for reference purposes. Complete details regarding the development and use of the transplant approach in San Diego Bay are provided in Salazar and Salazar (1995, 1996).

All animals were measured for WAWW and shell length weekly during the first 4 tests and on alternate weeks during the last 5 tests. The frequency of measurements was reduced when it was determined that weekly measurements reduced growth rates. Water samples were taken for measurements of seawater TBT and chlorophyll-*a* whenever mussel measurements were made. Temperature measurements were made at half-hour intervals at each site with an in situ temperature monitor. Temperature and chlorophyll-*a* were measured to determine their relative effect on mussel growth. Seawater TBT concentrations were used to estimate exposure. Repetitive measurements of mussel weights and lengths over time permit the integration of effects in much the same way as the mussels are integrating the water column for seawater TBT concentrations. At the end of the deployment period, shell length and WAWW measurements were made, in addition to soft tissue weights and empty shell weights. In each test, tissues were analyzed for TBT. In 4 of the 9 tests, tissues were also analyzed for selected metals. Tissue chemistry was used to estimate the dose. Because the mussels are sedentary and the exposure period defined, these measurements can be more informative than measurements of mobile animals such as fish.

Analyses of growth rate data from the early tests suggested that an EOTW was not as useful as a WAWW as an effects endpoint. Therefore, the characterization of effects in the Navy's TBT risk assessment was based on multiple measurements of WAWW. More recent analyses, such as the one provided here, suggest that EOTW can provide different information that can be just as useful or perhaps even more useful in the assessment of risk from stressors that have different modes of action on the organism.

Results and discussion

A reevaluation of the San Diego Bay mussel data supported the hypothesis that, under certain conditions, tissue weights can be more discriminating with respect to detecting differences between sites than growth rates estimated from multiple measurements of WAWW. End-of-test tissue weights were used to identify site-specific differences and to help explain the relationship between TBT exposure, dose, and response. They were also used to predict concentrations of TBT in seawater and tissues where effects will occur. This represents a significant refinement in the use of caged bivalves as a tool in the risk-assessment process. End-of-test tissue weight and tissue-chemical burdens are effective measurement endpoints because they provide valuable information with respect to characterization of exposure and effects. The following discussion will include a reexamination of the relationships between exposure, dose, and response; a comparison of relationships using both EOTW and WAWW; and the differences in the TBT risk assessment based on the evaluation of EOTW.

Exposure characterization

Seawater and tissue chemistry data indicate that juvenile mussels transplanted to SI, SID, NAV, and CON were exposed to different concentrations of several metals including the organometal TBT (Table 8-2). For TBT, Cu, and Zn, concentrations in mussel tissues were consistently highest at SI. Tributyltin exposure was characterized by chemical measurements of seawater and mussel tissues. It was the only chemical measured in seawater as part of this study, and the highest concentrations were always found at SI. Exposure to other chemicals was characterized by measuring the concentration of the chemical in mussel tissues. The temperature and chlorophyll-*a* data indicate that the physical conditions were also different among the stations. It is beyond the scope of this chapter to provide an in-depth discussion of the exposure characterization for chemicals other than TBT. Similarly, because TBT antifouling coatings were not used on vessels harbored at the Naval Station or the Control Site, the TBT discussion will focus on Shelter Island yacht basin. The information in Table 8-2 is presented to provide background information and assist the reader in making other comparisons.

Since both seawater and tissue TBT concentrations were so high in the Shelter Island yacht basin, these measurements became a critical part of the exposure characterization

Table 8-2 Parameters measured at SI, SID, NAV and CON during each test are indicated. All values represent means calculated from weekly measurements or measurements on alternate weeks over the course of the study. Grand means ( ) are shown for each parameter.

Test	Survival (%)		Seawater [TBT] ng/L		Tissue TBT (μg/g-dry)		EOTW (g-wet)		Growth rate- WAWW (mg/wk)		Final shell length (mm)		Tissue Cu (μg/g-dry)		Tissue Zn (μg/g-dry)		Temperature (°C)		Chl-a (μg/L)	
	SI	SID	SI	SID	SI	SID	SI	SID	SI	SID	SI	SID	SI	SID	SI	SID	SI	SID	SI	SID
1	100	-	530	-	13.5	-	0.12	-	17	-	14.4	-	-	-	-	-	21.1	-	2.95	-
2	94	94	360	200	8.5	5	0.11	0.37	17	54	14.7	18.9	-	-	-	-	16.5	16.0	1.61	3.00
3	94	100	200	64	11.5	5.5	0.34	0.77	70	147	19.3	24.8	171	79	-	-	18.9	17.4	2.36	5.42
4	95	100	169	36	4.7	5.1	0.45	0.93	81	182	20.7	27.2	-	-	-	-	19.9	19.1	2.55	4.06
5	100	89	105	62	15.8	4.7	0.62	1.29	160	279	26.2	31.8	197	37	185	102	16.9	16.2	1.93	2.75
6	100	94	86	22	12.2	3.5	0.79	2.33	160	378	25.7	35.0	135	9	160	60	19.9	18.7	3.77	5.02
7	89	100	82	15	4.2	3.5	0.85	2.01	181	380	28.3	35.3	171	20	175	112	20.4	19.4	2.40	3.72
8	100	100	87	52	9.8	6.9	0.38	0.71	76	138	21.0	25.6	-	-	-	-	14.6	14.4	1.89	2.00
9	89	100	72	19	8.5	1.7	0.47	1.46	140	303	24.4	31.6	192	30	204	102	22.0	21.1	3.11	5.39
x̄	96	97	188	59	9.9	4.5	0.46	1.2	100	233	21.6	28.8	173	35	181	94	18.9	17.8	2.51	3.92

for TBT. However, in terms of the exposure characterization it is extremely important to make similar comparisons among the other metals that were also present in high concentrations. A graphical presentation and statistical comparison of the exposure data for SI and SID is provided in Figure 8-2. Tissue concentrations of TBT, Cd, Cr, Pb, Cu, and Zn were higher in mussels from SI than from SID. These differences were statistically significant for TBT, Cu, and Zn. Additional replication may have shown that the differences for other chemicals were statistically significant as well. Perhaps most interesting of all is the fact that none of these site-specific differences between SI and SID would have been identified without the use of caged bivalves because mussels were not naturally found at depths in the Shelter Island yacht basin where SID was located.

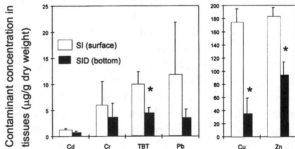

Figure 8-2   Exposure characterization. Mean concentrations of TBT and 5 metals in juvenile mussel tissues SI and SID in the most TBT-contaminated yacht basin in San Diego Bay. Means were calculated from every test where contaminants were measured (9 tests for TBT, 5 tests for Cu, 4 tests for other metals) with ± 2 SE. * = statistically significant difference (α = 0.05)

The mean seawater TBT concentrations at SI and SID were significantly different during each test and for data pooled across tests (Figure 8-3A). The source of TBT was ship hulls coated with TBT antifouling paints. Concentrations were higher at SI because 1) these mussels were very close to the ship hulls compared to the SID mussels, and 2) there is a thermocline in the Shelter Island yacht basin that prevents good mixing of surface and deep waters, particularly during the summer months. During Test 8 when the temperature difference and thermocline were minimized, differences in seawater TBT concentrations between the 2 sites were also minimized (Table 8-2). The concentration of TBT in seawater also decreased at both of these sites over time. This decrease was associated with restrictions on the use of TBT antifouling paint (Valkirs et al. 1991). The decline appears greater and more obvious at SI because the initial concentrations were so high (530 versus 200 ng TBT/L for SI and SID, respectively), but the seawater TBT concentrations decreased by about an order of magnitude at both sites (72 versus 19 ng TBT/L for SI and SID, respectively). The concentration remained higher at SI because some vessels were still coated with TBT antifouling paint.

In general, the concentrations of TBT in mussel tissue also decreased over time (Figure 8-3B). However, the consistent decline in seawater TBT concentration over the 4-y period was not directly reflected in the mussel tissue TBT concentrations. There was much more variability in the tissue TBT data at SI than at SID during the 9 tests. Surprisingly, the highest tissue TBT concentration (15.8 µg/g in Test 5) was not associated with the highest seawater TBT concentration (530 ng/L in Test 1), but a concentration that was lower by a factor of 5. In fact, the tissue TBT concentration for mussels at SI during Test 5 was as high as the tissue TBT concentration measured during Test 1 when seawater TBT concentrations were the highest.

These data indicate something other than TBT in seawater was regulating the amount of TBT accumulated in the tissues. Since previous analyses have shown that the TBT bioconcentration factor (i.e., concentration in tissues versus concentrations in seawater) is related to growth rate (Salazar and Salazar 1995, 1996), we believe that faster growing animals at lower TBT exposures accumulated as much TBT as slower growing animals at higher TBT exposures under certain conditions. Other possible explanations for this apparent anomaly include analytical errors associated with some of the first tissue measurements while the methods were still being developed and the fact that tissue analyses were made on a wet-weight basis and percent water was not measured in all tests. Assuming a composition of 80% water may have introduced another source of error in the measurements. These potential errors also explain relatively lower significance levels of the relationships between tissue TBT concentrations and mussel growth when compared to seawater TBT versus mussel growth.

During Tests 1 through 4, mussel metrics were measured on a weekly basis; an alternate week approach was used during Tests 5 through 9 when it was demonstrated that weekly measurements reduced growth rates. During Test 5 the mussels may have been in better condition, allowing them to accumulate a higher dose of TBT with less of an effect on growth. The decline in tissue TBT concentration over the next 4 tests could be reflective of availability or due to other factors influencing accumulation. It has previously been suggested that a seawater TBT concentration of 105 ng/L is the probable effects threshold. Between Tests 4 and 5 the seawater TBT concentration at SI decreased from 169 to 105 ng/L.

The relationship between exposure and dose for mussels in the Shelter Island yacht basin changes

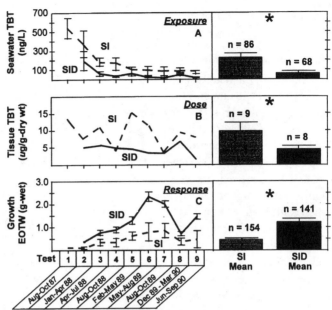

Figure 8-3   *Synoptic measurements in exposure-dose-response triad. Exposure (A) = seawater TBT concentration. Dose (B) = tissue TBT concentration. Response (C) = growth estimated by EOTW. Magnitude and spatial/temporal patterns of matrics are shown for 2 mussel transplant sites in Shelter Island yacht basin, San Diego Bay. SI =1 m below surface; SID = 1 m above substrate. Datapoints for seawater TBT concentrations represent 12-week means (± 2 SE). Tissue TBT and tissue weight datapoints represent end-of-test measurements only. * = statistically significant difference (α = 0.05)*

dramatically at a seawater TBT concentration of 105 ng/L (Figure 8-4A). The highest TBT concentrations appear to affect the way in which TBT is accumulated. It is evident from the trends shown in Figures 8-3A, 8-3B, and 8-4A that the relationship between TBT in seawater and TBT in mussel tissues is complex. A similar change in the relationship was found when all the San Diego Bay data were evaluated and the levels of significance were also similar (Salazar and Salazar 1995, 1996). At seawater TBT concentrations ≤ 105 ng/L, the slope is significantly higher than the slope at concentrations > 105 ng/L; the higher slopes are associated with higher bioconcentration factors. These higher slopes suggest that mussel physiology, filtration, and growth are less affected at lower seawater TBT concentrations and mussels may be able to accumulate more TBT without adverse effects. This was also demonstrated by using all the data. Approximately 60% of the variability in tissue TBT concentrations can be explained by seawater TBT. This relationship holds when data for just SI are analyzed and when data for all San Diego Bay are analyzed.

Effects characterization

The change in the relationship between the exposure and the dose near seawater TBT concentrations of 100 ng/L (Figure 8-4A) is reflected in the growth response based on EOTW (Figure 8-3C). Tissue weights were significantly higher at SID when compared to SI on a test-by-test basis and across tests. Surprisingly, mussel tissue weights did not continue to increase as TBT concentrations in seawater and tissues decreased after Test 6. For example, at SID between Tests 6 and 7, even though seawater TBT concentrations were low (approximately 20 ng/L) and tissue TBT concentrations remained constant at 3.5 µg/g, there was a statistically significant decrease in EOTW (α = 0.10). At the same time, tissue copper and tissue zinc concentrations doubled and chlorophyll-*a* concentrations decreased by about 25% (Table 8-2). Each of these factors could have contributed to the decrease in tissue weights at SID between Tests 6 and 7. However, there was no significant difference in growth rates based on WAWW (Table 8-2). This may be because WAWW (i.e., shell + soft tissue + internal water) may not accurately

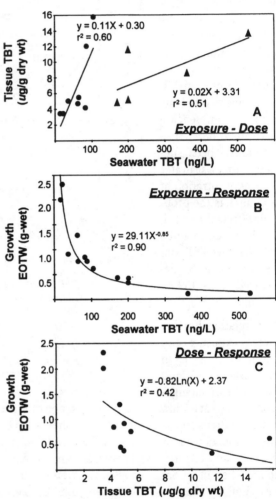

Figure 8-4   *Exposure-dose-response triad showing exposure-dose (A), exposure-response (B), and dose-response (C). Shown here are the relationships between seawater TBT and tissue TBT; between EOTW and 1) seawater TBT and 2) tissue TBT for SI and SID site in San Diego Bay. All regressions are statistically significant. Data from tests 8 and 9 were excluded because extremely low and high temperatures reduced EOTW tissue weights.*

reflect changes in tissue biomass. Bivalve tissues are approximately 80% water, so a loss in tissue weight would be difficult to detect by measuring whole-animal weights alone.

End-of-test tissue weights for mussels at SI never reached those for mussels at SID. Either the declining concentrations of seawater TBT continued to depress mussel growth or a combination of TBT and other contaminants (i.e., copper or zinc) or physical factors (i.e., available food, temperature) adversely affected growth. Between Tests 6 and 7 at SI, seawater TBT concentrations remained constant, tissue TBT concentrations decreased by about a factor of 3, tissue copper and zinc remained constant, and chlorophyll-*a* decreased by 36 percent. Therefore, it is not surprising that growth remained about the same between these 2 tests. Based on previous analyses of the San Diego Bay data (Salazar and Salazar 1995, 1996) and results from other studies that show reduced mussel growth at both low and high temperature extremes (Incze et al. 1980; Almada-Villela et al. 1982), the low tissue weights in Tests 8 and 9 are primarily attributed to low winter temperatures and high summer temperatures, respectively. See "Effects of temperature" section for a more complete discussion on the effects of temperature. The results for Tests 8 and 9 are similar to those reported previously using WAWWs to estimate growth.

The relationships and concentrations where the relationships changed significantly between seawater TBT and growth and between tissue TBT and growth were used to predict adverse effects on growth. The relationship between exposure and response (Figure 8-4B) improved significantly by using only the Shelter Island data instead of all data as in previous assessments of these data (Salazar and Salazar 1995, 1996). This demonstrates the importance of conducting site-specific assessments to reduce uncertainty instead of applying relationships derived from other areas, even in the same bay. Since the relationship between seawater and tissue TBT did not change significantly by using different datasets, it appears that the effects endpoints may be affected more by site-specific conditions than the exposure endpoints. In the previous analysis, using all the growth rate data (based on changes in WAWW), seawater TBT explained only 52% of the variance in growth. Using only the Shelter Island data and EOTW, 90% of the variance in growth was explained by seawater TBT. The relationship between dose and response was less predictive than the relationship between exposure and response. Nevertheless, the percent of the variance in EOTW explained by tissue TBT increased dramatically from 16% (using all San Diego Bay data) to 42% (using only Shelter Island data). Figure 8-4 represents pooled data for SI and SID. End-of-test tissue weight data associated with the highest and lowest temperatures (i.e., > 21°C and < 15°C; Tests 8 and 9) were not used in the regression analyses. These regressions examined the relationships between EOTW and seawater and between EOTW and tissue TBT. Temperatures in these ranges have been shown to reduce mussel growth (Incze et al. 1980; Almada-Villela et al. 1982). The resulting regression (Figure 8-4B) is significant with seawater TBT accounting for 90% of the variability in EOTW ($r^2 = 0.90$). Unlike the relationship between exposure and dose (Figure 8-4A), when the exposure-response data were separated at 105 ng/L, the relationship did not improve ($\leq 105\ r^2 = 0.69$; $> 105\ r^2 = 0.8$). The threshold concentration of seawater TBT for severe effects on mussel growth appears to be near 100 ng/L as suggested previously by using WAWW (Salazar and Salazar 1995). At seawater TBT > 105 ng/L, all EOTW were < 0.8 g. At seawater TBT concentrations < 100 ng/L, EOTW varied by as much as a factor of 2 for a given seawater TBT concentration, but tissue weights were always > 0.8 g. The relationship between EOTW and tissue TBT concentration (Figure 8-4C) is not as strong as that for seawater TBT. Only 42% of the variability in EOTW can be explained by the tissue TBT concentration ($r^2 = 0.42$).

The inability to use tissue chemistry to explain variability in growth can be attributed to the following:

- some of the first tissue analyses were not very accurate,
- all wet-weight analyses (mussel tissue weight and corresponding chemical analyses) include some error associated with water weight,
- replication was insufficient,
- relationship between the timing of accumulating critical tissue burdens and the manifestation of reduced growth associated with that dose was unclear,
- EOTWs represent only part of the exposure period, and
- growth rates and bioaccumulation were adversely affected by weekly growth measurements during the first 4 tests.

This variability led to the initial conservative predictions of probable adverse effects on juvenile mussel growth at tissue TBT concentrations > 7.5 μg/g dry weight and no effect below concentrations of 2.5 μg/g dry weight. It is not surprising, therefore, that the relationship between tissue TBT and tissue weights is less predictive than expected. It should also be added that the wet-weight tissue concentrations were converted to dry weight equivalents by assuming 80% water. This introduces another source of error in that mussels from different sites varied by more than 10%: from 79 to 90% water in Test 9. However, by dividing these data at the apparent effects threshold of 6 μg TBT/gm tissue, more information is gained and the actual tissue concentration of TBT for predicted effects can be more accurately defined. At tissue TBT concentrations greater than 6 μg/g, the relationship is poor ($r^2 = 0.27$), probably because there are not enough datapoints (Figure 8-4C). At tissue TBT concentrations less than 6 μg/g, the relationship improves dramatically ($r^2 = 0.66$). Further, the distinct drop in tissue weights at tissue TBT concentrations greater than 4 μg/g strongly suggests that 4 μg/g should be the predicted effects threshold.

In general, tissue TBT concentrations < 6 μg/g dry weight were associated with seawater TBT concentrations ≤ 105 ng/L. There is a significant change in the relationship between seawater and tissue TBT near seawater TBT concentrations of 105 ng/L, resulting in 2 separate groups (Figure 8-4A). The slope of the regression for the relationship at seawater TBT concentrations ≤ 105 ng/L is approximately an order of magnitude higher than the relationship at seawater TBT concentrations > 105 ng/L. It appears that the seawater TBT concentrations have a poisoning effect on mussels that reduces their growth rate, metabolic rates, and the rate of accumulation. It is also possible that the animals simply remain closed for extended periods of time to reduce their exposure.

A multiple regression analysis was used to test the relationship between seawater TBT, tissue TBT, and EOTW for all San Diego Bay data. The relationship is statistically significant ($P = 0.002$), but the predictive power is low ($r^2 = 0.15$). Nevertheless, the 3-dimensional surface plot of the relationship helps visualize the driving factors and the outlying points (Figure 8-5). By restricting the data to SI and SID in Tests 1 through 7, the relationship and the predictive power improve dramatically ($P = 0.018$; $r^2 = 0.90$).

In addition to using EOTW to understand the relationships between seawater TBT, tissue TBT, and mussel growth in the Shelter Island yacht basin and distinguishing differences between SI and SID, EOTWs were also used to help predict the effects of using TBT at NAV. This was one of the purposes of the TBT risk assessment. For NAV, comparisons between EOTW and WAWW as measurements of effects showed that they were clearly different (Figure 8-6). Mussel growth rates (mg/wk) estimated from changes in WAWW were significantly higher at NAV than at SI in all 9 tests. Since seawater and tissue TBT concentrations were lower at

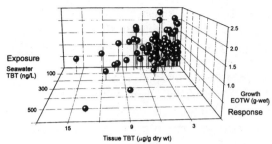

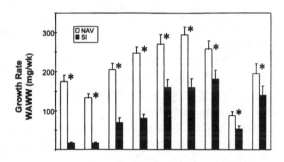

Figure 8-5   Exposure-does response triad data. Exposure-and-effects characterization using 3-dimensional scatterplot to depict exposure based on seawater TBT (ng/L), does based on tissue TBT (μg/g dry weight), and response = growth based on EOTW (g-wet). All datapoints are based on means of 12-week exposures at 18 different sites 1987–1990 in San Diego Bay.

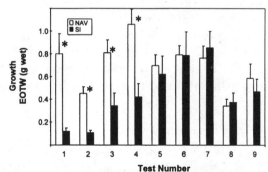

Figure 8-6   Effects characterization. Comparison of mussel growth at NAV and surface site in SI using 2 different metrics: growth rate (mg/wk) based on WAWW and growth based on EOTW. * = statistically significant difference.

NAV (Table 8-2), higher growth rates were expected. Surprisingly, growth estimated from EOTW was significantly higher at NAV only during the first 4 tests when mean seawater TBT concentrations at SI ranged from 169 to 530 ng/L, which are within the predicted probable effects level for TBT on mussel growth predicted previously (Salazar and Salazar 1995) and shown in Figure 8-4.

It is also important to put the EOTW data from NAV in the perspective of San Diego Bay as a whole by making comparisons with a control site. In these comparisons, growth was estimated from both EOTW and changes in WAWW. Growth rates based on changes in WAWW were significantly lower in 6 of the 9 transplant studies (Figure 8-7). End-of-test tissue weights were significantly lower than the controls in 8 of the 9 studies. Further, in the only test where there was no significant difference (Test 4), growth based on EOTW at the control site was lower than expected and survival was 70%, the lowest

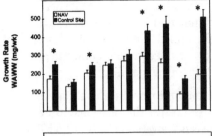

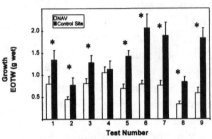

*Figure 8-7   Effects characterization. Comparison of mussel growth at NAV and CON using 2 different metrics: growth rate (mg/wk) based on WAWW and growth based on EOTW. * = statistically significant difference*

ever measured at this station. These data strongly suggest that tissue weights and WAWWs respond differently to environmental conditions. Seawater TBT was not considered a factor affecting mussel growth at either NAV or CON because concentrations in seawater were < 25 ng/L, the predicted no-effect concentration (Salazar and Salazar 1995). Tissue copper concentrations in mussels from NAV were a factor of 5 higher than tissue copper in mussels from the control site. Chlorophyll-*a* at NAV was only 50% of the mean chlorophyll-*a* concentrations at the control site and about 33% of the chlorophyll-*a* at SID. The lower chlorophyll-*a* concentrations at NAV may have been a factor contributing to the lower growth, even though no statistically significant relationships were found.

Effects of temperature

Using EOTW to estimate relative growth and mussel health demonstrates that caged juvenile mussels at NAV were under stress, particularly after Test 4, and that stress was most likely associated with high temperatures. Temperatures at NAV were > 22°C in 5 of the 9 tests, and yet growth rates based on WAWW suggested that mussels at SI were under significantly more stress from the high concentrations of TBT. Previous analyses have shown that mussels at SI had the lowest growth rates in every test when compared to the other 18 sites being assessed (Salazar and Salazar 1991). End-of-test tissue weights at NAV and SI were both among the lowest of all 18 sites in every test.

Other studies have shown that tissue growth and shell growth occur at different rates and are affected by different factors (Hilbish 1986). If different environmental factors have different effects on tissue and shell growth, it would be important to identify these as part of the characterization of effects during a risk assessment. It has also been suggested, however, that the effective concentration could change based on environmental conditions, such as temperature. In 6 of the 9 tests, seawater temperatures were above 20°C at NAV. It has been documented in both laboratory and field studies that temperatures above 20°C cause stress in mussels (Incze et al. 1980; Almada-Villela 1982; Bayne et al. 1985). Exposure to high summer temperatures may induce sufficient stress such that the NAV mussels may have been affected by seawater TBT concentrations in the no-effects range. These effects may have been detected with other more sensitive measurement endpoints. Adult mussels are particularly sensitive to temperature and nutritive stress during gametogenesis (Bayne et al. 1985). Therefore, adult mussels could be more sensitive than the juvenile mussels (Widdows and Donkin 1992) used for the in situ bioassays here. Further, both high temperatures and low chlorophyll-*a* measured at NAV could have more of an adverse effect on adult mussels. The addition of TBT exposure could then be significant.

End-of-test tissue weights were significantly affected by both seawater TBT concentrations and temperature. For all San Diego Bay data collected during the 9 transplant studies, the highest EOTWs were associated with temperatures near 20°C and seawater TBT concentrations < 10 ng/L (Figure 8-8). End-of-test tissue weights were lowest at temperatures above 20°C and below 15°C. The extremely low temperatures measured during Test 8 and high temperatures measured during Test 9 help explain the effects of temperature on changes in tissue weight and the relative effects of TBT. Maximum EOTW were predicted at 20°C. Previous analysis of the San Diego Bay growth data (i.e., based on WAWW) predicted a similar temperature for maximum growth

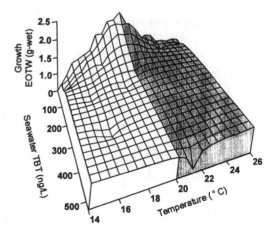

Figure 8-8 *Effects characterization. Effects of seawater TBT concentration and temperature on growth predicted from 3-dimensional surface plots using weighted means. Shaded area represents tissue weight reductions at temperatures about 20°C. Reduced tissue weights at low temperatures and high concentrations of TBT in seawater (>100 ng/L) are also apparent.*

(Salazar and Salazar 1995, 1996) as have other laboratory studies (Almada-Villela et al. 1982).

The importance of temperature and seawater TBT concentrations on both mussel growth rates and EOTW is shown in Figure 8-9. When seawater TBT concentrations were correlated with both growth rate (mg/wk) and EOTW (g), the correlation coefficients were consistently higher for growth rates, regardless of the seawater TBT concentration. Negative associations were found between seawater TBT concentration and growth rate and between seawater TBT concentration and EOTW. Different relationships were found when temperature was correlated with growth rate and EOTW. When all temperatures and low temperatures were evaluated separately, both growth rate and EOTW were positively correlated with temperature. At low temperatures, EOTWs were better correlated with temperature than were growth rates, but the difference is probably not significant. At high temperatures, both growth metrics were negatively correlated with temperature. The strongest correlation was found between temperature and EOTW.

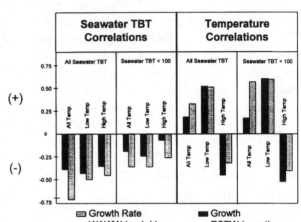

Figure 8-9   *Effects characterization. Effects of seawater TBT and temperature on mussel growth (whole-animal growth rate and EOTW) as estimated by correlation coefficients in predicted effects ranges for temperature and seawater TBT. All temp = 14 to 26°C; high temp = > 20°C. Positive correlations are above the center horizontal axis at 0, and negative correlation are below the line.*

Summary and conclusions

Using caged bivalves can be extremely useful in the risk-assessment process because information is provided on marine environmental quality that would not be available through routine chemical monitoring, biological monitoring of resident organisms, or laboratory bioassays. The caging methodology facilitates obtaining both effects and exposure (i.e., dose) information on the same animals as well as using bivalves in areas that they may not naturally inhabit. The transplant methodology combines the advantages of experimental control associated with laboratory bioassays and the environmental realism inherent in resident populations. This permits a higher degree of confidence in estimating risk than does using traditional approaches alone. The risk assessment is further enhanced by the synoptic evaluation of exposure and effects. These types of data can be used to help extrapolate or model site-specific conditions. Risk assessment applications include identifying site-specific differences, temporal and spatial variability, short- and long-term trends, and contaminant sources, as well as developing exposure-dose-response relationships.

The complex relationships between exposure, dose, and response and the effects of natural factors such as temperature and chlorophyll-*a* reinforce the need to include these measurements in the risk-assessment process. Using caged bivalves in the triad framework described here can clarify these relationships and help predict risk. The reanalysis of the San Diego Bay data presented here stresses the utility of soft tissue weights as a measurement endpoint. The first analysis of the mussel data based on WAWW was misleading with respect to evaluating the risk associated with the TBT application to ships berthed at NAV. The WAWW growth rates suggested conditions at NAV were not highly stressful to mussels and that adverse effects would result as seawater TBT concentration exceeded 100 ng/L or 7.5 µg TBT/g tissue as previously suggested (Salazar and Salazar 1995). However, EOTW suggested that animals at NAV were already stressed due to other chemicals and other natural factors, e.g., temperature and chlorophyll-*a*. If these stressors are additive, the potential ecological risk due to the presence of TBT would increase; significant reductions in mussel growth could be elicited at lower concentrations of TBT in seawater and mussel tissue. Although the other thresholds have not been reevaluated, the revised predicted threshold for probable adverse effects on mussel growth is 4 µg TBT/g tissue dry weight.

Including exposure, dose, and response data is highly recommended in the ERA process. The exposure-dose-response triad includes standard laboratory bioassays, analysis of field collected samples, and in situ field bioassays. The ability to accurately predict risk is enhanced by including all environmental variables and characterizing exposure, dose, and response under site-specific conditions. Caged bivalve studies can facilitate collection of synoptic exposure and effects data, but other species can be used in the field element of the triad. More effort should be directed toward developing standardized protocols for test species that are suitable for assessing exposure/dose (i.e., bioaccumulation) and effects (i.e., various sublethal endpoints) rather than separate protocols for exposure/dose and effects. This means including more sensitive effects endpoints as part of bioaccumulation tests and performing measurements of bioaccumulation as part of effects testing in standard toxicity tests. It also means a paradigm shift toward emphasis on measuring bioaccumulation in both laboratory testing and analyses of community structure.

Acknowledgments - We wish to thank all of the people who have helped us since we began conducting in situ field bioassays. Brad Davidson deserves special thanks. Without his help and support, the quality of the work would have diminished significantly. We also thank the following Navy personnel: Steve Hurley for providing the funding to begin this work; Sachio Yamamoto for allowing us to begin; and Pete Seligman for helping us in the final stages of development. We thank our past and present supervisors at NOAA and EVS for tolerating continued refinement of the methodologies and time spent in preparing this paper: Bill Conner, Doug Wolfe, and Bob Dexter.

References

Almada-Villela PC, Davenport J, Gruffydd LD. 1982. The effects of temperature on the shell growth of young *Mytilus edulis* L. *J Exp Mar Biol Ecol* 59:275–288.

Bayne BL, Brown DA, Burns K, Dixon DR, Ivanovici A, Livingstone DR, Lowe DM, Moore NM, Stebbing ARD, Widdows J. 1985. The effects of stress and pollution on marine animals. New York: Praeger Special Studies, Praeger Scientific.

Bedford JW, Roelofs EW, Zabik MJ. 1968. The freshwater mussel as a biological monitor of pesticide concentrations in a lotic environment. *Limno Oceanogr* 13:118–126.

Burgess RM, Morrison GE. 1994. A short-exposure, sublethal, sediment toxicity test using the marine bivalve *Mulinia lateralis*: statistical design and comparative sensitivity. *Environ Toxicol and Chem* 13:571–580.

Calabrese EJ, Baldwin LA. 1993. Performing ecological risk assessments. Boca Raton: Lewis.

Chapman PM, Power EA, Burton Jr GA. 1992. Integrative assessments in aquatic ecosystems. In: Burton Jr GA, editor. Sediment toxicity assessment. Boca Raton: Lewis. p 313–340.

Cook PM, Carlson AR, Lee H. 1992. Tissue residue approach. Sediment Classification Methods Compendium, U.S. Environmental Protection Agency, Office of Water.

Eganhouse RP, Young DR. 1978. In situ uptake of mercury by the intertidal mussel, *Mytilus californianus*. *Mar Pollut Bull* 9:214–217.

Friant SL, Henry L. 1985. Relationship between toxicity of certain organic compounds and their concentrations of aquatic organisms: a perspective. *Chemosphere* 14:1897–1907.

Godsil PJ, Johnson WC. 1968. Residues in fish, wildlife, and estuaries: pesticide monitoring of the aquatic biota at the Tule Lake National Wildlife Refuge. *Pest Monit J* 1:21–26.

Grovhoug JG, Seligman PF, Vafa G, Fransham RL. 1986. Baseline measurements of butyltin in U. S. harbors and estuaries. In: Proceedings, Oceans 1986 Conference, Washington DC., 23–25 Sep 1986, Organotin Symposium, Volume 4. p 1283–1288.

Hilbish TJ. 1986. Growth trajectories of shell and soft tissue in bivalves: seasonal variation in *Mytilus edulis* L. *J Exp Mar Biol Ecol* 96:103–113.

Incze LS, Lutz RA, Watling L. 1980. Relationship between effects of environmental temperature and seston on growth and mortality of *Mytilus edulis* in a temperate northern estuary. *Mar Biol* 57:147–156.

Landis WG, Chester NA, Haley MV, Johnson DW, Muse Jr WT, Tauber RM. 1989. Utility of the standardized aquatic microcosm as a standard method for ecotoxicological evaluation. In: Suter II GW, Lewis MA, editors. Aquatic toxicology and environmental fate. Eleventh Volume. Philadelphia: ASTM. p 353–367.

Landrum PF, Lee H, Lydy MJ. 1992. Toxicokinetics in aquatic systems: model comparisons and use in hazard assessment. *Environ Toxicol Chem* 11:1709–1725.

Laughlin Jr RB. 1986. Bioaccumulation of tributyltin: the link between environment and organism. In: Proceedings, Oceans 1986 Conference, Organotin Symposium. Washington D. C. 23–25 Sep 1986. p 1206–1209.

Lenihan HS, Kiest KA, Conlan KE, Slattery PN, Konar BH, Oliver JS. 1995. Patterns of survival and behavior in Antarctic benthic invertebrates exposed to contaminated sediments: field and laboratory bioassay experiments. *J Exp Mar Biol Ecol* 192:233–255.

Lenihan HS, Oliver JS, Stephenson MA. 1990. Changes in hard bottom communities related to boat mooring and tributyltin in San Diego Bay: a natural experiment. *Mar Ecol Prog. Ser* 60:147–159.

Long ER, Chapman PM. 1985. A sediment quality triad: measures of sediment contamination, toxicity and infaunal community composition in Puget Sound. *Mar Pollut Bull* 16:405–15.

Maguire RJ, Chau YK, Thompson JAJ. 1996. Proceedings of the workshop on organotin compounds in the Canadian aquatic environment. Sidney, British Columbia, 19–20 Feb 1996. NWRI Contribution No. 96-153.

McCarty LS. 1991. Toxicant body residues: implications for aquatic bioassays with some organic chemicals. In: Mayes MA, Barron MG, editors. Aquatic toxicology and risk Assessment. 14th Volume. Philadelphia: ASTM. p 183–192.

McCarty LS, Mackay D. 1993. Enhancing ecotoxicological modeling and assessment. *Environ Sci Technol* 27:1719–1728.

McKim JM, Schmieder PK. 1991. Bioaccumulation: does it reflect toxicity? In: Nagel R, Loskill R, editors. Bioaccumulation in aquatic systems: contributions to the assessment. Proceedings, International Workshop, Berlin. 1990. New York: VC. p 161–188.

McKinney AD, Wade DC. 1996. Comparative response of *Ceriodaphnia dubia* and juvenile *Anodonta imbecillis* to pulp and paper mill effluents discharged to the Tennessee River and its tributaries. *Environ Toxicol Chem* 15:514–517.

McMahon R. 1991. Mollusca: Bivalvia. In: Thorp JH, Covich AP, editors. Ecology and classification of North American freshwater invertebrates. p 315–400.

Meador JP. 1997. Comparative toxicokinetics of tributyltin in five marine species and its utility in predicting bioaccumulation and acute toxicity. *Aquatic Toxicol* 37:307–326.

Meador JP, Krone CA, Dyer KW, Varanasi U. 1996. Toxicity of sediment-associated tributyltin to infaunal invertebrates: species comparison and role of organic carbon. *Mar Environ Res* 43(3):219–241.

Mearns AJ. 1985. Biological implications of the management of waste materials: the importance of integrating measures of exposure, uptake, and effects. In: Purdy R, Bahner RC, Cardwell RD, editors. Aquatic toxicology and hazard assessment: Seventh Symposium. ASTM STP 854. Philadelphia: ASTM. p 335–343.

Moore DW, Dillon TM, Suedel BC. 1991. Chronic toxicity of tributyltin to the marine polychaete worm, *Neanthes arenaceodentata. Aquatic Toxicol* 21:181–198.

Page DS, Widdows J. 1991. Temporal and spatial variation in levels of alkyltins in mussel tissues: a toxicological interpretation of field data. *Mar Environ Res* 32:113–129.

Phillips DJH. 1980. Quantitative squatic biological indicators—their use to monitor trace metal and organochlorine pollution. London: Applied Science.

Salazar MH. 1986. Environmental significance and interpretation of organotin bioassays. In: Proceedings, Oceans 1986 Conference, Organotin Symposium. Washington DC. 23–25 Sep 1986. p 1240–1245.

Salazar MH. 1989. Mortality, growth and bioaccumulation in mussels exposed to TBT: differences between the laboratory and the field. In: Proceedings, Oceans 1989 Conference, Seattle, WA. 18–21 Sep 1989, Organotin Symposium. p 1188–1197.

Salazar SM, Beckvar N, Salazar MH, Finkelstein K. 1996. An in situ assessment of mercury contamination in the Sudbury River, MA, using bioaccumulation and growth in transplanted freshwater mussels. National Oceanic and Atmospheric Administration Technical Report.

Salazar MH, Chadwick DB. 1991. Using real-time physical/chemical sensors and in situ biological indicators to monitor water pollution. In: Wrobel LC, Brebbia CA, editors. Water Pollution: modeling, measuring and prediction. First International Conference on Water Pollution Modeling, Measuring and Prediction. London: Elsevier. p 463–480.

Salazar MH, Salazar SM. 1991. Assessing site-specific effects of TBT contamination with mussel growth rates. *Mar Environ Res* 32:131–150.

Salazar MH, Salazar SM. 1995. In situ bioassays using transplanted mussels: I. Estimating chemical exposure and bioeffects with bioaccumulation and growth. In: Biddinger GR, Mones E, Hughes JS, editors. Environmental toxicology and risk assessment - Third Volume. 216-41. Philadelphia: ASTM.

Salazar MH, Salazar SM. 1996. Mussels as bioindicators: effects of TBT on survival, bioaccumulation and growth under natural conditions. In: Champ MA, Seligman PF, editors. Tributyltin: environmental fate and effects. London: Chapman and Hall. p 305–330.

Salazar MH, Salazar SM, Paynter K, Gaffney P. 1995. Using transplanted bivalves to assess oil exposure and effects in Delaware Bay. Fifth Symposium on Environmental Toxicology and Risk Assessment: Biomarkers and Risk Assessment, ASTM Conference, Denver, Colorado. American Society of Testing and Materials, Philadelphia.

Salazar SM, Sandberg R, Hammermeister T. 1997. Using caged bivalves to assess exposure and effects at pulp and paper mills. ASTM Seventh Symposium on Environmental Toxicology and Risk Assessment, 7–10 Apr 1997, St. Louis, MO. Abstract only.

Taub FB, Kindig AC, Conquest LL. 1987. Interlaboratory testing of a standardized aquatic microcosm. In: Chapman GA, Landis WG, Adams WJ, editors. Aquatic toxicology and hazard assessment. 10th Volume. Philadelphia: ASTM. p 385–405.

Taub FB, Kindig AC, Conquest LL, Meador JP. 1988. Results of the interlaboratory testing of the standardized aquatic microcosm protocol. In: Suter II GW, Lewis MA, editors. Aquatic toxicology and environmental fate. Eleventh Volume. Philadelphia: ASTM. p 368–390.

URS Consultants. 1994. Phase I Technical Memorandum, Remedial Investigation/Feasibility Study (RI/FS), Operable Unit B, Puget Sound Naval Shipyard, Bremerton, Washington, CTO 0131, Volume 1. Prepared for Department of the Navy, Engineering Field Activity, Northwest, Southwestern Division, Naval Facilities Engineering Command, Poulsbo, Washington. Contract Task Order 0131.

[USEPA] U.S. Environmental Protection Agency. 1989. Risk assessment guidance for Superfund. Volume II. Environmental evaluation manual. U.S. Environmental Protection Agency, Office of Emergency and Remedial Response, Washington, DC.

[USEPA] U.S. Environmental Protection Agency. 1992. Framework for ecological risk assessment. EPA/630/R-92/001. Risk Assessment Forum, U.S. Environmental Protection Agency, Washington, DC.

[USN] U.S. Navy. 1984. Fleetwide use of organotin antifouling paint: environmental assessment. U.S. Navy, Washington, DC. 128 p.

Valkirs AO, Davidson B, Kear LL, Fransham RL, Grovhoug JG, Seligman PF. 1991. Long-term monitoring of tributyltin in San Diego Bay California. *Mar Environ Res* 32:151–167.

Widdows J, Donkin P. 1992. Mussels and environmental contaminants: bioaccumulation and hysiological aspects. In: Gosling E, editor. The mussel *Mytilus*: ecology, physiology, genetics and culture. Amsterdam: Elsevier. p 383–424.

Widdows J, Donkin P, Brinsley MD, Evans SV, Salkeld PN, Franklin A, Law RJ, Waldock MJ. 1995. Scope for growth and contaminant levels in North Sea mussels *Mytilus edulis*. *Mar Ecol Prog Ser* 127:131–148.

Young DR, Heesen TC, McDermott DJ. 1976. An offshore biomonitoring system for chlorinated hydrocarbons. *Mar Pollut Bull* 7:156–160.

Index

in DTSC guidance, 25–26, 34,
36–48, 51
Naval Weapons Station at Seal
Beach, 73–80
terrestrial, 36–44
Phase 1 site characterization and
screening, 84
Phase 2, Tampa Bay, National Status
and Trends Program, 121–122
Phase 2 determination of ecological
impairment, 84
Phase 2 validation study, in DTSC
guidance, 25–26, 44, 47, 51
Phase 3 bioassessment, 84–85
Phase 3 impact assessment, DTSC
guidance, 27–28, 48–51
photographs, 36
photolysis, 29
plant uptake
of metals, 89–90, 91, 93
of selenium, 98–99, 101, 102, 103
polychlorinated biphenyls (PCB)
on Camp Pendleton Marine Corps
Base, 81
effects on birds, Naval Weapons
Station, 77, 79
polycyclic aromatic hydrocarbons
(PAH), effects on birds, 77, 79
population effects, 28
potentially responsible parties (PRP),
24
Preliminary Endangerment Assessment (PEA), 25, 30
preliminary impact assessment, in
EPA Region 9 guidance, 13,
15–16, 20
problem formulation, in *Framework*,
13, 67

R
rainwater pools, 97, 100, 101, 102,
103–104
ranking, of locations within a site, 87
rare, threatened, or endangered species
(RTE), 30–31
RCRA (Resource Conservation and
Recovery Act), 11, 80
receptors. *See also specific animals*
aquatic, 44–48, 59–62, 103–104
for exposure parameter values, 49–50
identification of, in DTSC scoping
assessment, 30–31, 35, 36, 48
site, delineation of, 14–16
terrestrial, 38–44, 102–103
record of decision, Naval Weapons
Station at Seal Beach, 72
"Red Book," 3
reference areas, concurrent, 70
reference concentration
aquatic, 25, 45–47
terrestrial, hazard quotient for, 37–38
reference dose (RfD)
in DTSC guidance, Phase 1 and Phase
2, 25, 37–38, 48
scaled to body weight, 41, 43
values for representative species,
Phase 3, 49–50
regulations
incorporation of the risk-assessment
process, 1–2
restriction of tributyltin usage, 133,
134, 146, 162, 168
role of ERA in decision-making,
55–58, 62–63
remedial investigation/feasibility study
process, 5, 10
remediation guidance
cost *vs.* effectiveness in development
of, 3–4

in EPA Region 9 guidance, 13,
19–20
habitat damage *vs.* effectiveness in
development of, 20, 29
report structures, Phase 1 and Phase 2
study report, 47–48
representative species. *See* Receptors
research, feedback loop to practical
application, 3
Resource Conservation and Recovery
Act (RCRA), 11, 80
risk assessment. *See* Ecological risk
assessment; Human health risk
assessment
Risk Assessment Guidelines (RAGS), 39
risk assessors, communication with
risk managers, 5, 57, 66
risk characterization, 5. *See also*
Hazard quotient
aquatic, 47
Camp Pendleton Marine Corps
Base, 91–94
in EPA Region 9 guidance, 13, 18
in *Framework*, 13, 67
terrestrial, 43–44
risk management
in EPA Region 9 guidance, 13
in *Framework*, 13
route of exposure, toxicity variability
with, 31
runoff
from contaminated sites, effects on
invertebrates, 87, 95
stormwater, 59, 60–63

S

saltmarsh. *See* Naval Weapons Station
at Seal Beach
sampling. *See also* Field sampling/
monitoring

imprecision in, 17
in remediation guidance development, 19–20
San Diego Bay, Calif. *See* Tributyltin
San Pedro Bay, Calif. *See* National
Status and Trends Program
SARA (Superfund Amendments and
Reauthorization Act), 9
scoping
in DTSC guidance, 25, 29–36
in EPA Region 9 guidance, 13–14
screening
comparison with regulatory levels,
85–86
in Phase 1 site characterization, 84
Seal Beach, Calif. *See* Naval Weapons
Station
Seal Beach National Wildlife Refuge
(NWR), 71–80
seasonal effects, 17, 30
sea urchins. *See* Invertebrates, sea
urchins
sediment criteria, accuracy of, in
predicting toxicity, 118–123,
129
sediment quality assessments
accuracy of guidelines in predicting
toxicity, 118–123, 129
sensitivity of solid-phase amphipod
toxicity tests, 125–129
significance of ammonia, 123–125,
129
spatial extent of sediment toxicity in
industrialized bays, 114–118,
129
tributyltin, 139, 146, 147–149, 155–
156, 175–176
sediment quality triad, 171

selenium
  effects at Kesterson Reservoir,
    96–104
  effects on birds and eggs, 96–97,
    100, 101–102, 103–104
  effects on invertebrates, 101, 104
  effects on mammals, 101
site history, 31
  Camp Pendleton Marine Corps
    Base, 80–81
  Kesterson Reservoir, 96–97
  land-use map of, 33, 34, 36
  Montrose Chemical Corporation
    Superfund site, 59
  Pearl Harbor, Hawaii, 152–153
  San Diego Bay, 143, 168
Society of Environmental Toxicology
    and Chemistry (SETAC),
    Southern California Chapter, 1
soil, selenium concentrations,
    Kesterson Reservoir, 100
soil adsorption coefficient, 92
soil criteria
  use of background levels, 86
  use of Canadian quality criteria, 85
spatial extent/patterns
  of chemicals of concern, Naval
    Weapons Station, 79
  of sediment toxicity in industrial-
    ized bays, 114–118, 129
"special species"
  of California Department of Fish
    and Game, 30
  Naval Weapons Station at Seal
    Beach, 72–73
spills, chemical, 10
state agencies, role in federal ERA
    regulations, 9–10
stormwater runoff, 59, 60–63

Superfund Amendments and Reautho-
    rization Act (SARA), 9
Superfund sites
  Comprehensive Environmental
    Response, Compensation, and
    Liability Act, 9
  EPA guidance for. See Framework for
    Ecological Risk Assessment
  Montrose Chemical Corporation,
    58–63
  National Oil and Hazardous Sub-
    stances Pollution Contingency
    Plan, 9
  Superfund Amendments and
    Reauthorization Act, 9

T

Tampa Bay, Flor. See National Status
    and Trends Program
TBT. See Tributyltin
technical innovations, 3
temperature, effect on bivalve growth
    rate, 186–188
threatened species, 30–31
tidal saltmarsh. See Naval Weapons
    Station at Seal Beach
total petroleum hydrocarbons (TPH),
    Camp Pendleton Marine Corps
    Base, 83, 85, 95
toxicity tests
  amphipod sensitivity to, 111, 115–
    116, 118, 121–122, 125–130
  Camp Pendleton Marine Corps Base,
    87, 89
  clams, 126, 127, 128
  in confirmatory impact assessment
    phase, 17–18
  grass shrimp, 126, 127, 128
  imprecision in, 17
  sandworms, 126, 127, 128